To

The Memory of

WILLIAM DURRETT NICHOLLS

A Successful Farmer
A Discerning Economist
An Outstanding Educator
An Exemplary Parent

We Affectionately Dedicate This Book

Preface

This book outlines a procedure for teaching farm organization and farm management. This procedure is based on an analysis of management functions and is elementary enough to be understood by college students yet advanced enough to give them an integrated version of the so-called old and new approaches to farm management.

The text is designed for students on junior, senior, and lower graduate levels. The procedure followed is that used by teachers, professional farm managers, rural land appraisers, soil conservationists, research workers, and farmers. The presentation has vocational objectives, but the method used is procedural and analytical. Exposition of principles and problems are the main pedagogical devices used. The text is both a teaching device and a learning procedure. The first three chapters define the subject. The fourth introduces some common farm management terms. The remaining chapters handle problems of organizing and operating farms in a continuous, integrated process.

The procedure includes use of much of the findings of earlier farm management research as well as much of the early procedures. To this somewhat "traditional" approach to teaching farm management, we have added much of the so-called new approach. Generally, we regard this new material as an extension of the valid portions of earlier farm management approaches. Hence, we have added to the highly productive portions of the traditional approach rather than replacing them.

Both authors were trained in the traditional approach to farm management. Both of us have since studied and taught theory and principles of production economics with their applications in agriculture. Both of us have related the results of our studies to the data and methods of the traditional approach in teaching courses in farm management. This experience and training forms the basis for selecting from the "new" and the "old" the portions used in developing this textbook.

Despite our similar experiences, we originally placed somewhat different degrees of emphasis on the traditional and the so-called modern or theory approaches. Obviously these differences created some need to compromise with respect to content and emphasis. These compromises are regarded as having some value, as the need to compromise on these points is a need of the profession. Although we have attained a high degree of consensus, the results are probably not entirely consistent and satisfactory to both points of view. We hope that the results of our work will at least partially satisfy the current need in farm management for synthesis and integration. If this book does this, our labor of reason, patience, and compromise will be amply rewarded. We know that the task of integration and development has not been completed in this book—further, we anticipate that several years will pass before this highly desirable goal is completely attained.

Special attention is devoted in the book to (1) the tasks of management, (2) the principles for increasing the efficiency with which the managerial functions are performed, and (3) the problems created by the personal subjective wants and preferences of farm people. The materials presented were and are being developed, integrated, and tested slowly. We, therefore, have confidence that the materials and methods presented are sound.

The problem-solving approach through budgeting and dynamic marginal analysis is in ascendancy throughout the country. It forces students to give consideration to the general relationships among inputs used in farming, to specific relationships of management to changing conditions, to the subjective nature of farming, and to the control of output (and profits) through regulation of input.

A class case farm is used throughout the book to illustrate the organization and analytical methods being taught. Additional problems are also solved in the text for illustrative purposes. These may be supplemented with problems from local case farms if teaching resources, including staff members, transportation for students, time away from the campus, and suitable systems of management permit. In any event, one individual case farm should be selected by or for each student to use in connection with the problem exercises. Such individual case farms will frequently be the student's home farm.

The text is adaptable. It may be used, chapter by chapter and exercise by exercise, as presented for two semesters or quarters, or three quarters. If it is used for two semesters or quarters, the first might end with Chapter 21 and the second start with an intensive review and expansion of Chapters 8 through 12, followed by Chapters 22 to 26 and supplemental material supplied by individual professors. If it is used for three quarters, the first two quarters should be taught as a unit terminating with Chapter 21, the third quarter covering Chapters 22 through 26 with related supplemental material furnished by the professor. The book can also be used on a one-semester or quarter basis by dropping the problem exercises not pertaining to the budgets. The book is also a source of selected readings for professional farm managers and land appraisers, educators in agriculture, farm credit agencies, technicians, and farmers.

Much credit is due to many persons and agencies who have contributed directly and indirectly to this book. Our associates at the University of Kentucky, Michigan State College, in neighboring southern states, in the Tennessee Valley Authority, and in the North Central Farm Management Research Committee have contributed thought after thought and concept after concept, only a small portion of which are specifically recognized by references and footnotes. Specific mention should also be made of the Bureau of Agricultural Economics and cooperating land-grant colleges which have contributed so much input-output data to the profession of agricultural economics and, specifically, to Chapters 16, 17, and 18 of this book.

LAWRENCE A. BRADFORD
GLENN L. JOHNSON

May, 1953

Contents

PART 1 · ORIENTATION

PART 2 · INTRODUCTION TO ORGANIZING A FARM BUSINESS

PART 3 · OPERATING A FARM BUSINESS

Part 1

ORIENTATION

CHAPTER 1

Management and Its Meaning

The first part of this book deals with management: its nature, its tasks, and general principles for increasing the efficiency with which these tasks are performed. The second deals with the problems of organizing and reorganizing farms; the third, with the problems of managing a going farm business over a period of years.

Management Defined

Management is an intangible part of production which develops within the lives of men. It is first a mental process, a concentration of desires, a will power. Management functions when a farmer is (1) observing and conceiving ideas; (2) analyzing with further observations; (3) making decisions on the basis of the analysis; (4) taking action; and (5) accepting responsibilities. Management can be seen only through observing the decision-making process and its results. Managerial ability is doubtless partly inherited and partly acquired.

A good manager must be self-disciplined (i.e., pursue definite goals and objectives) so that he can:

> Direct thinking toward opportunity for attainment.
> Attack problems preventing attainment of his objectives.
> Extract the optimum information from his environment.
> Carry analysis for each decision to a favorable degree.
> Take prompt action on his decisions.
> Accept the consequences of his actions.

Obviously the decisions of management are reflected in (1) the process of assembling and co-ordinating the other factors of production—such as land, labor, cash, credit, and equipment; (2) the choice of products to be produced with the factors; and (3) the relationships which managers maintain with the outside business world. Equally obvious, but less discussed, the decisions of a farm manager deal with subjective choices which must be made between the farm business and the family, the reinvestment or consumption of current incomes, and the apportionment of energy between the farm business and the welfare institutions of the community.

Management Illustrated

Since the definition of management just given is somewhat formal, let us turn to a simple illustration. Free Enterprise, a pioneering farmer, carried water from a hillside spring to his home. The task took about an hour a day and the physical exertion was distasteful. The buckets, it seemed, were always empty at the close of toilsome days in the field. Free had an *idea!* Water ran downhill; why not make it run where he needed to use it? Free had been taught to "make his head save his heels." Make what? Make his head? Yes, force himself to think. Herein Free took the first step in management. He conceived an idea, a thought. A mental process was used; a thought product was born.

But how could the idea be put into use? He would have to do more thinking, and so he *analyzed* the problem. Now, *observation* is one of the principal tools of management and Free was a good observer. He concentrated on observing new things about moving water, elevations, and distances. You see, the spring was not directly above the house but somewhat around the hill, heading a stream circling off to the right. Could water be made to run around a hill as well as down a hill? Could some of the fall near the spring be saved to use near the house? From a point in a distant cornfield Free could see both the spring and the house at the same time, and he concluded that there was enough drop to meet his purpose.

The analysis was spread over weeks; all the while Free trod the path back and forth and weighed the pull of the heavy buckets against the trouble of building a flume to do the carrying. In so doing he was matching costs against returns. Would the idea work? How could sections of the flume be supported? What long and slender, yet straight trees could he use for sections? Who had an adz that he could borrow? Was the whole thing worth the effort? Would his neighbors laugh at him? Many personal considerations were involved in the pros (returns) and cons (costs) to be considered. Even if it did work some neighbors would probably say the contraption was the invention of the devil.

To continue meant revealing his plans. Free had not yet told a soul, not even his wife. To continue also meant the use of extra effort: both carrying water and hewing poles. Our entrepreneur needed *will power* to announce a *decision* and carry out his plan. This he summoned and told his wife.

Up to this stage Free had taken three of the steps in the management process. He had: (1) *conceived an idea* related to a problem, *observed* facts bearing on the problem and his idea of its solution; (2) *analyzed* the problem, including the uncovering of some new difficulties and readjustment of his solution; (3) made a *decision*, i.e., he *determined to take an action* and accept whatever consequences the actions entailed.

What consequences?

> Ridicule if he failed.
> Lost work if he failed.
> Praise, maybe, if it worked.
> More water.
> Less work.
> More time to do other things.

Free now took the next step in management. He went to work—physically as well as mentally now. He acted and accepted responsibility for those actions. To management he added labor—cut long straight trees, grooved them into troughs, whistled to keep up his courage, smiled when his curious neighbors twitted. Then in the twilight of an evening he fitted the first section. Ah! It worked! Water ran through it—moved closer to his house.

The next day's journey to water was not so long. Encouraged, Free worked all the following day, fitted section to section—water moved closer and closer. Then all the way. Success!

Now the riddle of this story is this: Where was management used, and what did it do? Labor cut the logs; capital furnished the adz and the ax; nature provided the trees. What did management do? Where was it? Could you see it, or taste it, or smell it? No, management is an intangible. It has no form that can be seen or weighed on scales. Yet without management no flume would have been made. Management (1) "thought up" the *idea* and *observed* things about a problem; (2) *analyzed* the observations and subproblems associated with the idea; (3) made a *decision;* (4) *acted;* and (5) accepted responsibility for the results. But these are intangible things. Could they be counted as inputs? Did a physical product result? If so, what physical product? What did management accomplish? How much did it accomplish?

Free may have inherited a portion of his managerial ability, and he may have acquired some of it through training. His neighbors would have said that he was a handy man—that he could do anything he set his mind to. His father was that type of dreamer who was always going to do something, his mother the type that got things done. As a boy, Free had made bows and arrows, tied paper bags on the house cat, roamed the woods, and learned of nature. His mother had taught him the virtues of industry and thrift, and pointed to the rewards of accomplishment. The fact that he made the flume and that it worked was no great surprise to some of his neighbors, who would probably have given credit for Free's ability to both inheritance and training. It has been said that "nothing succeeds like success," which means in this story that the hero was now better fitted to use management on the next problem.

Let us complete illustrating the definition of management. We have seen that capital was necessary, in the form of an adz and an ax, and that a product of the land (trees) was used. The largest physical input was labor—services of the disciplined, co-ordinated and skilled physical strength of a man. The decisions of the man were reflected through his judgments in assembling and co-ordinating these other factors, and through the thing he chose to do. In a commercial economy it would have been reflected also through contacts with the outside business world—prices and people. But Free was not yet through managing. He had more choices to consider, more judgments to formulate, more decisions to make. He had to apportion his earnings between his farming business and the needs of his family, between using them today or reinvesting them for larger uses tomorrow. Should he use the time saved to milk another cow or roam the woods with Free, Junior? He had also to apportion his earnings among his business, his family, himself and his community, because the end products of management are human satisfactions.

Management Examined Further

Since the management service is a human factor evolving within men and created only during the period of use, it is often associated with specific human traits called personality traits. Dr. Henry C. Taylor devoted a chapter in *Outlines of Agricultural Economics* to a description of some of the human traits that he considered essential to success in farming.[1] Among these, he said, are health and strength,

[1] Henry C. Taylor, *Outlines of Agricultural Economics*, Chapter X, The Macmillan Company.

skill in a variety of tasks, a clear vision, good judgment, knowledge, faithfulness, interest, honesty, courage, and patience.

Problem Exercise 1, to which students are asked to give consideration, contains a list of several traits that are likely to have some bearing on management. The items are to be checked with reference to men known by the student and considered to be good farm managers, and also with reference to other men considered to be poor managers. The list is not a score card. The items are not weighted, neither are the various individual traits considered of equal value or even separately essential. It is well recognized that good managers vary widely in personality. The value, then, in giving consideration to such a list should come through directing attention to some of the traits usually thought to be of either positive or negative value in management. The student should keep in mind that management has been analyzed in the definition and in the illustration of the definition as performing five tasks:

1. Getting of ideas and making observations.
2. Analysis of observations, including formulation and reformulation of problems and ideas concerning their solution.
3. Decision making.
4. Action.
5. Acceptance of responsibility for actions.

The list in Problem Exercise 1 consists of personality traits. Some of these traits can be readily associated with one or more of the five tasks. For example, determination is easily associated with action and acceptance of responsibility. The second on the list, easy going, is difficult to associate with any of the five. As a part of the exercise, would you like to see if you can make associations between the various traits and the five tasks given?

Learning and Management. Can one be trained to be a better manager? Are personality traits inherited or acquired? Or both? The basis for some of them is without question inherited. Physical strength —the residence of management—for example, has basis in the natural body, yet it is clearly easy to increase physical strength through feeding and exercise, or to diminish it through neglect. Mental strength, made up of such qualities as determination, the ability to reason abstractly, courage, persistence, and memory, likewise may be sharpened, increased, and developed. Encouragement from associates may help one to increase a man's determination. Faith of friends in one's abil-

ity to do things is one of the most compelling forces in individual behavior. Some sons learn to manage from their fathers. If teaching
is conscious on the part of parents, doubtless much learning to manage results.

The connection between the learning process and management cannot be overemphasized. Efficient learners among managers are able to
handle the affairs of their businesses more accurately and quickly than
inefficient learners. Efficient learners are close observers in their field
of interest, keen analysts, and adept concluders or decision makers.
The functional definition of management developed herein [1] appears
good but is undeveloped with respect to the relationships between the
learning process and management. What are the principles a manager
should follow in order to maximize his efficiency as an observer? As
an analyst? How does a manager equate the cost of an additional
observation or additional analysis with its value?

All thought processes are subject to error. Some managers are at
once quicker and more accurate in their conclusions than others. As it
takes time for a manager to reason, make observations, analyze observations, and draw conclusions, inefficient learners among managers
require more time to make business decisions with a given degree of
accuracy than efficient learners. Time for thinking and decision making is often purchased with resources held in reserve or in inefficient
uses. Net returns to a business, therefore, depend partly upon the
ability of its manager to learn effectively and rapidly. A rapid, efficient learner needs less time to learn, and hence keeps fewer resources
in reserve and inflexible, inefficient employments. The resulting differential in net income is conceptually traceable to management.

Management and Risk Taking. Some managers take large risks;
others are conservative. Overly conservative managers may never get
into business and, if they do, may never be able to learn enough about
an event to permit them to act. Overconservatism may require more
accuracy than is economically attainable. The result is that the more
audacious managers may beat the more conservative managers to
lucrative opportunities. On the other hand, the large-risk taker may
continually try to exploit opportunities about which he is poorly informed. Though the extreme gambler worries little about committing
errors, the results of such errors may "wipe him out." There seems to

[1] Glenn L. Johnson, "Needed Developments in Economic Theory as Applied
to Farm Management." *Journal of Farm Economics*, XXXII, 1950, pp. 1151–
1152.

be an optimum degree of risk taking. A little reflection indicates that the amount of *risk* a manager is willing to take depends upon such factors as (1) the amount of assets he has to lose; (2) the status of his family; (3) his age; (4) the society in which he lives; (5) the effect of possible gains or losses upon his social position; and (6) his love of adventure.

Capacity for Management. Industrial psychologists have given attention to measuring management capacity in men. A number of tests have been devised by them, for the purpose of appraising managerial capacity. Efforts in this field are reported to be only partially successful, but they indicate strongly that qualities for management are personal, and further that such qualities may be appraised. Their efforts correspond to the work of specialists in other fields who are attempting to find relationships between a number of factors and results, such as relationships between factors of soil fertility and soil productivity. A list of qualities claimed by the users of one management test to be associated with success in executive positions is reproduced in an article in *Fortune* magazine.[1] The article, the tests, and the lists refer wholly to hired management in industrial businesses and in no way imply that such tests or qualities apply directly to measuring the management capacity of farmers. However, the list is worth reviewing by those interested in the management factor in farming. The article says in part:

According to their [2] ··· findings, the successful executive exhibits eleven definite "traits" and the unsuccessful twelve. Here, greatly condensed, are their marks of the successful: (1) he is primarily motivated by the sheer accomplishment of work; (2) he accepts authority without resentment; (3) he has strong drives toward achievement first, then toward material rewards and prestige; (4) he can organize events or facts and see relationships that tie them together; (5) he is decisive, either on the spot or after detailed consideration; (6) he has firm conviction, knows what he is, what he wants, and has well-developed techniques for getting what he wants; (7) he has a constant drive to be moving and doing things; (8) he has a pervasive fear of failure; (9) he is aware of immediate realities and their implications; (10) he identifies himself with his superiors, regards his subordinates as "doers of work" rather than as people; (11) he has "left home," i.e., has broken his emotional ties to his mother but retains a positive tie to his father as the admired symbol of authority.

Gardner and Henry have found that the first ten of these traits are present to some degree in all efficient managers. (The eleventh is necessary in execu-

[1] *Fortune,* XLII, 1, July, 1950. Courtesy of the publishers.
[2] Social Research, Inc.

tives of large impersonal corporations.)   Conversely, they report that failure of an executive is usually due to a combination of several of these twelve traits: (1) he is detail-minded, he cannot see the forest for the trees; (2) he avoids responsibility, does not concern himself with changes or innovations; (3) he unconsciously desires to be in some other, non-executive work; (4) he unconsciously desires the social status of an executive, not the work itself; (5) he is intolerant of slow advancement through routine tasks; (6) he cannot cooperate with associates or accept criticism; (7) he resists authority; (8) he is arrogant with subordinates; (9) he interprets situations in terms of his own fixed ideas about himself and others; (10) he concentrates all his energy in his work; (11) he fears success, has an unconscious urge to fail; (12) he is overly self-critical, convinced he cannot succeed.

Some of the traits are perhaps more applicable to managers of farms than others.   The first seven and the ninth of the positive ones are easily related to one or more of the five management tasks, as listed. The latter division of the first, namely the acceptance of authority without resentment, is not applicable to firms whose sole managerial responsibilities are assumed by one individual.   However, if we were permitted to substitute "failure" for "authority," making the quality read "accepts failure without resentment," the new statement would appear to be wholly applicable to farm managers.   The tenth and eleventh are not applicable.

These traits may be checked against the five management tasks as an exercise.   Franklin Riess, at the University of Illinois, is completing a somewhat similar study concerning farm managers.

The Difference between Skill and Management.   Skill is usually thought of as being related to physical or mental proficiency.   One becomes skilled in carpentry or arithmetic, for example, through practice.   Skills are more often associated with labor than management: skilled carpenters, accountants, machinists, and animal husbandrymen are usual.   Distinctions between skill and management are easy to draw at the extremes; difficult at the center.   The parallel drawn between learning and management in this book provides the basis for distinguishing between management and skilled actions.   When a hired hand, who does not know how to handle modern farm machinery, decides to acquire such ability, it is necessary for him to perform the five managerial tasks noted in this chapter.   Thus, *in handling his own affairs* (not the affairs of his employer), a hired hand is performing a managerial action when he learns to operate modern farm machines.   Once this ability is acquired, he becomes a *more* skilled laborer.   The return for his managerial activity is the skill which he has acquired. As a result of his managerial actions, he reduces his ignorance and acquires a worth-while asset or skill. That skill is the return for his managerial action. When he sells the use of this asset to the farmer employing him he is not selling managerial services—he is selling skilled labor. His wages are a return for the skill which, in turn, was a return for his managerial activity.

When, as a result of observing, analyzing, deciding, taking action, and accepting responsibility, assets are acquired which have repetitive value, such assets, if personal, are ordinarily referred to as skills. Acquisition of such skills involves managerial activity. The sale of such a skill is not a managerial activity.

A large percentage of the problems encountered in running a farm business are not repetitive in nature. Such problems occur but once and the five managerial tasks must be performed for each such problem. Thus the farmer, handling such problems, repeats the managerial tasks over and over again without the acquisition of personal capacities (skills) having repetitive value, and we say that he is managing the affairs of his business.

What Are the Problems with Which Management Deals?

In a subsequent chapter, it will be seen that almost all the problems which concern managers can be classified under one of the following subjects:

1. Changes in prices or lack of information concerning existing prices.
2. Lack of information concerning existing production methods.
3. Changes in production methods.
4. Changes in personalities, and lack of information concerning personalities.
5. Changes in economic, political, and social institutions and lack of information concerning the existing institutions.

This book is predicated upon the conviction that managerial capacity can be taught and/or developed. The authors feel that people can be trained to become more efficient observers and analysts. The authors are convinced that people can be taught ways of attacking problems arising under each of the five subject matter categories described above. The authors are further convinced that students and farmers in general can be trained to see the consequences of their

actions and that such foresight will make them (1) better decision
makers, (2) more aware of their responsibilities, and (3) more likely to
take those actions which will lead to satisfactory attainment of their
various monetary and non-monetary objectives.

QUESTIONS AND PROBLEMS

1. Write definitions for: analysis, agronomy, judgment, capacity, ability, thrift,
efficiency, and resources.

2. Management has been traditionally defined as choosing crops, selecting livestock, directing labor, etc. How does this definition differ from the one given and
illustrated in this text?

3. What actions may students in colleges take to increase their managerial
abilities?

4. Distinguish between farm management as a subject and management of
farms as a vocation.

5. If Free Enterprise decided to start a business of building water conveyors
for neighbors similar to the one described in the illustration, of what would his
management problems consist?

6. Relate the five tasks of management to the decision of either (1) buying
feeder cattle or (2) going to college.

⁎ PROBLEM EXERCISE 1
Personal Characteristics of Managers of Farms

1. (a) Make a tabulation of the items as given on the next page. (b) Select
two men whom you consider good managers of farms and two whom you consider to be fair managers. (c) Give each of them a name or other identification
in the head of the columns as on the next page. (d) Mark each of the personal
characteristics listed as descriptive (+), or not descriptive (−) as related to each
of the men selected. (e) Summarize your observations.

2. List five of the personal characteristics, as given on the next page, that you
think may be associated with each of the management tasks.

A. Observing and   B. Analyzing   C. Making decisions
   getting ideas

_____   _____   _____
_____   _____   _____
_____   _____   _____
_____   _____   _____

D. Acting   E. Accepting responsibility

_____   _____
_____   _____
_____   _____
_____   _____

Personal Characteristics of Managers of Farms

Characteristics	Names or Other Identifications of Farmers Rated			
Determined Easy going Domineering—bossy Tactful Headstrong				
Alert to opportunities Trades quickly Decides carefully Industrious Thrifty Adaptable				
Courageous Aggressive Acts in risky situations Conservative Big talker Adopts new practices Analyzes carefully				
Neighborly Honest Bargain driver				
Physically strong Studious Persistent Hard worker Self-disciplined Has good memory Keeps ahead of work				
Uncanny judgment Lucky Foresighted Plans work Holds to life purpose Interested in job Observes closely				

Made most of money by:
  trading
  inheritance
  crop production
  livestock production
  taking risk
  slow accumulation				

Slow to give advice Quick to accept advice Good supervisor				

PROBLEM EXERCISE 2

1. Make a list of the things you suggest doing to develop managerial ability in a 10-year-old boy.

2. (*a*) Relate the applicable personal characteristics listed in Problem 1 to a fellow student whom you consider well above average.

(*b*) Write a description of the student selected for item (*a*) from the point of view of management of his present academic and associated work.

3. From the positive and negative lists of management traits used by Gardner and Henry for testing management in industrial organizations list eight that you think most applicable to good farm managers.

CHAPTER 2

The Subjects Which Managers Must Study

This chapter discusses, in general terms, the five subject matter areas with which managers must be concerned. The authors feel that almost all subjects which a manager must study can be classified under one of the five subject matter areas mentioned in Chapter 1. These five subject matter areas—existing production methods, forthcoming changes in production methods, prices, personalities, and institutional settings—provide the outline around which this chapter is written.

Stability in farming is abnormal—change and the need to study and adjust to change are normal. In farming, as elsewhere, partial ignorance is universal: the need to learn and adjust is the main problem of farm management. The questions arise, what are the kinds of changes which farmers are continually experiencing and what are the subjects about which farmers need to learn? Those subjects are grouped into meaningful categories, categories which have sufficient unity to be studied as a whole with some assurance that generalizations applying to the category can be drawn.

It appears that almost all the changes which a manager must study and handle can be grouped under one of the following five categories:

1. A manager's own imperfect state of knowledge concerning existing production methods.

2. Forthcoming changes in production methods.

3. Price changes and lack of knowledge concerning existing prices and price relationships.

4. Changes in the personalities and lack of knowledge concerning the individuals closely associated with the farm business.

5. Changes in and ignorance concerning the economic, social, and political environment in which the business is being operated.

Because a farmer does not know all the production techniques which might be useful to him, he continuously faces the problem of acquiring knowledge concerning such methods and of taking action concerning them.

In the twentieth century with its rapid rate of invention, changes in production methods occur annually, monthly, and, seemingly, almost daily. Thus, managers must try to avoid making fixed investments in machinery, buildings, and equipment which will soon be rendered obsolete by subsequent inventions. One has only to think of the threshers, the heavy old-fashioned tractor, and the obsolete horse-drawn equipment of the past decade to realize the importance of changes in the technology of production.

Price changes are another bugaboo of the twentieth-century farmer —World War I inflation, high prices paid for items of production in the twenties, the price depression of the thirties, the World War II inflation, and the widely anticipated post-World War II depression.

Farm businesses are continuously being affected by personality changes—a son becomes reckless, the manager himself becomes shiftless or careless, a wife becomes dissatisfied, a creditor becomes less lenient or, perhaps, even "shady" in his dealings, or a theft occurs. Any of these may have serious consequences for a farm business, and a manager has to spend part of his time watching, learning, and adjusting to such changes in personalities.

Again, the economic, social, and political setting in which a farm business operates is continuously changing: tax structures change, available markets change, social values change, acreage allotments and marketing quotas change, and the political strength of groups of producers change.

Changes in Production Methods and Imperfections in Knowledge Concerning Production Methods [1]

Farmers rarely find themselves in possession of all that is to be known about the production processes that they are employing or might employ on their particular farms. In the first place, such processes are continually developing, thus causing the information which farmers possess to become obsolete. And, in the second place, farming is such a complex business that farmers are rarely successful in acquiring all the existing knowledge concerning the production processes which they employ. Thus, farmers are ordinarily curious

[1] W. E. Hendrix, "Availability of Capital and Production Innovations on Low Income Farms," *Journal of Farm Economics*, XXXIII, 1951. Emily L. Day and E. L. Barber, *Physical Risks in Farm Production—Selected References*, 1930–1948, Library List No. 49, U. S. Dept. of Agriculture Library, August, 1949.

persons, highly interested in production methods and willing to "talk shop" at the "drop of a hat" concerning different ways of producing crops and livestock.

The demand for knowledge and production know-how occasionally develops farm management men who are "jacks of all trades" rather than masters of management. Despite this statement, a knowledge of production methods is one of the basic requirements for managing a farm. However, such knowledge is not management; it is knowledge of production methods and, as such, is a fundamental for farming. This book, in developing its first overall procedure for "roughing out" the organization of a farm, will make extensive use of knowledge and information concerning the capacity of soil to produce different kinds of crops without irreparable damage to itself. The authors refer to this procedure as the land-use approach to farm organization. It is based, in a very fundamental sense, on knowledge concerning the technical subjects of agronomy (both soils and crops) and animal husbandry.

Researchers and specialists in the technical agricultural sciences are important sources of technical know-how. So also are the commercial companies which produce fertilizers, feed, and machinery for the agricultural industry. The private farm management services should not be forgotten. Probably the most important single source of technical knowledge is the experience of other farmers.

Knowledge of agricultural production processes can be broadly classified into two categories. The first category concerns questions of *how* to produce a certain product or products. The second category of knowledge concerns questions about *how much* of a certain product or products should be produced. For decades American agriculture has been developing technical know-how at the most rapid rate in the history of civilization. Hence, the questions of "how" have been of very great importance. In periods of rapid change this type of question eclipses questions of "how much"; thus, a great part of the extension work and of the research work of our colleges of agriculture has concentrated on questions of "how." Similarly, the advertisements of our feed, fertilizer, and machinery companies have tended to concentrate on the same type of questions.

Economic theorists using concepts based upon assumptions of an unchanging know-how have tended to miss the importance of answering questions concerning how different farm products should be produced. Instead, they have tended to concentrate upon questions of how much of the various inputs pays and how high yields should be in order to maximize profits from a given production method.

Obviously, on reflection, it is evident that neither the persons concentrating on questions of "how" nor the persons concentrating on questions of "how much" are in balance. The balanced researcher, extension man, or farm manager alternates the two types of questions in accordance with their relative importance in the problems which he faces.

The tendency of the technical agricultural scientist to concentrate upon questions of "how" to produce in contrast to questions of "how much to produce" has resulted in a dearth of research results useful in answering questions of how much. Chapter 16 of this book on pork production, Chapter 17 on dairy production, and Chapter 18 on beef production present some of the most useful data produced by the physical scientists on answering the question of how much. All these studies were designed by teams of agricultural economists and physical scientists working together. Answering questions of "how much" requires the use of economic principles, which will be rather fully developed in subsequent chapters and will not be discussed further at this point.

Our agricultural society has developed a wide variety of agencies for providing information to farmers concerning productive processes. First, the agricultural press feeds information, in the form of special articles, to farmers on a daily, weekly, and monthly basis. The success of the publishing companies in selling such material to farmers attests the high esteem attached to this source of information by the people actually managing the farms of the United States.

The companies which buy advertisement space should be noted in connection with the farm publications. All the major farm machinery companies, the fertilizer companies, the feed companies, and companies producing the drugs used by farmers employ farm magazines as a means of disseminating information on how to produce various products. Probably the agricultural press is the most important direct contact between persons possessing productive know-how and the persons using that know-how.

The agriculturists of the United States have called upon various governmental agencies to do research on production questions and to disseminate the results of such research to farm people. Chief among the agencies disseminating such information are the agricultural extension services connected with our state colleges of agriculture, the vocational agriculture system, the soil conservation service, and other agencies of the United States Department of Agriculture.

In addition to the agricultural press and governmental agencies mentioned above, various privately organized farm management services disseminate a great deal of information to farm managers, farm owners, and those having business dealings with farmers. The farm management services regularly (1) mail to their clients information on production processes and (2) hold demonstration meetings for their clients.

Several farm organizations also play important roles in distributing production information among farmers. A list of such organizations includes the American Farm Bureau, The Grange, The Farmer's Union, and various special associations formed among the producers and processors of particular products such as milk, citrus fruits, cotton, soybeans, and tobacco. The list includes also the various farmer cooperatives which find it advantageous in their sales programs to disseminate production information.

Forthcoming Changes in Production Methods [1]

In addition to the lack of knowledge concerning existing production methods, farmers naturally lack knowledge concerning the inventions and innovations which will occur in the future. Thus, even the best-informed modern farmers are likely to have their businesses upset by inventions and developments which render investments in machinery, buildings, and equipment obsolete and their existing knowledge more or less out of date.

Such changes cannot be accurately foreseen. They may be anticipated by persons in the vanguard or by persons closely associated with people making the inventions and bringing about the developments in technology. It appears that the need for protection against such changes is more important than the need to try to predict such changes. Thus, farmers often find it advantageous to refrain from making large-scale investments for the production of certain products when such investments could be easily rendered obsolete by minor inventions and developments. The wide-awake farmer protects himself against such changes by "not being the one upon whom the new is tried or the last to lay the old aside." By avoiding being experimented upon, a farmer can avoid the losses involved when an inven-

[1] Hendrix, *op. cit.*

tion or development proves to be a "dud." On the other hand, by not being the last to lay the old aside, a farmer can remain in position to salvage a part, at least, of his investments in old production methods.

Price Changes [1]

Only a farmer's interest in production methods exceeds his interest in price changes. When farmers gather, sooner or later their conversations turn to the prices they are receiving for what they produce, the prices they are paying for what they have to buy, or prospective changes in both, including the relationship between prices paid and prices received.

For purposes of discussion, it is advantageous to distinguish between two kinds of price changes. Prices change in absolute level, i.e., the price of corn may go up from $1.10 to $1.40 and back to 90 cents a bushel. The other kind of price change is illustrated when the price of one commodity or group of commodities changes relative to another commodity or group of commodities, i.e., the price of corn can change from one-half that of a bushel of wheat to three-fourths that of a bushel of wheat to one-fourth that of a bushel of wheat. Or an index of livestock product prices can be twice as high as an index of feed prices at one point in time, and, at another point in time, be at the same level.

From the World War I period to the depths of the depression, prices received by farmers fell drastically. This decline in the absolute level of prices upset plans made by farmers. All debt commitments, which are ordinarily in absolute dollar terms, became difficult to meet as the absolute level of prices received fell. In the same period, prices paid by farmers fell but not so rapidly. Hence, even debt-free farmers suffered serious consequences in the 1920–1933 period. They suffered these consequences because the prices they received fell in relation to prices that they had to pay for the items which they purchased. Thus, net income (measured both in dollars and in purchasing power) fell because the prices of products which were produced fell relative to the prices of items purchased.

[1] D. Gale Johnson, *Forward Prices for Agriculture,* Chicago, University of Chicago Press, 1947.

W. W. Wilcox, "Effects of Farm Price Changes on Efficiency in Farming," *Journal of Farm Economics,* XXXIII, 1951.

D. B. Williams, "Price Expectations and Reactions to Uncertainty by Farmers in Illinois," *Journal of Farm Economics,* XXXIII, 1951.

By the early 20's, it was evident to farm leaders that instability in prices and the inability of farmers to predict price changes were greatly reducing the efficiency with which farm products were being produced in the United States. It was further evident that these price instabilities were having adverse effects upon the welfare of farm people. Thus, action was taken, on the part of the Federal Government, to provide farmers with more adequate information concerning prospective price changes. This work became known as "outlook work." Since April, 1923, a series of continuous studies have been conducted by the Bureau of Agricultural Economics in Washington, D. C. These studies deal with each of the important farm commodities and, in addition, deal with income and overall demand. The results of these continuous studies have been published in a series of situation reports. Currently, the Bureau of Agricultural Economics publishes monthly situation reports on the following commodities and subjects: cotton, dairy, fats and oils, feeds, fruits, livestock and meat, poultry and eggs, tobacco, vegetables, wheat, wool, sugar, demand and price, farm income, marketing and transportation, food, costs, and the general agricultural situation.

Once in the fall of each year the monthly situation work is summarized and presented in the form of forward-looking "outlook statements" to all interested agencies, especially the state extension services. This summary is presented at the Annual Outlook Conference in Washington. Some state extension agencies and others then carry the situation and outlook information to the various states, adapt it to the peculiar situations existing there, and pass it on to the farm press, county agents, and, thence, to individual farmers, businessmen, and others interested in agricultural prices, production, income, etc.

By and large, the outlook and situation workers have done an efficient job of predicting changes in the prices of farm products relative to each other. They have also done a moderately good job of predicting changes in the prices of items which farmers buy relative to prices of the items which they sell. On the other hand, the record of the situation and outlook workers is much less impressive when the accuracy of their predictions concerning the general level of prices is considered. Economists, state extension people, bankers, federal workers, and, apparently, the rest of us do a very poor job of predicting changes in the general price level. It appears that the highly advanced American economy has a rather unstable price level easily thrown out of balance by wars, psychological trends, and other more

or less random and, hence, relatively unpredictable factors. Despite this difficulty, the continued support of the situation and outlook work indicates that it is helping ease a felt difficulty. Undoubtedly, this work has contributed tremendously to the productive efficiency of American agriculture and to the welfare of the United States.

Several other sources of price information are available to individual farmers and agriculturists. The many commercial sources feed a continual flow of price information to farmers. The daily and weekly newspapers and the weekly and monthly magazines furnish farmers with a continuous series of statements and articles concerning changes in both absolute and relative prices. Commercial men—feed dealers, fertilizer distributors, and machinery dealers—also serve to keep farmers rather continuously informed concerning changes in the prices of the products which they buy. Among the private agencies disseminating price information to farmers perhaps none are more important than (1) the private agencies extending credit to farmers, and (2) the farm management services. Because the safety of loans extended to farmers depends in major part upon price developments, the people administering credit agencies spend a great deal of time studying price outlook and advising borrowers about prospective changes in prices.

Government price-supporting agencies also disseminate important information to farmers in the form of announcements concerning price support levels and programs. It is also very important to note that such programs reduce price variations and, hence, (1) make it easier to predict future prices, and (2) reduce the consequences of errors in predicting prices.

The individual farmer plays a very positive role in bringing information concerning prices to his business. It is he who seeks out price information, observes it, and analyzes it as a basis for making decisions affected by prospective price developments.

The individual farmer draws his information from the sources listed above as well as from a wide variety of other sources such as the experiences of others, trips which he takes about the country, conversations with other people, political developments, and international decisions which might result in war or peace.

In local markets, where personal considerations affect the price of such items as land, major items of equipment, and labor, the farm manager gathers information from local sources which serves to help him locate and take advantage of bargains.

Changes in the Personalities Closely Associated with a Farm Business [1]

As previously pointed out, the personalities that affect a farm business change continuously. They change with respect to the values which they attach to various commodities, services, and activities. They change with respect to their capacity to render services to the farm business. They change with respect to their honesty and integrity, and they change in response to the actions taken by the farm business. The first and last of these four types of changes are rather closely related. They can be separated on the basis of strategy; i.e., the changes in responses of individuals to actions of the business are involved when the strategies of handling people are considered, whereas changes in beliefs and convictions held by people will be considered in a much broader sense.

Changes in Values Held by People Associated with a Farm Business. The value structure of a person is made up of the importances which he attaches to commodities, concepts, services, and activities. Value structures vary from person to person in accordance with their psychological make-up, their moral and esthetic training, the society in which they live, and a wide variety of other influences. Value structures are usually considered to be important on the consumption side of economics. Thus, they are often ignored in studying production and management problems. However, it will be noted that the chances which farmers take, the managerial decisions made, the problems considered, and the results of their decisions depend upon the values which they attach to possible losses and gains in income and the value which they attach to performance of the five managerial tasks of observing, analyzing, deciding, acting, and accepting responsibility. A little further reflection indicates that the actions of farmers are determined to a much greater extent than commonly realized by their concepts of what is important, i.e., the values which they hold. Persons who have watched a farmer enjoy such assets as a new tractor, a well-bred, fine animal, or a cool, restful woodlot know that a great deal of consumption occurs on the business side of farming. Values

[1] J. M. Brewster and H. L. Parsons, "Can Prices Allocate Resources in American Agriculture?" *Journal of Farm Economics,* XXVIII, 1946.

J. D. Black et al., *Farm Management,* The Macmillan Co., 1949, pp. 88–102.

J. von Neuman and O. Morgenstern, *Theory of Games and Economic Behavior,* Princeton, Princeton University Press, 1947.

J. McDonald, *Strategy in Poker, Business and War,* W. W. Morten and Company, 1950.

such as those mentioned above are held by managers and are important aspects of managing a farm.

The values held by the members of a farm family also play important roles in the operation of farm businesses. If a farm family values increases in earning power much more highly than increases in current consumption levels, it is easier to expand and develop a farm business. If the family values a costly level of living highly, it may become very difficult for a farm manager to stabilize the consumption pattern of his family enough to accumulate savings for needed investments in the farm business.

Similarly, the importance attached to various activities and services by the businessmen with whom a farmer deals has important impacts upon a farm business. A conservative banker may seriously restrict the credit available to a farmer capable of using it wisely. On the other hand, a reckless lender may encourage a farmer to take unusually large risks in purchasing land, machinery and livestock. The importance which the businessmen dealing with the farm manager attach to honesty and integrity may have important effects upon a farm business. The authors know, for instance, of more than one farm operation which has been liquidated or put in serious difficulty by the failure of lenders to make a promised extension of shortrun credit arrangements.

Changes of the nature described above need to be studied almost continuously by a farmer. He needs to see such changes developing and take steps to protect his business against them or to take advantage of them. Written contracts, bonding arrangements, deposits, etc., are ways of protecting a business against certain undesirable changes in "outside" personalities.

Further, a business can be protected against undesirable changes in the personalities of the farm manager and his family by conscious attempts to develop desirable value structures. Self-study of such problems as family education, public education, religious education, and a general attempt to develop desirable moral and esthetic values are important and have significant eventual implications for the successful operation of the farm business.

Changes in Personal Capacities of Individuals Associated with a Farm Business. The personal capacities of individuals are both physical and mental. Changes in the physical and mental capacities of the people associated with a farm business have important consequences for the successful operation of the business. On most commercial, family-type farms, the farmer and members of his family contribute most of the labor. The physical and mental capacity of farm families changes with the life cycle. Thus, farm businesses need to be adjusted to utilize the increases in the physical capacity of the manager and members of his family as such increases occur. Conversely, certain activities within the business have to be curtailed as the capacity of the operator and his family diminishes in the later years of his life or as the services of family members are lost for one reason or another. Mental capacities change in much the same way as physical capacities, and the same conclusions apply.

Investments can be made in both mental and physical capacity. Sons and daughters can be given educations which increase their mental capacities for purposes of managing and operating farm businesses. Farmers may invest in their own mental capacities by attending meetings, purchasing educational literature, and by self-study. Similarly, investments are often made in the physical capacity of the members of farm families. Medical care is given, mechanical aids are used to prevent physical breakdown, and a wide variety of other investments are made which contribute to the physical capacity and durability of individuals.

Responses of Individuals to Actions Taken by a Farm Business.[1] People differ from inanimate objects and animals in that they think and adjust their actions to the actions of others. Thus, the actions taken by a manager are important determinants of the actions taken by people closely associated with his business. Study of these actions and reactions falls in the realm of personal strategy. This type of change in the personalities associated with a business can often be anticipated and, for that matter, determined by the actions which the manager himself takes. Thus, it is necessary for a farm manager to study and learn a great deal about the reaction of others to his actions. This subject is of particular importance in handling hired laborers, members of the farm family, creditors, businessmen, and the influential members of the farm community.

Changes in Economic, Social and Political Environment in Which a Farm Business Operates

The American economy is one of the most changeable in the history of civilization. The world situation is one of the most controversial and fluid in the history of civilization. Consequently, the political, economic, and social environment in which American farms are oper-

---

[1] J. von Neuman and Oskar Morgenstern, *Theory of Games and Economic Behavior,* Princeton, Princeton University Press, 1947.

ated changes continuously. Philosophies behind government actions change and, as a result, the political framework in which American farms operate changes. Wars occur, populations grow, the country becomes urbanized, etc. All these changes have their influence upon the farm businesses which produce the food, fiber and other raw material for our changing society and industries. These rapid changes influence the values held by farm people, render productive techniques obsolete, eliminate and create demands for certain types of products; in short, any farm business must be continually adjusted to such changes.

Some of the most direct forms in which political, social, and economic changes have their impact on farm businesses are found in the government programs. Production controls and price supports now play very important roles in American agriculture. From 1850 to 1900, public subsidies in the construction of railroads were playing similar roles. Also, from 1800 to 1900 the governmental policy of distributing land at virtually no cost was having its lasting impact upon American agriculture. This land policy rendered certain types of farms obsolete and created entirely new production. We now have the river development plans, the soil conservation legislation and publicly supported research and extension services. In addition to these direct influences to which farm managers must adjust, the modern American farmer is called upon to adjust to the impact of war and defense preparations, new tax structures, new educational systems, new transportation policies, etc.

The techniques which farm managers employ in learning about and adjusting to this general category of changes are not unique. Fundamentally, forthcoming changes must be anticipated and adjustments made thereto. In carrying out these processes, farmers often find it advantageous to avoid large fixed investments in production processes dependent for profitability upon governmental arrangements. Farmers also often find it advantageous to preserve ability to readjust their business as changes occur in the varying political-economic-social environment. Farmers also find it advantageous to spend a considerable amount of time (1) observing and learning about such changes, and (2) trying to bring about desirable changes (a) through regular governmental channels, and (b) through their own special farm organizations. These various activities are being carried out to an optimum degree when the value of carrying these activities further is just sufficient to offset the additional cost of carrying them out.

CHAPTER 3

Management, Its Functions, and Elementary Managerial Principles

This is the third chapter which deals specifically with the tasks of management. It examines in further detail the discussion opened in Chapter 1. The objects are to (1) ascertain more specifically what management does and (2) to present, in general, some principles for increasing the capacity and efficiency with which the managerial tasks are performed. With few exceptions, the subject matter with which management deals plays a secondary role in this chapter. The emphasis is upon management, its tasks, and how to perform these tasks effectively.

This book is written around a definition of management which makes learning a definite component of management. The student should probably reread the definition of management in Chapter 1. These earlier pages defined management, in functional terms, as the performance of five tasks—observation, analysis, decision making, action and acceptance of responsibility. This definition has many implications, only a part of which have been thoroughly worked out.

The definition implies, for instance, that management is needed only in situations involving change and ignorance (more or less complete). It is because knowledge is imperfect, or changes are imperfectly foreseen, that it is necessary to observe, analyze, conclude, etc. If all owners of resources were perfectly informed, managers would not be needed to allocate resources properly.

A carpenter who knows how to construct complicated roof structures is not classified as a manager when doing such work. By the same token, a man who knows how to handle a herd of high-quality dairy cows is not a manager when handling them; instead, he is a herdsman, a skilled laborer. On the other hand, a beef producer observing the feed and livestock markets while accepting responsibility in buying, selling, and feeding beef animals on the basis of what he can learn about the everchanging cattle markets is ordinarily classified as a manager—he is operating in a situation of imperfect knowledge and change and spends time performing the five managerial tasks referred to above. A farmer engaged in deciding how many hogs to raise the next year or a farmer engaged in planning for the construction of a new barn to be used in beef production over the next 20 years is performing a managerial function. By the same token, a farmer who does not know how to grow a new crop, who does not know what the inputs involved in producing such a crop amount to, or what can be expected in the way of returns is engaged in managerial activity as he learns about the crop, makes decisions, acts, and accepts economic responsibility for his actions. If a farmer did not know how to build a gate and spent some time learning how to build various gates before taking action and accepting responsibility for the results, he, too, would be engaging in a managerial task. Once ability to build the gate is acquired, the farmer does not differ from a carpenter (skilled laborer) who could have been hired to build it.

Actions involving a portion of the five managerial steps may be classified as partial but not as complete managerial actions. Thus, "old Uncle Jake" who sat around the cracker barrel in the local store figuring up scheme after scheme on how to make a million dollars was engaging in but one phase of managerial actions. He never got beyond the point of observation (perhaps, faulty) and analysis. He never completed the managerial processes by deciding and taking action along with acceptance of responsibility. Similarly, many hired farm managers are engaged in only partial managerial activities. Hired farm managers may be limited, by their contractual agreement with the owner, as to the types of decisions which they can make; further, they rarely accept more than a small part of the economic responsibility for the actions which they take.

Degrees of Perfection in Knowledge

As has been noted above, a prime function of management is to improve knowledge (through observing and analyzing); therefore, it seems important, at this stage in the study of management, to classify the degrees of knowledge which a manager (farmer) may have concerning any event or process in which he is interested. Knowledge of a situation may range all the way from knowing nothing about a future event or process to knowing everything about that event or process. In setting up this classification, the authors (and contributing thinkers) have attempted to construct a classification which is meaningful in further studying and examining the managerial process. The classification begins with the least perfect knowledge situation and ends with the most perfect. Five knowledge situations are distinguished as follows: [1]

1. Inactive situation. The inactive situation exists when a manager does not foresee a future event well enough to take positive action, and does not value prospective increases in his knowledge more than the cost of making such increases. In other words, a manager remains inactive in the sense that he does not take positive actions if he (a) does not know enough to be ready, willing, and able to act, and (b) does not think acquisition of such knowledge is worth the effort and cost involved in acquiring such knowledge. He, therefore, does not act positively and does not try to learn; his action is of a negative nature.

2. The learning situation. The learning situation exists when a manager (a) does not foresee a future event well enough to take positive action concerning it, but (b) does value prospective improvements in his knowledge more than the cost of making such improvements. He, therefore, engages in the positive act of attempting to learn more about the event before taking positive action concerning that event.

3. The forced action situation. A forced action situation exists when a manager does not foresee a future event well enough to be *willing* to take a positive action but is forced, nonetheless, to take such actions.[2]

4. The subjective risk situation. A subjective risk situation exists when a manager does not foresee future events perfectly but, nonetheless, sees them, or thinks he sees them, well enough to be ready, willing, and able to run the risks of taking a positive action.

[1] Frank Knight, in classifying knowledge situations in *Risk, Uncertainty and Profit* distinguished between risk and uncertainty only; the classification presented here has evolved over the years in the writing of many people (i.e., those of Marshak, Hart, and Tintner) and in the minds of the authors and their associates.

[2] In one sense, it is hard to distinguish this situation from the risk situation; i.e., the outside force could be regarded as one which (1) greatly reduces the value of more information or (2) greatly increases the cost of new information, *thereby* bringing about the condition to be subsequently defined as subjective risk. The difference is to be found in the existence or non-existence of such forces.

5. The subjective certainty situation. A subjective certainty situation exists when the manager operates and makes decisions as if he knew future events perfectly.

For inactive situations (the first of the above categories), few principles are applicable. Those which do apply deal mainly with determination of the chances which a manager is willing to run in taking a positive action. Obviously, the size of these chances must be considered by a manager before he knows his knowledge is so imperfect that he is unwilling to act.

In the second of the above categories (the learning situation), many principles of inductive (learning about the whole from a small part) and deductive (learning about small parts from knowledge of the whole) learning processes are applicable. *Budgeting and economic principles are particularly important aids to farmers in the learning situation.*

In forced action situations, many principles from the field of strategy are applicable. It may be, for instance, that in such a situation a manager would want to select actions such as taking out insurance which would minimize the possible losses that might be incurred. On the other hand, a manager might want to select a course of action which would maximize his possible gains at the expense of incurring larger probabilities of incurring moderately large losses.

In situations of subjective risk, all the principles of formal and informal insurance apply. Informal insurance includes such techniques as (1) discounting probable returns in order to acquire safety margins, (2) maintenance of reserves against possible unfavorable developments, and (3) diversification.

In the learning, risk, and forced action situations, strategic operations are important. In some cases these operations are impersonal; in others personal.

In the last and most perfect of the five degrees of knowledge (subjective certainty), the principles of static economics and of traditional budgeting are particularly applicable.

A Classification of Managerial Principles

The five tasks of management outlined in this book indicate that management is very closely tied in with the process of acquiring new information or learning. The last two functions, those of taking action and accepting economic responsibility, indicate that strategy and personal considerations are also important in management. Thus, it appears that principles for increasing the efficiency of management would fall into one of the following categories:

1. Principles of learning.
    (a) Deductive (going from the known or assumed to details).
    (b) Inductive (going from details to more widely applicable conclusions).
2. Principles of strategy.
    (a) Personal.
    (b) Impersonal.

A Statement of Principles for Increasing the Capacity and Efficiency of Management

Managerial principles, as distinguished from ordinary economic principles,[1] deal with the process of economizing in the performance of the five managerial tasks, these tasks being made necessary by the existence of imperfect knowledge and change. It *costs to perform* these tasks, and their performance has value. As is the case with the ordinary economic principles, *the core of the managerial principles is the equating of additional costs and additional returns as a condition defining an optimum position.* Obviously, it pays to increase costs only so long as the resultant additional returns cover the additional costs. The additional (marginal) cost of performing the various managerial functions must be equated with the additional (marginal) value of having such functions performed. The value of performing such functions is not ordinarily measured in dollar terms but is measured, instead, in personal terms; thus, the cost of performing the managerial functions must also be reckoned in personal, subjective terms if marginal costs and returns are to be equated. This is realistic: the cost of learning, for instance, is likely to be in personal terms; i.e., mental activity on the part of a manager is likely to involve more personal inconvenience than dollar costs.

Questions of how and how much are continually asked. Ordinary economic principles place heavy emphasis on answering questions of how much; i.e., marginality principles and input-output studies concentrate on answering questions concerning how much of different variable inputs should be used and how much of the various products

[1] On the production side, ordinary economic principles deal with the process of economizing in the use of scarce inputs in the production of some output which has value. On the consumption side, ordinary economic principles deal with the process of economizing in the use of consumption goods and services so as to derive a maximum of satisfaction from the limited income which a person has to spend. On both the production and consumption side these principles tacitly, if not specifically, ordinarily assume perfect knowledge and unchanging conditions.

should be produced. Ordinary economic principles place less, but still considerable, emphasis on choices between different *known* production methods, i.e., on questions of how to produce. Economists ordinarily leave the problem of learning new production techniques to technicians and physical scientists, i.e., animal husbandrymen, agronomists, etc.

Managers also face the questions of how and how much with respect to the five managerial tasks. For example, how should observations be made? How many observations should be taken? How much analysis should be done? What analytical procedure should be followed? In accepting economic responsibility, how much insurance should be acquired? The dynamic managerial principles answer the questions of how much in personal terms, i.e., in terms of equating the marginal personal cost of additional information with the marginal personal value of such information. These same principles are also capable of selecting which method of securing the information is best. Like ordinary economists, managerial theorists draw upon scientists for information concerning the various alternative "how's." The economist, the statistician, the logician, the psychologist, the mathematician, and the strategist all make their contributions to the development of managerial principles by furnishing data and procedures for performing the managerial tasks.

Learning Principles. It is important that the student understand the role which logic plays in management. Actual farm managers continuously employ both deductive and inductive thought processes in handling the everyday problems of farming.

Farmers often reason deductively from general facts, known or assumed to be true, to conclusions concerning the details of their farming operation. They are very prone to assume the truth of certain propositions, reason out the meaning and implications of these propositions, and take action accordingly. For instance, a farmer, knowing that hogs require substantial amounts of protein, reasons out the details deductively as to how to supply the protein as cheaply as possible. Also, on the assumption that they are in business to make money, farmers proceed to reason out the details of various business transactions and production processes ahead of time so that, when they actually close the transactions or perform the production process, they will be relatively sure of making a certain amount of money.

Farmers also continuously engage in inductive thought processes. As a rule, farmers are close observers and generalizers. Thus, on the basis of one, two, and perhaps three years of experience with a new crop, farmers often draw general conclusions concerning the long-time profitability of that crop or production process in their farm operations. From observing the individual animals in a herd or drove, farmers are prone to make generalizations concerning the value of different feeds, forages, and production techniques.

In addition to the general principles of deductive logic, management people have several subbodies of logic which serve as aids in the learning processes. These subbodies of logic serve as a basis for *visualizing* problems. In a sense, they provide perceptual images for a manager to use.

The *first* such important aid is the budget, which is a way of visualizing the results (in money terms) of employing various quantities of different inputs in the production of certain products. This approach, long used by farm management analysts, has been given renewed impetus by Boulding's *Reconstruction of Economics* which adopts a balance sheet approach in economic analysis. The *second* such important perceptual aid is the body of economic principles. These principles provide mental pictures (models) of great value in visualizing problems and arranging information for their solution.

Another important set of perceptual images involves techniques for visualizing the importance of various *fixed* factors in planning and organizing a farm business. For instance, professional farm-management men, operating in areas where land has a limited range of physical capacities, often adopt the land-use approach in "roughing out" the organization of a farm business. Similarly, other farm-management men, working in areas of flexible land resources in close competition with urban industrial employments, find it advantageous to formulate thought patterns built around the supply of available labor as the most rigid fixed factor of production. These concepts are, of course, closely related to the concepts of fixed costs, fixed assets, and planning spans found in systems of economic theory and principles.

In acquiring information, the inductive thought processes are generally important. And, as the field of statistics deals with inductive thought processes, many of the management principles involving inductive thought and learning processes are statistical in nature.

In knowing how much information or accuracy should be acquired, it is important to know the make-up of accuracy. In making estimates, errors are involved. The manager is interested in two things about errors: (1) their size and (2) the probabilities of committing the error. Similarly, in choosing between two alternatives, error is involved—in fact, two kinds of errors. For instance, one estimating whether it will or will not rain could incorrectly conclude that it will not when it will. This is a different error from incorrectly concluding that it will rain when it will not. The fact that a difference exists can be seen by examining the respective consequences of the two types of errors. If one cuts hay on the basis of an incorrect conclusion that it will not rain when it will, he loses his hay. If he does not cut hay because he incorrectly concludes it will rain when it will not, he loses only the opportunity of getting his hay in. In the first 6 years after World War I many farmers suffered the consequences of incorrectly concluding that land prices would not come down when, in fact, they did. Conversely, in the first 6 years after World War II many farmers suffered the consequences (lost opportunity to profit) of incorrectly concluding that land prices would come down when, in fact, they did not.

The amount of information which can be extracted from a given set of facts is increased by the use of budgets, economic principles, and the various fixed-factor approaches. It should also be pointed out that accuracy (information) has a long-term value as well as a value in solving immediate problems; this long-term value is referred to as the value of experience. Thus, this value should be included in weighing costs against value in the learning process.

Both the statistician and the farm manager face diminishing returns in the sense that additional observations or facts yield decreasing amounts of new information. Conversely, additional information (accuracy) ordinarily has decreasing value (at least beyond some limit). These two statements indicate that the cost of acquiring accuracy increases as more accuracy is acquired and that the value of accuracy decreases. Both cost and value as used here are personal subjective

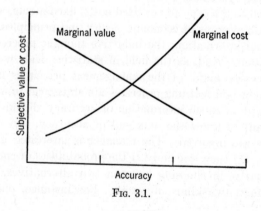

Fig. 3.1.

things. Free Enterprise, in Chapter 1, experienced personal costs in exerting efforts to observe, analyze, and decide. Similarly, the value of what he learned was personal. The first principle in management is to *acquire additional information only so long as the cost of such additional information does not exceed value.* Figure 3.1 shows a marginal (additional) value and a marginal (additional) cost curve. The proper amount of accuracy equates marginal cost and value.

Strategy Principles. In taking action and in deciding to act a manager can often select and control the situation in which he will act. Such control procedures are, in a broad sense, strategies and are especially important when he is managing on the basis of conclusions subject to error.

In impersonal situations one important principle is to discount expected results so as to build up reserves against errors. Thus, a man expecting to get 80 bushels of corn an acre may "count on" only sixty. A creditor may take notes and mortgages on the basis of 6 percent interest but "figure on" averaging only 4 percent after allowance is made for bad debts, etc. In discounting, safety is acquired and opportunities are foregone. Here, the economic principle *is not to sacrifice more in terms of foregone opportunities, when acquiring additional safety through discounting, than the additional safety is worth.*

Also, in impersonal situations, risks may be spread. Additional enterprises may be added to a farm business in order not to leave all one's eggs in one basket. Similarly, insurance schemes may serve as a way of spreading risks over a large number of farms. In general, insurance schemes can be formal involving contracts, premiums, and liabilities or informal within a given business. Thus, a farmer buys formal life and fire insurance and uses informal insurance by maintaining reserves of cash and feed and diversifying his enterprises. The economic principle here is not to spend more on additional amounts of such insurance than such additional amounts are worth.

When information is becoming available slowly and with the passage of time, a manager often desires to select situations which permit him to readjust to improved information. Such situations are flexible, and the ability to readjust, which they grant, is referred to as *flexibility.* Flexible situations are often less productive of income and, hence, can often be maintained only at a cost. For instance, cash on hand is a source of flexibility but is not as productive of income as cash invested in livestock and crop production. *When additional flexibility has a cost, that cost should be matched against the value of the addi-*

tional flexibility. The value of flexibility, depending as it does (among other things) on the ability of a manager to learn (observe and analyze), is a personal subjective thing.

In addition to the above impersonal situations, managers often want to select among and influence situations involving other people. In such situations the probable changes depend on the strategies of the other people as well as on impersonal considerations; i.e., interactions occur between persons. In such situations it is desirable to learn what the other person is going to do. It is also desirable to get him to do what you want him to do. It is often desirable to keep him from knowing what you are going to do even to the extent of leading him to expect you to do differently from what you are going to do.

In selecting situations, managers sometimes desire to minimize risks —certain kinds of risks. For instance, they may desire to minimize the maximum loss which they could incur. Or they may desire to maximize the possible gain which they might receive. A person buying insurance is minimizing or reducing the maximum loss which can be incurred. A person taking a long chance on a farm purchase, on the other hand, may be maximizing or at least increasing his chances of making a large gain.

In exchanging a situation involving one set of risks for one involving more or less risks, costs are often involved. Such costs include premiums and costs of changing situations, such as brokerage fees and title transfer costs. Hence, in making such exchanges, managers should be sure that the new situation is preferable to the old one.

In order *for a new situation* involving (1) a much smaller chance of incurring a large loss and (2) a much larger chance of a small loss *to be preferable* to the old situation, the importance of losses must increase at an increasing rate. This is the exchange commonly made when buying insurance. The loss insured against is so important that the manager insured is willing to give up a premium large enough to cover profits and administration costs as well as the amount needed to "average out" the losses for all those insured.

In order *for a new situation* involving (1) a larger chance of making a large gain and (2) a much larger chance of making a small loss *to be preferable* to the old situation, the importance of gains must increase at an increasing rate. This is the exchange commonly made in taking long chances. Before it "pays" to incur expenses in order to take such chances the large gain must be so important to the manager concerned that he is willing to incur not only the losses necessary to "average out" the gains but the expenses in addition.

This discussion of insurance and long-chance-taking principles makes it desirable to describe a limited number of psychological patterns.

Psychological Patterns. Familiarity with these psychological patterns increases our understanding of actions taken by managers and others. Among persons reasonably well accustomed to their present incomes and social-economic status, small gains and losses probably have about equal value. However, as losses become larger—large enough to change the socio-economic status of the person or family involved—losses assume increasing importance. The same is true of gains. Thus, the more or less "normal" psychological pattern is for persons to attach increasing importance to losses and increasing importance to gains. This, in turn, often results in managers being simultaneously conservative (i.e., they insure) and speculative (i.e., they also gamble or take long chances).

"Less normal" people include those who have recently suffered large losses or benefited from large gains. Such people vary from individual to individual. Both groups contain "abnormals" who will either insure or take long chances but not do both.

This subject is discussed in more detail in Chapter 12, entitled "Getting and Maintaining Control of Assets."

A Look Ahead

The remainder of this book will be divided into two main parts. The next part, consisting of Chapters 4 to 21, will present and demonstrate various techniques for organizing and reorganizing a farm business. These techniques will be concerned mainly with the land-use approach, traditional farm-budgeting techniques, various rules of thumb, and economic principles useful in organizing, planning, and budgeting a farm business. This part will have as its main objective the teaching of students to use these organized systems of thinking in organizing and reorganizing farm businesses.

The second remaining part, consisting of Chapters 22 to 26, will be concerned with the day-to-day and year-to-year problems of managing a farm business subject to various types of change and imperfections in knowledge. As such, this part will give attention to methods of anticipating changes and strategies as well as to insurance and long-chance-taking principles.

Each of the remaining major parts of the book lead to budgeting chapters designed to illustrate the application of what has been learned to individual farm businesses (Chapters 21 and 25).

Part 2

INTRODUCTION TO ORGANIZ-
ING A FARM BUSINESS

The next eighteen chapters have a specific purpose—they teach a student how to organize a farm business. Chapter 4 teaches him the parts of a farm business. Chapter 5 outlines an approach and, along with Chapters 6 and 7, indicates the important considerations determining the kinds of businesses which can be developed for a given man or a specific farm. Chapters 8 through 12 acquaint the student with the ordinary economic principles useful in organizing farms. Chapters 13, 14, and 15 teach the student how to rough out crop and livestock systems for a particular farm. Chapters 16, 17, and 18 present specific data for pork, dairy, and beef production for use in budgeting. Chapter 19 is devoted to a discussion of labor and working capital, and Chapter 20 is devoted to prices. Chapter 21, the final chapter of Part 2, is on budgeting a farm business.

CHAPTER 4

The Parts of a Farm Business and Income Statements

Before proceeding with the problem of farm organization, the student should be introduced to the components of farm businesses. One way to do this is to examine the parts of a farm business operating statement.

A farm business is made up of physical entities (things, parts) and actions. The physical parts of a farm business are:

1. Land.
2. Improvements, including such items as buildings, fences, and water systems. (Improvements are fastened to the land or become parts of it.)
3. Laborers.
4. Machines and other types of equipment.
5. Feeds, fertilizers, seeds, etc.
6. Usually productive livestock.
7. Money for operating.
8. The farm family with its wants, preferences, goals, and desires.

The parts of a farm business may be studied by examining a financial operating statement. One part of such a financial statement is given in Table 4.1. The statement is of a farm business for the year 1949 which is called Case Farm One.

Table 4.1 is a summary of the capital invested in this farm business as it was organized on a specific day, March 1, 1949. Had the business been inventoried on any other day, the statement would have been somewhat different. For example, a week or a month later the livestock could have been worth more and the supply and value of feed less.

Inventorying then introduces the concept of time. A concept of time and a period of time are necessary because of the action portion

Table 4.1. Inventory of Assets of Case Farm One

Investment (also called capital investment) as of March 1, 1949

Land (306 acres)	$ 65,000
Improvements	35,000
Machinery and equipment	10,678
Feeds	2,700
Supplies	1,220
Livestock	28,773
Cash	3,000
Total investment	$146,371

of the farm business. A farm business is a continuing thing, a stream of actions. The stream may be long, covering the business lifetime of a family or even of a succession of families. In order to examine a farm business, we must lift out a segment of this stream of time. What is the best segment? Segments of 1 year each are the most used, because of the seasonal cycles of production and because of usual business statements.

Farming is biological. It is concerned with growth—growing crops and growing livestock. Growth of crops is seasonal. Most farm crops require a year or a multiple of years for maturity or production. Wheat, corn, and tobacco are annuals; alfalfa and tree fruits are perennials. Whether growing annuals or perennials, production is seasonal. Little is produced in winter, much in summer. Years are, therefore, good segments of time for the farmer to divide his farming business into, because of the natural forces involved. The necessity of filing income tax returns by most farmers makes segments of one year each convenient, whether the return filed is on the cash or on the accrual basis.

The inventory is a device used to completely divide the farming business into time periods for purpose of analysis. Two inventories are thus needed. The first is taken at the start of the time period, in this case at the beginning of the year's business; a second at the end of the time period, in this case at the end of the year's business or the accounting period. Change between the values of the item at the time of the beginning inventory and at the time of the ending inventory are parts of the returns to the business for the period being used in making the operating statement. However, inventories do not account for all actions within the year.

Crops. The second part of this farm business statement concerns the crops produced. Table 4.2 is a list of the crops grown in 1949, together with the acreages and the yields of the individual crops.

Table 4.2. Crops and Crop Yields, Case Farm One

Crops	Acres	Yield
Corn (raised by a cropper)	30	72 bu.
Wheat	20	22 bu.
Clover hay	20	2 tons
Alfalfa hay	15	6 tons
Soybean hay	1	3 tons
Burley tobacco	1.5	1,728 lb.
Burley tobacco (cropper produced)	15.5	1,714 lb.
Garden and truck	3	
Rotation pasture	170	0.5 unit
	—	
Total tillable land	276	
Other land	30	
	—	
Total land	306	

Livestock. The third part of this farm business statement deals with the productive livestock. Table 4.3 lists the kinds of livestock on this case farm, the number of each kind, and the principal products.

Table 4.3. Livestock on Case Farm One

Kinds of Livestock	Number	Principal Products	
Milk cows	29	Milk	$7,673
		Heifers (5)	900
		Cows (2)	425
Beef cows	28	29 calves	
Feeder cattle	6		
Ewes	54	60 lambs	900
		Wool	265
Chickens (hens)	139	Eggs	758

Receipts. The fourth part of a farm business statement is a table of the receipts. Receipts may be defined to include:

1. The cash values of the items sold.
2. The value of inventory increases.
3. The value to the operator of the use of the house, a personal consumption of a part of the farm real estate investment which is therefore treated as a receipt to the farm business.

4. The value of the farm products produced by the farm business and used by the farm families.

The items of the last two groups are called perquisites.

Table 4.4.　Receipts of Case Farm One

Crops

Corn sold	$　900
Wheat sold	202
Burley tobacco (cropper)	11,088
Burley tobacco (self)	1,162
Use of garden	200
Livestock (net increases)	
Dairy sales and increases	9,268
Sheep net increases	1,079
Beef cattle net increases	3,339
Poultry net increases	951
Increase in feed inventory	200
Use of house (10% of value)	1,650
Total	$30,039

Why are net increases of livestock used instead of gross sales in Table 4.4? An explanation is needed. This is a statement for a one-year period. Some of the livestock on farms is carried over from the previous year; some is carried over to succeeding years. Our objective is to study the business for 1 year, the year 1949. We must, therefore, separate values produced in other years from values produced in the year under study. The result of this separation gives us a figure called net increase. For example, a farmer might have $500 in value of hogs at the beginning of a year and $1,000 in value at the end. Further, suppose that he purchased $300 worth and sold $800. His net gain or net increase for the year for this particular kind of livestock is:

$$\left. \begin{array}{c} \$1{,}000 \text{ at end of year} \\ + \\ \$800 \text{ sold} \end{array} \right\} - \left\{ \begin{array}{c} \$500 \text{ at beginning} \\ + \\ \$300 \text{ bought} \end{array} \right. = \$1{,}000$$

The $1,000 (not $1,800) is the net increase in production of hogs on his farm for the year, and is called the livestock net increase on hogs.

In order to get similar increases for the various kinds of livestock, inventories at the beginning and at the end of the year's business are made for each kind. Purchases and sales complete the financial story.

Thus, an inventory item for the beginning of the year's business acts as an expense for that year's business. It has been brought into the business (of the year) the same as if purchased. Similarly, an inventory item at the end of the year's business acts as a receipt. It is a contribution of the year. The same method is used for the handling of feed and supplies. This procedure is used by businessmen and accountants whether determining the net income of a railroad, a store, a farm, or other business. It is the only known way of reducing the long life of a business into segments for examination.

Expenses. Expenses are the fifth part of this or any farm business. Table 4.5 gives a list of the expenses for the farm business being analyzed.

Table 4.5. Expenses of Case Farm One

Expenses	Cost
Buildings and fences	$ 2,019
Machinery and equipment	623
Crop expenses	2,229
Feeds bought	1,862
Hired labor	1,405
Cropper labor (i.e., share of crop)	6,444
Tractor, truck, and machine hire	473
Farm use of auto	306
Taxes and insurance	444
Other inventory decreases	1,080
Miscellaneous	197
Total	$17,082

What are expenses? Of what are they composed? The term expenses must be arbitrarily defined for use in business statements. Outlay is a synonym which helps clarify understanding. One needs to know the meaning of the expenses of a farming business for the same reasons that one needs to know the meaning of the receipts.

Expenses are of four types:

1. Expenses of the first type or kind involve items which are wholly used within the year. These cash items include costs of seed, feed, fertilizer, purchased labor, fuel oil, repairs, taxes, insurance, etc. These cash items are sometimes called *current expenses*.

2. Expenses of the second type or kind involve depreciation of properties. Each year the business uses up (or wears out) a portion of the value of the buildings and the machines not offset by cash expenditures for repairs and maintenance. These are outlays, or

costs or inputs, of the year's business and must be included in the statement if one is to get an accurate picture of the year's business. These expenses are included in the list in Table 4.5.

3. Expenses of the third type or kind are decreases in inventories of operating capital, feed, and supplies other than feed. These are included in Table 4.5 as "other inventory decreases."

4. Expenses of the fourth type or kind are the uses of the labor services performed by members of the family other than the operator but not paid for in products or cash. A word of explanation is needed for including this input as an expense item. The present objective is to estimate returns to (1) the manager as an individual, and (2) the capital investment as an entity. In order to accomplish this objective an arbitrary value must be placed on family labor.

Recounting the types or kinds of expenses, we have:

1. Cash items.
2. Depreciation of physical properties.
3. Other inventory decreases.
4. Money values of family labor.

Examining Parts of the Business

Having completed compilation of parts for the business statement, we may now study it further. How shall we proceed? Did the operator do well; that is, did he manage the business successfully? Are there weak places? Did he spend too much money? Were his crop yields low or high?

First, suppose that we summarize further, as follows:

Investment	$146,371
Receipts	30,039
Expenses	17,082
Business gain	12,957

Business gain (receipts − expenses), $12,957, is also called *farm earnings*. This is the return to the operator for his management and labor, and the capital investment.

The farm-earnings figure can be further subdivided only by putting an arbitrary figure on either (1) the use of the investment or (2) the value of the operator's management and labor services.

Not all the business gain came from the operator's labor and management. A part of it came from his investment. How can we deduct a charge for use of the investment? One method is by placing a value on the use of the investment. The opportunity cost basis may be arbitrarily used. He had $146,371 invested. He could have put this investment in Government bonds and received 2½ percent or in other good bonds and received 3 or 4 percent. He might have loaned it out on real estate mortgages and received 4 or 5 percent. Suppose we arbitrarily say that he could have gotten 4 percent for the use of it. Then $146,371 × 0.04 = $5,854.84 which is the amount he sacrificed (opportunity cost) for keeping his money in a farming business. If we subtract from the business gain the $5,854.84 item we have:

$$\$12,957 - \$5,854.84 = \$7,102.16$$

as the calculated net returns to the operator for his labor and management. This item is customarily called the *operator's net earnings*—a residual to labor when the use of the investment is valued at 4 percent. A farmer might also be interested in estimating the returns to his efforts plus returns to his owned assets, in which case only interest on borrowed money would be charged. A family might also be interested in finding the returns to its efforts and owned assets, in which case no charge for family labor would be made.

Receipts per Dollar Expenses. Were the operator's net earnings good? If so, what made them good? Crop income? Livestock income? Care in buying and selling? High prices? Efficiencies in farming? First let us take a look at the gross receipts in terms of the expenses. The receipts may be called output(s), the expenses input(s). There was put into the business an investment of $146,371. A charge for the use of this investment has been subtracted as opportunity interest. There was also put into the business the manager's services for the year and $17,082 in value of other outlays (inputs). Let us find the amount of output per unit of input, or expressed in terms of dollars, the dollars received per dollar of expenses.

$$\frac{\$30,039 \text{ (receipts)}}{\$17,082 \text{ (expenses)}} = \$1.76$$

which means that the business under examination received $1.76 for each dollar of values (other than interest) put into it. Was this a good showing? What measures can be used?

One standard is that of comparison with farmer competitors for a similar period. National gross farm income figures compiled by the Bureau of Agricultural Economics, although not exactly comparable in items, suggest themselves. For example, the receipts per dollar of production expenses for the national industry as a whole for the five-year prewar period of 1935–1939 were $1.82. For the five-year period 1944–1948 the receipts per dollar expenses were $2.01.[1]

In view of the above indications, use of a closer test is justified. The farm organization could be tested to see if additional expenditures at any one point would have yielded additional net income. For example, at the existing milk-hay and milk-grain price ratios, would it have paid to feed the dairy animals to higher levels of production? Would additional expenditures on fertilizer have proved profitable or would an additional tractor pay its way?

We should emphasize at this point, that the first measure is a very rough measure, a first approximation. Yet it provided an indication that further analysis was needed. It served as a "warning stop-and-think light." The tentative answer is that this farmer was somewhat on the low side in receipts for the 1949 year or, said in another way, somewhat on the high side in expenses per dollar received and that input-output relationships needed to be examined enterprise by enterprise. The expenses per dollar received may be determined as follows:

$$\frac{\$17,082 \text{ (expenses)}}{\$30,039 \text{ (receipts)}} = 56.8 \text{ cents}$$

The average national for 1944–1948 was 49.7 cents.

Capital Turnover. Now let us look at receipts per dollar invested, called capital turnover. Again average output per unit of input.

Investment $146,371
Receipts   30,039

$$\frac{\$30,039}{\$146,371} = \text{How much?}$$

20 some? Yes, 21.9 cents or 21.9 percent. High? Low? How can we judge? By what can we measure "height" of capital turnover? As compared with other industries farming is a business of low capital turnover. In farming investments are high in proportion to gross receipts. That is, fixed capital inputs are very high in proportion to operating capital inputs. The investment-receipts ratio is about 5 to 1. A farmer showing better than average in a particular measure of

---

[1] Gross farm income 1935–1939, 52,121 million dollars; production expenses, 28,650 million dollars. For 1944–1948 comparable totals were 148,775 million dollars and 73,912 million dollars.

output presents an indication—not a fact—that he is strong in respect to that particular resource. Let us see what the usual capital turnover for farming is. The average gross national farm income from 1944–1948 was 29,755 million dollars. The 1949 investment in agriculture was 127,300 million dollars. The capital turnover was thus 23.3 percent.

With the capital-turnover measure and the expenses-per-dollar receipts measure, we find indications as to which of the two figures, receipts or expenses, is out of line. For example, if the capital turnover of a particular general farm business was 30 percent and the expenses per dollar receipts were 80 cents we would look for the difficulty first in the expenses rather than in the receipts. But if the capital turnover were 15 percent and the expenses per dollar receipts were also low, say 40 cents, we should search for the difficulty first in the receipts, or in the size of the investment.

Land Husbandry. Crop production is the basis of most farming. Profitable commercial livestock production on general farms is developed by first producing feed efficiently and then feeding it to livestock efficiently, the highly specialized livestock farms purchasing all feed being special cases.

Profitable crop production comes through two sources:

1. Putting the land in the "best" (most economic) crop or crop combinations.
2. Adjusting inputs and, hence, yields (returns per acre) to optimum rates.

Did this farmer use his land to good advantage from both physical and price standpoints? Were his crop yields high? Too high? These are questions requiring specific analysis for specific answers. Good land use depends upon the kind and quality of land, its topography, its fertility, governmental programs, and other factors such as price relationships. Let us, therefore, reserve analysis of land use and crop yields for later study, contenting ourselves at this point with having acquired the notion that crop programs are important in the successful operation of general farms.

Livestock Husbandry. More than half the sales and increases from this farm came through livestock. Livestock sales are indirect sales of feed, labor, and capital investment. An investigation into the profitableness of the use of these factors is therefore necessary in the analysis of farm businesses involving livestock. Here again an indication may be found with such rough measures as:

Dollar return per dollar of feed fed.
Returns per animal or per animal unit.
Returns per $100 invested in livestock.

or in more specific terms such as:

Cost per unit of product, as per hundredweight of milk or per pound of beef produced.
Output per unit of the resources used.

Again this is a long story which should be reserved for special treatment in a later chapter. Let us rather retrace our steps and take a second look at some of the procedures used thus far.

A Second Look at How to Examine a Farm Business

Let us review some of the items of information needed by a beginning student in farm management. He needs to acquire the names and uses of the various parts of a farm business and of a farm business statement. Just what is a farm business statement? What does it include? What is the usual length of time implied? Suppose that we review the answer to the last question first. One year is the usual period of which we speak. Since farming involves biology, we usually make the farm business year cover a crop production year beginning sometime between January first and April first and ending 12 months from the beginning.

Now let us review the question, what does a farm business analysis include? This question is again answered through use of the following condensed summary or record of a year's business for 26 corn, beef cattle, hog farms for the year 1940:

At the beginning of the business year the average investment picture on these farms was:

Crops and supplies	$ 149
Feeds	1,060
Machinery and equipment	935
Real estate	14,102
Dairy cattle	119
Work stock	623
Hogs	498
Sheep	146
Beef cattle	1,084
Poultry	55
Total business investment	$18,771

Receipts. The average total cash receipts from the year's business on these 26 farms was $3,622. In addition, the farm business furnished products to the farm family (frequently called perquisites) worth $427. Again in addition to these two items, the value of the operating capital increased $274 (inventory increases). The sum of these three items, called *farm receipts*, is $4,323.

Expenses. The average expense incurred in operating the year's business was $2,289 ($2,183 plus $106 for the value of family labor). When these expenses are subtracted from the total receipts of $4,323, we have left $2,034, which was the net income to (*a*) the farm business investment, and (*b*) the farmer for his labor and his management. This figure is called *farm earnings*.

As a means of separating income to investment from income to the farm operator for his labor and his management, we can subtract interest at an arbitrarily selected rate on the total investment from the farm earnings. In this case interest at a rate of 5 percent on the total investment of $18,771 is $938. Subtracting the $938 from the farm earnings figure ($2,034), we get $1,096 as the average net income to the farmers themselves for their labor and management. This figure is called *net earnings* or *operator's net earnings*. Had we subtracted interest on borrowed money only and not subtracted a charge for family labor, we should have arrived at a figure showing returns to the farm family and owned investment.

Summarizing, we have the following:

Total investment	$18,771
Total farm receipts	4,323
Total farm expenses	2,289
Farm earnings	2,034
Interest on investment	938
Net earnings	1,096

It should be re-emphasized that net earnings are not entirely cash. They are returns to the farmer in products, cash, and inventory changes. The term is widely accepted in agricultural circles and thus has the sanction of use.

Returns to Investment. In separating farm earnings into returns to investment and the returns to operators, we arbitrarily used interest as the value of the use of the capital investment, and assigned the remainder as a residual to operator's labor and management. We may likewise use an arbitrary value of operator's services and let returns to investment be the residual. For an owner of a farm not operating the farm himself, this method is preferred, as such an individual is more interested in what he gets out of his investment than what he gets for his personal services. Using this method we might have:

Farm earnings	$2,034
Value of owner's services	100
Returns to investment	$1,934

Owners of property which they do not operate themselves are interested in reducing such a figure to a percent return on investment. To find the percent return on investment we divide the net returns to investment (in this illustration, $1,934) by the value of the total investment.

$$\frac{\$1,934}{\$18,771} = 0.103 \text{ or } 10.3 \text{ percent}$$

Early Methods of Examining a Farm Business

A frequently used technique for studying farm businesses has been to:

1. Select a group of farms.
2. Make business operating statements of them.
3. Divide the statements into subgroups such as:
   (a) Those showing high net earnings.
   (b) Those showing low net earnings.
4. Make comparisons between averages of the subgroups, or between one individual and averages on the factors thought to affect earnings. The usually used factors are: (1) size of business; (2) crop yields; (3) livestock returns; (4) labor returns.

Though these comparisons may be invalid or misleading in many cases, they serve as flashing red lights indicating those parts of the business likely to be the source of existing difficulties.

Let us take a look at some of these factors. The data used are taken from the study of a group of 26 corn, beef, hog farms for the crop year 1940. Averages have been made of the items in the business for the group as a whole and also for the 10 which made the highest net earnings.

Table 4.6 presents some of the factors thought to affect earnings of both groups and provides a basis of comparison.

Table 4.6. A Comparison of 26 Farms with the 10 Farms Having the Highest Net Earnings

	Average 26 Farms	Average 10 Highest
1. Net earnings	$ 1,096	$ 1,834
2. Acres operated	230	222
3. Acres tillable	206	206
4. Total receipts	$ 4,323	$ 5,176
5. Total expenses	$ 2,289	$ 2,268
6. Total investment	$18,771	$21,472
7. Percent land in corn	24	28
8. Percent land in wheat	11	16
9. Percent land in clover hay	9	15
10. Percent land in alfalfa hay	1	1
11. Percent land in other legumes	2	1
12. Percent land in plowable pasture	36	29
13. Yields of corn	36 bu.	38 bu.
14. Yields of wheat	19 bu.	20 bu.
15. Yields of clover hay	1.9 tons	2.0 tons
16. Number of sows, per farm	8	9
17. Number of hogs bought	12	12
18. Hog receipts per sow	$ 123	$ 129.51
19. Pounds pork per sow	2,162	2,286
20. Beef receipts per animal unit	$ 40.39	$ 46.08
21. Beef receipts per $100 feed fed	$ 105.39	$ 114.85
22. Sheep receipts per ewe	$ 9.57	$ 10.09
23. Dairy receipts per cow	$ 62.29	$ 53.74
24. Poultry receipts per hen	$ 1.75	$ 1.69
25. Man work units accomplished	498	571
26. Men per farm	1.9	2.0
27. Man work units accomplished per man	252	285
28. Total receipts per tillable acre	$ 20.98	$ 25.13
29. Total expenses per tillable acre	$ 11.11	$ 11.01
30. Expenses per $100 total receipts	$ 52.94	$ 43.81

Crop Yields. A significant factor in management of farms is the use of the land and the yield of crops. There is an indication of better use of land by the 10 best farmers compared with the group as a whole on lines 7–15. They produced more cultivated crops and secured higher yields, two indications but not "sure signs" of good crop management for that particular year.

Large acreages of adapted high-yielding crops are essential to good farming. Ordinarily, yields must exceed the average to put a farmer "out in front." Good land husbandry involves using all the land for the crops best adapted to it (economically) and making the land yield the most economical quantities per acre. The test of whether good land use has been attained is whether changes can be made which will return more than they cost.

Livestock Returns. The indications are that 10 high-income farmers probably excelled in handling their livestock (lines 16–24). They had somewhat more livestock and handled their livestock so as to get higher average returns. The average returns per $100 in feed fed to livestock, though low in both cases, were higher for the 10 farmers. One farmer received $179 and $199 for $100 in feed fed to hogs and beef, respectively. The data do not permit us to determine whether additional expenditures on the various livestock enterprises would have yielded returns in excess of costs.

Labor Returns. In the use of labor the 10 farms show some indications of superiority. They used more labor, probably more machinery, and accomplished more work with both machines and men per man (lines 25–27). A productive day's work accomplished is the product of work done by both men and machines on the average of a large number of farmers per day. It is not the number of days worked.

Intensity and Quality. Rough indications are that the 10 farmers were more intensive and better users of the factors of production (lines 28–30). They received more dollars per tillable acre. They also averaged lower expenditures to get a dollar. We have no way of knowing why this was true—perhaps the 10 highest farmers had smooth fertile land and, hence, received high yields from low-fertilization and ground-preparation costs.

The forces creating these small differences in (1) size of business, (2) land husbandry, (3) livestock returns, (4) labor returns, and (5) intensity and quality made for large differences in the earnings; in fact, a difference of more than 60 percent above the overall average. If we compare the best 10 farmers with the poorest 16 farmers, the difference is more than 100 percent. The highest man made a net earning of $2,837, whereas the lowest man lacked $28 of making anything for his labor and management.

Another Approach to Analysis of Farm Businesses

The primary objectives of this chapter are to:

1. Teach the meaning of some of the terms used in farm management.

2. Teach the use of these terms in their intended places.

3. Gain an introduction to procedures in examining farm business statements.

4. See some of the relationships among the parts of a business.

5. Find some rough measures of success and some input-output ratios.

The summarized record of a year's business on a 306-acre farm was presented by parts with explanations. The summary of a group study of 26 corn, beef cattle, hog farms was also looked at from the standpoint of

Size of business.
Land use and crop yields.
Livestock returns.
Labor returns.
Intensity and quality.

We can now advance our attention to the analysis of some farm businesses with a somewhat different approach. The change in approach is in the methods by which the businesses are examined and the measures used. We may think of the methods and the measures as additions to those used in the first part of the chapter. Still further methods of analysis will be presented later in the text.

The data to be studied next were developed by the Department of Agricultural Economics of the University of Illinois from some farm businesses in western Illinois.[1] Illinois has perhaps carried on more work with farm records than any other state. In this particular study returns from farming and from farm enterprises are measured in terms of *total outputs per dollar* of total inputs. Attention is called to the relationships among the factors of production—land, labor, operating capital, and management.

Again let it be noted that our primary interest in this chapter is to acquire concepts of farm business statements, terms, and methods. Said another way, we are interested in concepts and *methods of examination*, whereas these particular farmers were doubtless more interested in the results of the examination.

An examination was made of five systems of farming, namely (1) cash grain, (2) hog, (3) feeder cattle-hog, (4) beef cattle-hog, and (5)

[1] R. H. Wilcox, A. C. Renne, and R. C. Ross, *Inputs and Returns as Related to Systems of Farming and to Production of Crops, Livestock and Livestock Products in Western Illinois, 1948,* Mimeograph Release AE 2750, June, 1950, University of Illinois.

dairy-hog. Analysis was made also on six crop and six livestock enterprises. For simplicity we shall use but two of the systems. The parts of the business and the data are given in Table 4.7.

Table 4.7. Selected Data on Some Illinois Farms, 1948

	Grain	Dairy-Hog
1. Acreage	303	126
2. Capital investment (Av. 8 farms)		
Land	$58,112	$16,866
Buildings and fences	4,491	6,089
Machinery and equipment	3,936	3,266
Horses	13	81
Sheep	—	52
Poultry	151	245
Cattle	3,177	2,494
Hogs	1,189	3,708
Feed, grain, seed	6,300	6,178
Total	$77,369	$38,975
3. The crops (acres)		
Corn	114.1	37.1
Soybeans	29.0	2.1
Oats	63.9	21.2
Hay	17.6	13.9
Other hay	11.1	3.0
Pasture, total	50.5	40.8
4. The livestock		
Milk cows	3.0	15.0
Units feeder cattle	7.2	—
Units other beef cattle	5.6	—
Litters pigs	14.0	19.0
Number hens	88.0	134.0
5. The returns (receipts)		
Crops	$12,135	$ 516
Livestock and products	6,704	14,679
Other returns	358	247
Total	$19,197	$15,442
6. The inputs (dollars)		
Land	$ 2,740	$ 956
Labor	2,355	2,977
Operating capital	7,303	7,898
Management	986	1,020
Total	$13,384	$12,851

Such is the picture of the businesses of these two groups of eight farms each with two systems of farming in western Illinois. Now the questions that the owners of these farms and other farmers doubtless wanted answered were how good were the businesses? and how could they be made better? The additional question we want answered is how to find out how good the businesses were and why? By what methods did the research workers who conducted this study measure the efficiencies of these systems and of the individual businesses, and of the individual enterprises? Also how did the methods and measurements used in this study differ from the ones previously used in this chapter?

What Are the Differences in Approach? In the Illinois study, charges for use of the four factors, land, labor, operating capital, and management are determined as follows:

1. Land—interest on value of naked land plus taxes.
2. Labor—cost of hired labor plus value of family labor valued at current wage rates.
3. Operating capital.
   (a) Cost of seed, feed, fertilizer.
   (b) Interest on improvements.
   (c) Depreciation and repairs.
   (d) Cost of power, machinery, and equipment.
   (e) Livestock expense.
   (f) General farm expense.
4. Management—value of hired professional farm management services at current rates (equal to about 7 percent of receipts but figured on an input basis).

The totals of the input determinations are given for the two systems of farming. The total value of the inputs may thus be determined and any residual left as net returns. The method used for the 306-acre and the 26 farms determines the cost of the cash expenses, in the same manner. Also the costs of depreciation, taxes, and family labor. Receipts less these expenses leave the remainder of the receipts as farm earnings. From these farm earnings (see page 51) interest on total investment is subtracted in one sum and the residual called net earnings (returns to the operator for management, risk, and his labor).

The problem exercises provided are intended to develop the relationships of the two methods for the purpose of concentrating attention on terms, methods, and meanings of terms.

The student should solve Problem Exercises 3 and 4 in connection with studying this chapter.

As previously stated, five systems of farming were analyzed in this study and also twelve enterprises. Provisions were made for checking the inputs and outputs of each individual farmer against the averages of farmers in the enterprise studies who produced that enterprise on significant scale. For example, for 14 of the 39 farmers the dairy enterprise was analyzed. These 14 farm dairies were divided into 2 groups, (1) those with cows giving less than 7,500 pounds of milk, and (2) those with cows giving more. The returns per $100 of inputs were $90 for the lower group and $102 for the higher. The gross returns per $100 of feed fed were $194 for the lower and $219 for the higher.

More Advanced Analyses of Farm Records Could Be Made

Three elementary methods of examining farm businesses were presented in this chapter—the class case farm, the comparison of 10 best farms with averages for 26, and the recent Illinois approach. All these examinations had the common shortcoming of requiring arbitrary charges for fixed assets in the absence of estimates of the earning power of such assets. Thus, once cash expenses were deducted from gross income, further deductions were necessarily arbitrary. Hence, the resulting residuals (such as operator's net earnings, etc.) have similar shortcomings.

After the student has mastered the economic principles to be presented in subsequent chapters, another method of analysis will be presented. This method will eliminate a portion of the shortcomings referred to here through providing estimates of the earning power of the fixed assets. (See the last portion of Chapter 9.)

Record Books as a Learning Device

The farm record book is a production tool for farmers. For students the record is widely recognized as a good teaching device. It is a system of logic and a deductive tool. When students have made the entries of a year's farm business in a farm record book they will have:

1. Gained further knowledge of the nature of expenses.
2. Gained further knowledge of the nature of receipts.
3. Gained further knowledge of fixed capital investment, working capital, and operating capital, and thus of fixed (overhead) and variable (operating) costs.
4. Learned some of the mechanics of keeping and analyzing farm records.
5. Learned to summarize a farm financial record.

The farm record book is introduced at this point in the course for the above purpose. The point of view expressed is that records are a device for learning new terms and a procedure for learning the meaning of the terms.

The record book exercise proposed consists of using two devices:

1. A record book.
2. A list of items of a year's business.

The lesson is set up in the Problem Exercises. *The record book used should be the one regularly used in the student's home state.* Such books are issued by the colleges of agriculture, the federal agencies, and commercial publishers. The data for the business to be used may be supplied by the instructor. It is well to use data of some farm within the state or, better, the type-of-farming area if such are available. One list is mechanically as good as another, but a list for a local farm business conforms to local practices. Since it takes considerable time to prepare and check such a list, local lists may not be available. For this reason a list is given with the Problem Exercise. In order to minimize the mathematical computations, the values have been rounded to the nearest dollar, and the repetitive items, such as milk and egg sales are given in lump sums.

Problem Exercise 5 may be used at this point.

QUESTIONS AND PROBLEMS

1. Define (not illustrate): receipts, expenses, farm earnings, interest on investment, output, capital turnover, perquisites.

2. Compare calculating operator's net earnings as measures of returns (on the basis used) with farm earnings as returns to the family and the firm.

3. How do owners of farms meet depreciation costs?

4. What objection can you see in appraising a factor affecting earnings (as crop yields) on the basis of averages? What are the assumptions underlying such comparisons if the comparisons are to be used as indicating strong or weak spots in a particular business?

5. Compare the recent Illinois method of appraising businesses (as given in this chapter) with that given in the "Second Look" section of this chapter. What added assumptions are required?

6. When are *returns to investment* a more appropriate measure of earnings than operator's *net earnings?*

7. The income tax laws provide for payment of income taxes on either the accrual or the cash basis. Most farmers choose the cash basis. Why? What are the differences?

8. Does your state Farm Record Book provide for finding the cost of producing products? If not, what other data are needed?

9. How does an accountant's point of view on costs differ from that of an economist? (See Chapter 12.)

PROBLEM EXERCISE 3
Methods of Examining a Business

Having partially acquired a few of the more general methods, we need to do a bit of productive work—practice—in examining farm business statements. Failure to use new concepts or methods results in loss of them. Misty notions of concepts precipitate scant drops of knowledge. They precipitate best through individual reflection and action. This book is making use of problems to consolidate ideas and data into knowledge. Thinking is a matter for individual initiative, and problems present opportunities for individual thinking. Suppose that we take a problem—take a look at another farm business, get some data on it, and make our own examination. Here is a good farm business statement for this purpose. Picture the business from the following.

We approach through the front gate; "Not much house," inventoried at $810. The tenant says that there is a total of 320 acres of land—304 tillable.

I. Capital investment. We find the investment to be:

Land and improvements	$19,000.00
Dairy cows (2)	450.00
Workstock (4)	485.00
Brood sows (16) ⎫ Other hogs (166) ⎭	3,837.00
Sheep (64)	1,370.00
Poultry (25)	25.00
Machinery and equipment	5,905.00
Feeds	5,423.00
Crops and supplies	289.00
Cash to run business	5,000.00
Total	$41,784.00

II. Organization of enterprises. Looking around we find:

A. Land use and crop yields

75 acres were in corn	Yield 60 bu.
35 acres were in wheat	Yield 20 bu.
15 acres were in rye	Yield 30 bu.
25 acres were in oats	Yield 20 bu.
20 acres were in barley	Yield 25 bu.
30 acres were in clover seed	Yield 9 lb.
7 acres were in clover hay	Yield 4½ tons
20 acres were in lespedeza hay	Yield 1¼ tons
10 acres were in strawberries	Yield 110 crates
1.5 acres were in garden	
65.4 acres were in rotation pasture	

B. The livestock program consisted of (March 1):

2 milk cows for home use
4 workstock
16 brood sows
166 other hogs (13,000 pounds)
64 ewes
25 chicken hens

III. The cash receipts for the year

A. Crop

Barley	$ 451.00
Wheat	120.00
Clover seed	400.00
Rye	409.00
Strawberries	5,156.00

B. The livestock net increases

Dairy cattle	$ 342.00
Milk	150.00
Hogs	8,756.00
Sheep	1,077.00
Beef cattle	210.00
Poultry	178.00
Eggs	150.00

In addition to the above receipts there was produced by the farm and used by the family:

Fruits and vegetables	$ 150.00
Use of house	81.00

The farmer also received $343 in government payments. The inventories of supplies showed an increase of $66.

Find the value of the total receipts (or incomes) as defined:

Total of Receipts $_____

A. Are they as large as reasonably expected:

1. In terms of the total capital investment used?
     Capital turnover _____
2. In terms of acres used?
     Receipts per tillable acre _____

Now take a look at the expenses in relation to the receipts. The cash expenses were:

Seed	$ 522.00
Fertilizer and limestone	2,630.00
Other crop expenses	1,065.00
Feeds bought	2,780.00
Hired labor	2,643.00
Cropper labor	458.00
Truck and tractor expense	1,318.00
Automobile	162.00
Taxes and insurance	374.00
Miscellaneous	79.00

In addition to the cash expenses, the inventory changes shown by the record book were:

Net decrease in value of feeds	$1,700.00
Net decrease in machinery equipment	1,862.00
Net decrease in value of farm improvements	1,701.00

The value of family labor other than that of the operator was placed at $500, and the value of the operator's labor at $1,800.

As defined what is the total of the farm business expense (as defined in Chapter 4) for the year (beginning March 1, 1949 and ending February 28, 1950)? _____

Figure the operator's net earnings:

Total capital investment	$_____
Total receipts	_____
Total expenses	_____
Farm earnings (business gain)	_____
Interest on investment (4%)	_____
Operator's net earnings	_____

Is it high?

Where do you begin to look for the difficulty? _____

Are the expenses high or the receipts low? _____

How do you know? What are expenses per dollar receipts? _____

What are the parts of the farm business in which one can look for the difficulty:

I. Size of business is one. Compare the size of business with that of the case farm analyzed in Chapter 4 and the 26 farms.

II. Land husbandry is one. Examine it. Are there major criticisms in use of the land for crops? (Explain.)

III. Livestock efficiency is another. The returns per dollar of feed fed can be estimated as follows:

1. Estimate the value (round to nearest dollar) of feed fed by:
   A. Putting a value on the feeds produced

75 acres corn, 60 bu. @ $1.50	$_____	
35 acres wheat, 20 bu. @ $2.20	_____	
15 acres rye, 30 bu. @ $2.20	_____	
25 acres oats, 20 bu. @ $1.00	_____	
20 acres barley, 25 bu. @ $1.00	_____	
7 acres hay, 4½ tons @ $25.00	_____	
20 acres hay, 1¼ tons @$20.00	_____	
65.4 acres pasture @ $4.00 per acre	_____	
Total value of feeds produced	_____	$_____

   B. Less sales (barley, wheat, rye)   _____
   C. Net value of feed fed from year's production   _____
   D. Plus value of feed bought   _____
   E. Plus value of decrease in feed inventory   _____   _____
       Total value of feed fed   _____

2. Livestock net increase $10,863.00

3. $$\frac{\$ \text{ Livestock net increase}}{\$ \text{ Feed Fed}} = _____$$

   Write your conclusion.

4. Now compare the gross value of the crops produced with the value of the crop and livestock receipts:

Total value feed crops produced (Item III total, subitem 1A)	$_____	
Total value of crops sales (clover seed $400, strawberries $5,156.)	$_____	
Total value all crops produced		$_____
vs.		
Total value crop and livestock receipts		$_____

What does this indicate as to the livestock program?

Were the prices used the source of the difficulty?

Would this farmer have made more money if he had dropped the live-stock portion of his business and sold all crops as such? What other factors would be involved if he followed such a plan?

IV. Another department of the farm business is the labor and equipment pro-gram. Labor is one of the two important basic factors of production in farming. While the authors do not think it a wise procedure to introduce the analytical tools for detailed examination of labor efficiencies (output per unit of labor input) at this point of our inquiry, it will perhaps do no harm to generalize on the labor inputs and outputs of this farm business. This could be done as follows:

Hired labor costs	$2,643.00
Cropper labor costs	$ 458.00
Value all unpaid family labor	$2,300.00
Total value labor used	$_____

This $_____ in labor added to:

$1,862 in machinery and equipment expenses

    plus

$1,382 in truck and tractor costs

    makes a total of

$_____ labor and equipment costs put into producing $17,385.00 [1] of crops and in caring for the livestock.

Suppose that the operator had rented out the farm on a 50-50 basis, the tenant furnishing all labor and equipment, half the feed, seed, and crop expenses, would he have had larger farm earnings?

The receipts would have been:

$$\tfrac{1}{2} \text{ of } \$18,039.00 \text{ or } \$9,019.00$$

The owner's expenses would have been:

Seed	$ 261.00	
Fertilizer	1,315.00	
Other crops	532.00	
Feeds bought	1,390.00	
Decrease in feeds	850.00	
Auto	162.00	
Taxes and insurance	374.00	
Miscellaneous	74.00	
Farm improvement	1,701.00	
Total	$6,659.00	$6,659.00
Farm earnings		___

[1] $11,830 in feed crops plus $5,556 clover seed and strawberries produced. Approxi-mate value of labor and equipment $8,645.

What does this indicate as to use of labor and equipment? _____

What difference in operator's net earnings would charging interest at 2 percent and labor at $100 per month have made?

Supposing that the family had a 100% equity in the business, what were the returns to the farm family and the investment?

PROBLEM EXERCISE 4
Methods of Business Analysis

1. From the data in Table 4.7 of the Illinois study, calculate:

	Grain Farms	Dairy-Hog Farms
Net returns (receipts less inputs)	_____	_____
Net returns per $100 inputs	_____	_____
Gross returns per 100 acres	_____	_____
Net returns per 100 acres	_____	_____

2. Calculate returns to management and to ownership separately as residuals:

(a) Total returns _____ _____
    Less inputs of land, labor and operating capital _____ _____
    Residual to management _____ _____

(b) Total returns _____ _____
    Less all inputs other than interest on capital investment [1] _____ _____
    Residual to investment _____ _____
    Percent return on investment _____ _____

3. Determine the average net earnings for each group of Illinois farmers in the spaces below:

(The average of total hours of labor used on the grain farms in the Illinois (1948) study were 3,555, and on the dairy-hog farms 4,499. On the grain farms the operator himself put in 65 percent of these hours, on the dairy-hog farms 75 percent. This labor was valued by the investigators at an average rate of 71.6 cents per hour. With this and the data given in Table 4.7, figure the average net earnings of the farmers in terms of the method illustrated for the 306-acre farm described as case farm one. See Chapter 4.)

	Grain Farms	Dairy-Hog Farms
Receipts (returns)	$19,197	$15,442
Inputs	13,384	12,851
Net returns (difference)	_____	_____
Value operator's labor plus	_____	_____
Value management as charged	_____	_____
Operator's net earnings	_____	_____

[1] Figure interest on capital investment at 4 percent. Subtract the answer from the total dollars of inputs.

4. On the basis of the method used for the 306-acre farm and the data given for the Illinois farms:

    (a) What is the gross capital turnover?   ——————   ——————

    (b) What are the gross receipts per dollar
           expenses?   ——————   ——————

PROBLEM EXERCISE 5
Analyzing Farm Businesses

Directions:

1. Take either: (a) the list of items of the business of Hustling Sam included with this exercise, or (b) a list handed you by the instructor.

2. Secure a Farm Record Book.

3. Record the items from the list selected in the record book. Check (✓) each item on the list after it has been recorded.

4. Summarize the record.

5. Analyze the farm business from the record made.

A Day to Day Financial Record of a Small Farm Business

On January 1, 1953, a farmer whom we shall call Hustling Sam took an annual farm inventory and thus started his 1953 record book. The items in this list were taken from the record, but rounded to the nearest dollar.

   I. Beginning inventory

      A. Real estate (total land and improvements)

30 acres land	$3,000.00
Farm house	1,411.00
Laying house (26 x 80)	940.00
Brooder houses (3)	210.00
Barn (30 x 40)	200.00
Fences	203.00

      B. Livestock

3 milk cows	350.00
1 heifer	150.00
10 pigs (1,000 lb.)	232.00
510 chicken hens	638.00

      C. Power and equipment

Tractor	802.00
Plows	67.00
Disc	104.00
Wagon	157.00
Other crop equipment	187.00
Miscellaneous	34.00

      D. Crops

Wheat (8.5 acres)	27.00

      E. Feed and supplies

Corn (300 bushels)	375.00
Supplies	5.00

II. Crops produced during the year were:

Corn (9 acres)	495 bu.
Wheat (7 acres)	187 bu.
Hay (7 acres)	8 tons
Tobacco (1.1 acre)	1,900 lb.

III. Financial transactions during the year were:

January

3	Bought 1 ton egg mash	$ 80.00
15	Paid real estate taxes	44.00
31	Cream sales for month	20.00
31	Egg sales, 20 cases (30 dozen each)	300.00

February

10	Bought 1,600 lb. of 5-10-10 fertilizer (tobacco)	54.00
10	Bought 3,600 lb. of 2-12-6 fertilizer (corn)	72.00
10	Paid trucking bill	10.00
15	Eggs sold, 10 cases	150.00
15	Sold 510 hens	1,071.00
25	Bought 800 sexed pullets	220.00
25	Bought 1 ton starter mash	95.00
25	Bought 2 tons egg mash	165.00
28	Cream sales for month	28.00

March

5	500 lb. fertilizer for garden	10.00
23	2 tons growing mash	160.00
30	Feed grinding	20.00
30	Cream sales for month	40.00
30	Received PMA payment	18.00

April

8	Fencing wire	50.00
15	Bought 3 pigs	44.00
15	3,600 lb. growing mash	144.00
20	Feed grinding	50.00
30	Cream sales for month	40.00

May

10	Materials for improvements on house	400.00
20	2 tons mash	160.00
20	Sold 2 cows	200.00
20	Sold 2 calves	115.00

May

20	Trucking	$	5.00
27	Feed grinding		25.00
31	Cream sales for month		10.00

June

10	Paid for crop insurance	13.00
15	Sold 2 calves	131.00
15	Paid for trucking	8.00
28	Bought 200 bushels corn	340.00
30	Cream sales for month	45.00

July

11	Bought 1 ton egg mash	83.00
30	Cream sales for month	35.00

August

13	Paid for hired labor	15.00
13	Paid for fire insurance	30.00
20	Bought 2 tons egg mash	150.00
20	Paid for baling hay	45.00
26	Bought 4 calves (1,800 lb.)	380.00
30	Cream sales for month	30.00
30	Egg sales, 10 cases	120.00

September

10	Sold 11 hogs	507.00
10	Bought 1 ton egg mash	78.00
30	Cream sales for month	30.00
30	Egg sales, 15 cases	225.00
30	Sold 84 cull pullets	69.00

October

15	Paid for 20 tons ground limestone	68.00
15	Paid for 2,700 lb. of 2-12-6 fertilizer	54.00
31	Cream sales for month	20.00
31	Egg sales, 30 cases	450.00

November

15	Bought 1 ton egg mash	75.00
30	Egg sales, 30 cases	420.00

December

15	Paid Farm Bureau dues	5.00
15	Purchased a truck	1,620.00
15	Truck license	5.00
23	Sold tobacco	1,069.00
23	Cream sales for month	15.00
30	Egg sales, 25 cases	300.00

IV. On December 31, 1953, Hustling Sam prepared to close the record of the year's business by entering the following miscellaneous items:

Charged tractor fuel for year	$ 70.00
Milk used by the family during year	48.00
Butter used by the family during year	50.00
Hogs (2 weighing 800 lb.) killed for home use	120.00
Poultry used by household	10.00
Eggs used by household	32.00
Fruits and vegetables used	50.00
Charged use of auto	88.00
Value of use of house @ 10%	141.00
Off-farm work	59.00
Charged farm business for electric current	21.00
Recorded value of own labor	1,000.00

V. The closing inventories showed the following:

A. Real estate

Land (30 acres)	$3,000.00
Dwelling house	1,775.00
Laying house	900.00
Brooder houses	200.00
Barn	190.00
Fences	200.00

B. Livestock

2 milk cows	300.00
4 beef calves (2,200 lb.)	500.00
675 chicken hens	945.00

C. Power and equipment

Truck	1,620.00
Tractor	700.00
Plows	55.00
Disc	90.00
Wagon	150.00
Other crop equipment	260.00
Miscellaneous equipment	30.00

D. Crops

Wheat (9.3 acres)	36.00
Cover crop (1.1 acre)	5.00

E. Feed and supplies

Corn (300 bu.)	375.00
Hay (75 bales)	56.00

CHAPTER 5

The Approach to Farm Organization and Reorganization

With what does one begin when he organizes or reorganizes a farm business? Is there a scientific approach? What factors of production form the most stable basis (tend to be the most fixed) for use as a starting point? Do tenants organize businesses on the same basis as owner-operators? Would one approach "livestock" farming through the same avenues as those used for cash grain farming?

It appears so easy to develop a successful farm business that many venture into it with little consideration of the strength of economic currents dictating the production opportunities which may be profitably followed. Questions of how best to handle a given farm consisting of the land, the man-made improvements thereon, a given amount of other financial resources, and a farm family confront all those interested in farming, and challenge students of organization and management. How may the available assets be best used? What crops will be grown? What proportions of the land should be used for each crop? What livestock should be kept? What pieces of equipment are needed? What production practices should be employed?

Many Farms Are Organized on the Basis of Experience and Observation

Most farmers have grown up in the area in which they farm and have learned what they know about farming as apprentices at the business. They have thus usually adopted the system of farming prevalent in their communities, adjusted it to their own farms, and followed the practices usual to their areas. If we examine carefully the use of this "apprenticeship" approach, we find that the organizations of farming businesses based upon it have been developed historically around the products rather than around the land and other resources, primarily labor. The experience of farmers runs simultaneously from product back to land and labor inputs, and thence from land, labor, and capital inputs back to product. This is in accord with sound economic principles. Farmers interested in making profits and enlarging their holdings have increased the quantity of things put into the production of those products which have proved profitable for them in their particular circumstances. The apprentice or experience approach to learning organization and management is an effective one. For students in agriculture, however, this approach is not sufficient because:

1. It is incomplete for application by them to numbers of farms.
2. It takes too many years to learn.
3. The knowledge gained is not transferable to other workers.

A Common Error in Organizing

A farming business is both complex and complicated—complex because it contains many individual parts; complicated because these parts are both intertwined within the business and interwoven with the competitive influences of other businesses.

Because of this complexity, thousands, perhaps millions, of disasters have occurred in organizing farm businesses. Our forefathers had little but trial and error (or success) to guide them; currently the uninitiated think that farming is a simple business with which one can profitably produce almost everything that he wishes in almost any place he wishes, or in any given quantity. For example, an Army Colonel recently wrote:

I'm interested in buying or renting about 600 acres of land in central Kentucky and planting or having it planted with wheat, and following the wheat harvest with crops to grow for hay.

Will you send me whatever information you consider appropriate for my information and guidance in this undertaking?

Particularly recommend parts of the state. Can I have the land prepared and sown and the wheat and hay harvested or will I have to buy machinery and do these things myself?

The Colonel's questions reveal a not-unusual lack of understanding of approaches to profitable farming. He elects Kentucky as the place and wheat as the crop. He should either have elected a wheat state such as Kansas or Nebraska if he wished to succeed with specialized wheat farming, or have selected tobacco or thoroughbred horses as his principal enterprises if he wished to carry on specialized farming in central Kentucky—that is, if he wished to farm for profit. Land values have been forced too high in central Kentucky by tobacco and race-horse prices to permit specialized wheat farming to be profitable. Wheat can be profitably grown in too many areas where tobacco and race horses cannot, to make specialized wheat farming in Kentucky a profitable venture.

Literature is replete with accounts of frontiersmen trying to grow crops in wrong places, i.e., of people who have ignored the fixed (in the short run, at least) characteristics of land including climate and markets. Often the trial was on a large financial scale or involved many people—sometimes both. Early New England farmers were forced to center their farming around subsistence while cutting timber and developing factories. At the same time, middle and southern Atlantic farmers were concentrating on tobacco, cotton, and indigo. Western frontiersmen took with them the plants and the production practices learned in the east, only to find through trial and error that the land and climate of the West were not well suited to most of them. As late as 1862 Congress made the sad mistake of establishing 160 acres as the size of a homestead for all states and territories. Farms of 160 acres had proved to be a very good size for family farms in the humid plains. Such mistakes made by relying completely on experience need not be made today.

The professional farm manager, the farm appraiser, the extension specialist, the county agent, teachers of agriculture, and the Soil Conservation Service farm planner must understand the great underlying principles of comparative advantage and decreasing returns upon which sound farm organizations are developed on specific farms and must have practice in applying them, if they are to do effective teaching.

Answers to questions of organization depend upon the fixed conditions faced by the potential operator, i.e., the amount of money available, his ability, certain fixed assets which he may own, his purpose in farming, price relationships (reflecting marketing opportunities and partially determining costs), personal tastes, and knowledge of farming.

Some Items Are More Important Than Others in Developing a Farm Organization

Successful farming is based upon a variety of considerations. One can easily say that success depends upon this or upon that, but the facts are that it depends upon many things functioning together.

However, some of the factors upon which profitable farming rests (in the sense that a house rests on a foundation) are more basic—more fundamental or important—than others.

What are the factors of basic importance in organizing farm businesses and what are the factors of minor importance? What things in farming are the most fixed and what are the most varied? Experience and economic reasoning dictate that an organization must be created within the limits imposed by the fixed conditions. The one most fixed factor for every farmer is the assets which he possesses—money, property, personal capacity, credit, family labor, etc. Once a fixed land asset is acquired, it and its climate, composed of such things as amount of rainfall, distribution of rainfall, frost-free days, average temperature, maximum temperature, and minimum temperature are fixed. Climate is probably more fixed than any other characteristic of a piece of land. Because little can be done about changing climate and land, crops and livestock must be adjusted to the limits imposed by it. So far as the present day is concerned, nature, our forefathers, and Experiment Station workers have determined what crops will succeed in a given climate. Therefore, within an area farmers conform to the climate factor by sticking to the range of crops and livestock which have proved successful in the neighborhood.

Land, then, is sometimes a dominating fixed factor in determining the organization of a given farm. Usually, land merely imposes ranges within which the farm must be organized. Land is composed of climate, topography, depth of soil, presence or absence of rocks, trees, gulleys, alkali, free water, and many other things. Usually a given piece of land will grow many useful plants, but the number it will grow well is limited, and the number it will grow well enough to sell to advantage under a given set of price relationships in competition with other producers is often narrowly limited. Sometimes land can be economically used for but one kind of plant, as small grains, pasture, or trees, in which case it is the fixed factor around which a given farm must be organized. Ordinarily, available financial resources, the characteristics of other fixed assets, personal capacities, prices of products and inputs at the farm, and personal preferences impose joint restrictions on what can be profitably produced. Only in special cases do personal preferences and special price advantages become completely dominating influences in the use of land.

Nature and "Usual" Price Relationships Point the Way in Developing Farm Business Organization

Let us consider the results of some of the physical, biological, and economic forces which have given shape to farming as a whole, to individual farm businesses, and to the things that farmers produce. Collectively, these forces have influenced both areas and the people who compose them. By flogging men for trying the wrong things and rewarding them for correct analysis, these physical and economic forces have without mercy pushed them and their children into producing crops and livestock in places of relative advantage, thus giving a pattern to production. Physical and economic forces are both cause and effect. They are tide, backwash, and undertow. They entrench some men in secure positions and grind others into poverty. In farming these forces are composed of rainfall and the lack of it, of the demand for products and the supply of labor and other inputs (all reflected in "usual" or "normal" price relationships), of the heat of summer and the cold of winter, of diseases and mosquitoes and cattle ticks, of acid soils and alkali soils, of steep hillsides and gentle slopes, of trees to cut, ditches to dig, of frost-free days and zero days, of distance to market and distance of others from the same market.

Natural and economic forces acting throughout the years have thus forced farmers into producing the crops for which they have the highest comparative advantage. Southern farmers still organize farm businesses around cotton production, midwest farmers around corn, Appalachian Mountain farmers also around corn, as a subsistence crop, Plains farmers around wheat and grass, seaboard farmers around truck crops, central Kentucky farmers around tobacco, and Aroostook County (Maine) farmers around potatoes. There must be reasons for such patterns. The reasons are found in the interaction of the capacity of land to produce with the demands (reflected in prices) for products and the supply of other inputs. The principle of comparative advantage holds true for both general and specialized farms. There are cranberry bogs in Massachusetts, corn and livestock farms in the corn belt, rice fields in Louisiana, sugar camps in Vermont, and many associations of crops in selected areas.

Distance to the centers of demand and ease and costs of shipping products have been generally referred to in the previous section as economic forces. The center of demand is the place toward which the "last case of eggs" or "bushel of wheat" moves to be priced. For example, farmers at "Podunk" produce a few eggs more than they consume, trading their extras for some things at the country store. The Podunk country store finally gathers a few cases and ships them to a dealer in a near-by town or city. Here a few are consumed, and when the dealer has collected a small truck load from farmers and other country stores the surplus is moved to a wholesale handler or jobber in a larger city whence they are moved to the "best" city market. Generally, prices at each point are such that costs of handling are collected by each handler. The point to be noted is that the egg producer near the demand center of consumption will have the highest-priced market and may be more advantageously located for profitable egg production than for other products. If the product is both bulky and perishable, such as fluid milk, the producer will certainly have an advantage if he is located near a consumers' market.[1] These economic advantages coupled with the physical advantages (or disadvantages) as given are thus important influences in determining the crop enterprises that may be profitably grown on a specific farm.

Farming is further complicated by seasonality of production. There is seed time and harvest time for most crops, with cultivating or simply waiting in between. Hay crops and small-grain crops are excellent examples. Even cows which must be milked every day are not milked all the day. There is an idle period between milkings. In order to fill in the gaps between morning and evening milkings and between seed time and harvest for one crop and for other reasons, typical farmers usually find it to their advantage to produce more than one crop and/or keep one or more than one type of livestock, thus giving rise to general farming, i.e., farms producing several different products. What combinations will be best for a specific farm? Those having the highest combined comparative advantages. The analysis of these combinations further complicates the problem of organizing farming businesses.

Fixed Factor Approach to Organization

The authors of this book approach the problem of farm organization as follows. They first evaluate the fixed conditions facing a given farmer at a given time. After having determined these, they proceed through the organization procedure by considering land and improve-

---

[1] A consumers' market is a market made up of direct consumers, whereas a producers' market is a marketing center located in an area because the product is produced there. For example, ice cream in a city suburb vs. grain elevators and cotton gins in producing areas.

ments, then cropping systems, livestock systems, labor and equipment programs, and finally integrate and adjust the component parts on the basis of (1) price and production relationships, (2) the ease with which the inputs and component parts can be adjusted, and (3) the wants and preferences of the farm family.

QUESTIONS AND PROBLEMS

1. Given a specific farm, why is organization likely to prove uneconomic if one approaches organization through planning to use the enterprises that one likes best?

2. X and Y are operators of adjoining farms. X is "King of the Golden River," Y a one-gallus hillbilly farmer. X can grow corn at the rate of a bushel per 20 minutes of labor, and Y can grow corn at the rate of a bushel per 7 hours of labor. Under what conditions would they both grow corn and under what conditions would Y buy corn from X?

3. Write a one-page description of the uses of enterprises in your home neighborhood and the economic reasons for the choices.

4. It has been said that: (*a*) "Ten acres is enough"; (*b*) "Three acres is liberty"; (*c*) "Five acres will produce abundance." What is lacking in such statements?

5. Enumerate the limitations of the land-use approach to organization.

6. Under what conditions is it economic to fit the crops program to the livestock selected?

7. What changes in uses of resources must be made in shifting from harvest crops farming to pasture farming?

8. Why may an absentee owner with abundant finances organize a business differently from an owner-operator limited in finances?

9. Do general price levels have any bearing on sizes of farms and on enterprises used on farms?

CHAPTER 6

Capital Limitations, Capacities and Goals or Objectives

When we narrow our realm of inquiry to organizing or reorganizing a farm business for one specific farmer, the farm to be operated for the purpose of providing a living—through production largely for sale —how do we begin? What crops does he grow? What seed does he use? How does he determine production rates? What size and type of tractor(s) are best? What other machines can he afford? What livestock should he keep?

The problem is not too difficult if one selects the important fixed factor or set of fixed factors and then considers the other variables in the order of their fixity and in the order of their income-producing capacities. Financial resources and personal capacities, wants and preferences, and land and climate tend to be the important fixed factors around which farm businesses are organized. One starts organizing or reorganizing a farm by appraising the characteristics of the fixed factors or conditions which one faces. *Thus, this chapter will consider first the influence of available capital on the problem of organizing and reorganizing farms and, second, the capacities, wants, and preferences of the individual farmer concerned.*

An Overall Look at Capital Requirements

Before examining the effect of capital limitations on the organization of a farm business, the student needs to take the overall look at capital requirements. This section provides such a look.

Commercial farming is rapidly passing into the category of a big private business. Higher land prices, machines, improved practices, higher market requirements, and higher alternative incomes from job opportunities off the farm are contributing causes. Though the amount of money necessary for fixed investments has recently increased almost threefold, the proportionate cost of annual operating expenses has become larger than the cost of the use of the fixed investments.

A large amount of capital is required to finance a farm business that gives reasonable prospect of success. However, the operator need not furnish all the capital. A tenant furnishing everything but real estate capital will need at least $4,000 to $8,000. To set up as an owner-operator $14,000 and upwards will ordinarily be required for real estate and $4,000 to $8,000 for personal property, a total of $18,000 or more,

reports the North Central Regional Land Tenure Committee, a group made up of agricultural economists from 14 north central states, a representative from the Farm Foundation, and one from the U. S. Department of Agriculture. Perhaps their estimates are on the conservative side. More capital would be needed at 1953 prices. Commercial farm businesses with investments of about $30,000 are more nearly the rule than the exception. For example, a modest farm of 150 acres of improved land that can be used for general crops and livestock production is difficult to find today (1953) at less than $30,000, a unit of machinery and equipment easily costs another $5,000, and 20 fair dairy cows are hard to find at $5,000. Cash to run the business must be added to these items.

The money required to purchase a good farm has always been large, relatively speaking. When land was sold by the Government of the United States at $1.25 per acre, $1.25 was hard to get. Besides, the land was usually bare unless covered with things of negative worth such as trees, rocks, or water. On the negative side, there were no buildings on farms, no roads, no schools, no churches near them. The improvements on land are a large part of the value of farms today. Improved farms now tend to sell at about the replacement cost of the farm improvements and community social services.

Money costs of obtaining a farm have gone up because:

1. The value of money has gone down.
2. Capital structures on farms and elsewhere have been added.
3. Farms are relatively more scarce; i.e., the number demanded is larger.

As pointed out by the Land-Tenure Research Committee, one need not have the total capital needed, provided that he is willing to follow good financing procedures. It is not necessary that one have $30,000, or even $20,000, of his own to do a fair job of farming. One can:

1. Operate other people's farms; thereby obtaining use of the large investments others have made in the real estate. The land-

lords can also furnish a part of the operating capital. Many renters make good earnings on share or cash contracts with landowners by furnishing only labor, machinery, and some of the productive live-stock. If one cannot buy a farm big enough to match his managerial capacities, he will have larger earnings by renting one. There is constant demand for well-trained, experienced, and dependable tenants on good-sized farms. This is a good outlet for college graduates who are willing to prove themselves first.

2. Borrow about 50 to 65 percent of the needed money for either fixed investments or working capital, or both.

3. Do part-time farming, especially if trained for city employment.

4. Combinations of the three listed above.

The term "capital" is used in this chapter, as in business circles, to mean the money value of all items. This meaning is synonymous with "capital investment" and includes value of real estate (as well as the item defined as capital when capital was defined as a factor of production); it is expressed in terms of money.

Fixed, Working, and Operating Capital. Capital requirements include money for:

Real estate, i.e., land and the fixed improvements thereon.
Machinery and equipment.
Products in process, as growing crops.
Livestock and poultry.
Cash to run the business, including investments in the home and family as well as maintenance thereof.

Fixed capital is often regarded as that part of capital invested in real estate and the improvements attached thereto. A definition of working capital could include those things which would be moved if the farm were sold, such as machinery, tillage tools, livestock, feed, and supplies. A more general definition of *fixed capital* would include assets not subject to variation by the manager, the term *working capital* being reserved for assets subject to variation by the manager. This definition would be realistic but would have the disadvantage of depending upon the particular circumstances in which each manager happens to be at a given time. Working capital can also be subdivided on the basis of function.

On another basis, there are at least five groups, namely:

1. Labor-displacing capital, such as tractors, cultivators, balers, including product-handling capital, such as wagons, trucks, milk bottles, and sacks.
2. Product-improving capital, such as hay driers and milk coolers.
3. Product-increasing capital, such as plant foods and seeds.
4. Product-converting capital, such as productive livestock.
5. Family and home maintenance capital.

As noted above, the division of capital into categories or subdivisions is not always the same. Sometimes such items as machinery and equipment or breeding stock are classified as fixed capital. They are fixed within the business for a time, but ordinarily for a shorter run of time than buildings, for example. Operating or working capital is a short-run type of capital. In this category one places seed, feed, fertilizer, feeder cattle, grade hogs, poultry, and cash to run the home and business. The usual length of run from the time of making such investments or expenditures until time of sale is about a year. The classification depends somewhat upon the construction of the bookkeeping system and the size of business. All of this emphasizes the fact that classification into fixed and variable depends on the planning span or length of run under consideration.

Capital Needs for Machinery and Equipment. Money needs for machinery and equipment have increased more percentagewise during the past two decades than needs for most other purposes. This increase has been caused by:

1. Transition from horse power to mechanical power.
2. Transfer of investments in workstock to machinery and other livestock.
3. Self-propelled machinery and motor-attached units.
4. Product-improving machines such as hay driers, grinders, milk coolers, and brooders.
5. Additions of electric motors for small jobs.
6. Rubber tires on machinery.
7. Farm workshops.
8. Portable farrowing houses, range shelters, etc.

Machinery and equipment values on typical family-operated farms, as determined by studies of the Bureau of Agricultural Economics in cooperation with some of the land-grant colleges,[1] for selected areas

---

[1] "Typical Family-Operated Farms, Adjustments, Costs and Returns," *FM* 55 and *Supplement,* Bureau of Agricultural Economics.

in 1945 and 1948 at current values (probably largely values at prices of used machinery and equipment) are:

	1945	1948
Dairy farms—central New York	$1,477	$1,832
Dairy farms—southern Wisconsin	1,582	2,246
Hog-dairy farms—corn belt	1,737	2,209
Cash-grain farms—corn belt	2,403	3,458
Hog-beef raising farms—corn belt	1,333	1,870
Hog-beef fattening farms—corn belt	1,940	2,734
Wheat-corn-livestock—northern plains	1,648	2,641
Wheat-grain sorghum—southern plains	2,868	4,249
Cotton—Delta of Mississippi	200	250

This survey of capital requirements indicates the importance of available capital in farm organization. Available capital is a basic limiting factor in organizing a farm business.

Capital Distribution by Systems of Typical Farms. The volume of capital and the distribution of it are given in Table 6.1 for typical family farms in 15 selected areas. These are farming units, not census farms.

Table 6.1. Capital Investment on Typical Family Farms, 1949 [1]

System and Area	Land and Buildings	Machinery and Equipment	Livestock	Crops
Central New York dairy farms	$10,584	$2,003	$6,795	$1,873
Southern Wisconsin dairy farms	16,359	2,403	6,438	3,711
Hog-dairy corn-belt farms	23,635	2,412	5,289	4,338
Corn-belt hog-beef fattening	39,405	2,875	9,026	6,275
Corn-belt hog-beef raising	22,134	2,068	5,419	3,696
Corn-belt cash-grain farms	54,520	3,453	4,069	7,275
Spring wheat-corn livestock	18,119	2,899	4,850	4,229
Spring wheat-small grain livestock	18,927	2,797	3,508	4,692
Wheat roughage-livestock	17,017	2,308	5,604	4,089
Winter wheat farms—wheat	37,820	4,448	4,391	2,768
Winter wheat-grain-sorghum	40,470	4,672	3,571	2,933
Cattle ranches	25,610	3,278	32,956	3,394
Cotton farms—Southern Plains	15,975	1,920	1,509	693
Cotton farms—Black Prairie	20,010	1,496	1,235	525
Cotton farms—Delta of Mississippi	8,145	275	574	469

[1] "Farm Costs and Returns, 1949, with Comparisons, Commercial Family-Operated Farms in 7 Major Farming Regions," *FM* 78, Bureau of Agricultural Economics.

Steps in a Sound Procedure for Acquiring Capital

Over periods of time capital limitations can be overcome in various ways. The following steps are useful in considering the problem of acquiring capital:

1. The first step for one who wants to acquire capital to operate a farm business is to establish a good reputation for himself and his family. The reputation is well based upon punctuality, honesty, complete sobriety, superior managerial ability for his age and situation, and evidenced thrift. The morals of both himself and the members of his family should be high.

2. The second step is to acquire operating capital. A money-making minimum is (a) a team or tractor, (b) land-tillage tools, (c) feed for a half-year's supply, (d) enough cash or credit to operate through one season, and (e) on some farms, productive livestock. This will probably necessitate a total investment of about $5,000 as a minimum at 1953 prices. The investment should provide enough operating equipment and cash to rent a farm, large enough to keep the operator and the members of his family productively employed most of the year. Many farmers try to buy farms too soon in their financial careers and find themselves with a small or poor farm, a heavy debt and no funds either to improve the farm or to operate it advantageously. If the purchaser has used his full resources plus his credit to buy the farm, he is in a weak position either to improve and develop the farm or to operate it. Operating capital, if wisely invested and used on larger farms of fair to high productivity, will return more than the same amount invested in land. The turnover is faster.

All farmers should keep themselves in a strong operating position, that is, keep a few hundred dollars (of cash or credit) in reserve for "bargains" and for bargaining purposes. "It takes money to make money," is an oft-quoted adage, and it is probably quoted more often by those who do not have it than by those who do. Many thrifty young couples can in a year or so, accumulate a thousand dollars. Usually it is best not to tie so small an amount up in long-run fixed properties such as land, but to use it as good opportunities arise in short-time uses. Most farmers are currently $1,000 behind in place of $1,000 ahead, until after they have accumulated one farm, reared the family, and paid the real-estate mortgage. Money spent for increasing productivity levels is important at this stage and so is restraint in living expenditures. Assets cannot accumulate until income exceeds living expenses.

3. The third step is to enlarge the amount of operating capital and cash into a reserve until it can be wisely invested in a farm. This may require one to several years. Many good tenants (cash or share basis) have as much as $10,000 invested in operating good farms on a share basis. Some have millions. A few of the largest farm business operators in the United States are tenants (renters).

4. The fourth step is to buy as much land as can be financed without unduly limiting operating capital and credit. If sufficient land cannot be bought to keep the family productively employed, additional land or additional crops can be rented.

5. The fifth step is to improve the land owned to a profitable productiveness. If water is available for crops, this level is probably indicated by yields of about 80 bushels of corn per acre, 3 tons of hay per acre, and pasturage for a unit of livestock on 2 to 3 acres of pasture on such lands as those of the eastern corn belt. Yields should, of course, be determined by economic productivity, depending in turn upon the fixed costs, the variable costs, and prices of the products. This procedure usually means spending money first for soil improvements, water control, and crop fertilizers.

6. The need for fences and buildings enters the finance program on livestock farms. No general rule is applicable as to the time to add them (if usable ones are not already on the farms). The system of farming is one determining factor. The type of crops grown and the climate are others. A generalization, however, may be followed. Buildings and fences are not directly productive. They are long-run fixed investments not usually recovered in less than 25 to 50 years. Operating capital costs, however, such as seed or fertilizer, are usually recovered in 1 year.

7. If one has attained the position of being able to operate and command a sufficient amount of productive land to (a) pay farm operating costs, (b) provide for the family, (c) retire existing debts, (d) maintain the physical properties of the farm, and (e) still have unused managerial capacity, he is in sound position to purchase additional land with credit as fast as the new purchases can be improved and/or profitably operated.

8. Family expenses will increase as the family increases in size and age. The maximum requirements are usually reached when the children are of high school and college age. Therefore, young farmers usually have a heavy financial load composed of improving a farm, retiring debts, and providing increased funds for family use at one and the same time. Family development is a primary objective in

good farming, and it cannot come from farming except through sound farm financing and sound family management.

Capital Problem Solutions Are of a Long-Run Nature. Solution of the financial problems of a farmer is largely a long-run proposition. One may well spend a lifetime accumulating a good farm. On ranches, the value of the livestock is about equal to the value of the real estate. For other systems the major portion of the capital requirements is in real estate. Houses, barns, fences, and water systems are expected to last 50 or more years; money invested in machinery and equipment 10 to 20 years; basic land improvements should likewise last as long. Frequently the interest payments on real estate mortgages, when totaled over the life of the loan, exceed the principal. Money is needed also for annual or short-run expenses such as feed, fertilizer, livestock, labor, and fuel. One of the distinguishing characteristics in the nature of farming is that it is a business of high fixed costs and low capital turnover. This characteristic is a factor of importance in farm financing. It subjects the safety of loans to long-time price cycles and also to the long-time changes within the borrower's family. One may borrow 100 percent of the value of commercial paper for 30 days, but only about 65 percent of the value of farm real estate; the difference is in rate of turnover and length of run involved.

The capital problem is of a long-run nature in contrast to the problem of organizing a farm at a given point in time. At a given point in time, little can be done about acquiring owned capital. Capital limitations constitute an important aspect of the fixed situation faced by the organizer.

The Problem of Capital Limitation Is Basic to Farm Organization. Regardless of the long-run nature of its solution, the individual farmer in organizing or reorganizing a farm must first deal with the immediate problems composed of his capital limitations. *These limitations fix the boundaries of the type of organization or reorganization that he may undertake.* These limitations partially determine whether it is advisable for him to be a part-time farmer, cropper, share-tenant, renter, indebted owner, or debt-free owner, etc. This question is never properly settled in isolation from other aspects of farming. Instead, it is settled in relation to (1) the form in which a man holds his assets (i.e., he may own equipment, he may have only cash and credit, he may own land, he may stand to inherit land, or his only assets may be farming "know-how" and managerial capacity), (2) the goals of the farmer and his family, (3) the crops and kinds of livestock that the man knows how and desires to produce, and (4) a wide variety of other considerations. Once capital limitations, personal capacities, and goals are assessed, the problem of selecting a farm or changing farms may arise. This problem arises for the entire range from part-time farmer through tenants to debt-free, commercial, owner-operators.

Personal Capacity—a Fixed Asset

Future chapters on economic principles will make it abundantly evident that all decisions concerning the organization of a farm are interrelated. Fixed assets can be appraised in partial isolation as a basis for such interrelated decisions. Family labor and personal capacity, confused as they are with management and the farm family, sometimes take on the nature of fixed assets. The fixed nature of labor, therefore, justifies separate evaluation of the family labor and personal capacities as assets more or less fixed which may or may not impose definite limits on the type of farm selected and the cropping system and livestock enterprises appropriate to the farm organization.

In a sense, owner and family labor, and associated management, are the long-run fixed (controlling) factor of all farm businesses. Their own labor is the factor on which men consciously economize most. "Not worth the effort," "not worth the time it takes," "too much trouble to be bothered with," and "costs more than it's worth" are frequent expressions of farmers.[1]

The Overall Problem of Using Personal Capacities. People who farm have but two sources of things to sell. These are their personal services and the services of their owned (not borrowed) investments. In a farming business the productivity of labor is tied so closely to the equipment and supplies that it uses that the amount of labor services a farmer can market at any given time depends largely upon the assets he owns and the amount he can borrow or rent.

To many of those who operate farms the farming business is primarily a means for providing a job. A farm business that is small in terms of capital investment provides little opportunity to sell personal services at acceptable rates, and one that is large provides a large opportunity. The farmer's first problem, therefore, is to associate sufficient capital with himself and his family. Each year, he has at his disposal 365 days in which to do things, or 365 days of labor and management services to use. These days are devoted to laboring,

[1] In economic terms these statements mean that the marginal returns to human effort measured in personal terms are not worth the outlay of human effort.

managing, laboring and managing, and living according to the size and nature of the business. If the capital investment is large enough to employ profitably some four or more laborers, the operator's days will be largely spent in planning, directing, supervising, selling, and buying; if smaller, as on the typical family farm, the days will be devoted to laboring and managing; if still smaller, as on farms where there is no need for additional laborers and frequently little need for a full-time manager, the days must be devoted largely to laboring. Thus, opportunity to use potential labor services efficiently are created by:

Finding units of capital investment to associate with labor.

Finding enough units for full-time employment.

Distributing the labor resources among enterprises (hence, over the year).

Returns to Labor and Management in Agriculture Indicate That They Are, in Part, Fixed Assets

Returns to farmers, expressed in terms of money wages, real wages, labor and management wage, or total returns, are traditionally low. Realized net income to the some 6 million farms in the United States has varied within the past 20 years from 4.3 billion dollars in 1933 to 18.+ billion dollars in 1949, averaging around $750 per farmer in 1933 and $3,000 in 1949.[1] These net returns are expressions of returns to labor, management, and owned investment, in the form of both net cash receipts and products used on the farm. If interest at a rate of 4 percent is subtracted from the realized net income, a residual average annual return which may be arbitrarily attributed to labor and management varies from about $475 to $1,220. The reasons for these low labor earnings are not hard to find; two are outstanding.

First, about 3 million of the farm businesses are near the level of subsistence production, employing but little capital investment and producing but approximately 10 percent of the farm products entering commercial channels. Output per industrial worker in the United States is traditionally high, partly because workers are associated with large investments in machines, averaging about $12,000 per worker. In comparison "the man with the bull tongue plow and a mule," eulogized so eloquently in poetry by Jesse Stuart, has failed for various reasons to equip himself with sufficient capital to raise the marginal

[1] *Annual Outlook Reports,* Bureau of Agricultural Economics, USDA.

value productivity of his labor to that of his "brothers" engaged in industry and commercial farming. Thus, the good use of labor on farms, i.e., high and sustained marginal returns, is largely dependent on the proportions in which capital (including land) and labor are combined. In small farm businesses there are not enough days of work if laborers are equipped with the usual machines; if they are not so equipped the returns to labor are low. The small-farm operator is between the proverbial "devil and the deep blue sea." If he adds equipment to make his labor services more productive, he cannot use such equipment enough to get back the total money expended; if he does not add such equipment, he produces little. In both cases he has little ultimate product through which to sell his time. Perhaps more than half of all farmers in the United States fall within this class, as do by far the majority of those who till the soil in other countries.

Second, farmers are in a highly competitive and yet highly personalized business. Competition forces low product prices, and the personalized aspects of the business make low prices bearable. Several reasons explain why farm people accept lower than "going returns" for their labor. Family and operator's labor is, in a sense, a fixed asset. As long as earnings of additional labor on the farm do not exceed what it costs to bring labor onto the farm, no labor is ordinarily hired. Conversely, as long as earnings of additional labor on the farm do not fall below the net return (wage rate less transportation costs, etc.) for off-farm work, discounted for various conditions peculiar to farm operator families, labor is not sold off the farm. Considerations explaining the discounting include: (1) being one's own boss, (2) family loyalty, (3) the amenities of rural life, (4) the uncertainties of the city (especially employment uncertainty), and (5) imperfect knowledge of city conditions and trade. Thus, on many farms the family labor supply, including the operator, is a fixed asset over the above range of returns and is worth, within that range, just what it produces. Thus, in organizing a farm one tries to utilize the operator's and family labor at a rate falling above the lower extreme. If the rate earned at the margin cannot be brought above the lower limit, then labor must be classed as variable and arrangements made for off-farm employment. If the rate earned at the margin exceeds the upper limit, then labor must also be classed as a variable input for the farm as a whole and arrangements made for hiring labor. Regardless of whether labor services are hired, sold off the farm, or neither, a properly adjusted farm should be earning equal returns on the last unit of labor applied to each activity.

Labor as a Fixed Asset—the Labor-Use Approach

In organizing or reorganizing farms for which labor is a more or less major fixed asset, such as farms situated on land having a wide range of physical capacities located close to urban industry, a labor-use approach often yields successful preliminary approximations to farm organizations. Oftentimes, the farm family, plus a certain amount of outside labor, can be definitely counted upon to operate the farm. In most such cases a certain labor supply is willing, for one reason or another, to work on the farm at less than the rate of wages obtainable in the near-by industries. Reasons for doing this were listed above. In such instances, the factor imposing the most serious restrictions on farm organizations often becomes the supply of labor available at the lower wage rate. When such a situation is faced, it is often advantageous to select a cropping system and a livestock production system which will utilize the fixed quantity of labor most advantageously.

By and large, the labor-use approach consists of figuring out how many productive man-work units of labor can be performed by the available labor supply and then setting up, as the first approximation, a cropping and livestock system which will utilize that number of productive man-work units. Once a farm organization is roughed out on this basis, it can be refined by considering various adjustments on the basis of additional costs vs. additional returns. As long as adjustments can be made in the system roughed out by the labor-use approach which will return more than the cost, the organization of the farm is obviously being improved. By the time an optimum or near optimum organization has been devised, it becomes apparent that the labor-use approach is not basically much different from the land-use approach. Both techniques are methods for inventorying the fixed assets, a process basic to the marginal analysis approach. Both the labor- and land-use approaches described depend for refinement upon application of the additional costs vs. additional returns technique. Subsequent chapters will be devoted to developing the details and applications of the marginal approach. Labor as a *variable* in contrast to labor as a *fixed* asset will be treated in a subsequent chapter.

Appraisal of Goals and Objectives for a Farm

Along with the consideration of capital and personal limitations, a person organizing or reorganizing a farm should consider the goals of the farmer and family involved. In the society of the United States, which places high value on free expression of individual wants and preferences, it is not appropriate for an "outside planner" to impose his scheme of values upon the farmer and his family. It is proper and necessary, however, that the adviser point out the necessity of developing and integrating a farmer's (and his family's) concepts of the relative importance of various objectives into a set of goals which the farmer and his family can be reasonably expected to achieve. A farm family is likely to be concerned with the following objectives: accumulation of extra assets (such as a home, land, and modern conveniences), soil conservation, home employment for sons, educational investments, investments in family health, security, self-expression, and a wide variety of other considerations too numerous to be mentioned here.

The *first point* to be made is that these objectives must be considered early in the selection of a farm and in the organization or reorganization of a farm.

The *second point* to be made is that, after the objectives are integrated into goals, they must be reconciled with the income-producing capacity of the farmer (and his family) and the assets which the farmer owns.

If a farmer, his family, and his assets are capable of producing a high income and if desires are modest, reconciliation of goals and the means of attaining goals is easy. If, however, the farmer, his family, and his assets are not capable of producing a high income and their desires are high, reconciliation is difficult. The job of reconciling goals with income-producing and financing capacity is the core of economics and a prime problem in farm organization.

Class Case Farm and the Individual Case Farm

The second main part of this book, of which this chapter is a portion, concentrates on the problems of organizing or reorganizing a commercial farm. For purposes of illustrating this procedure, a *class* case farm is used. It is expected that each student will select an *individual* case farm to be used in connection with the problem exercises at the ends of the chapters.

Our task at this point is to appraise the asset limitations, wants, preferences, and "fixed" labor supply of the farmer and his family to be connected with the class case farm. A problem exercise provided at the end of the chapter will help students to follow the same procedure in connection with their individual case farms.

Asset Limitations, Wants, Preferences, Capacities and Fixed Labor Supply of the Class Case Farmer and Family

It is assumed that the class case farmer has recently inherited a one-third interest in a 335-acre farm to be described later, that he is presently operating a 110-acre farm, worth $300 an acre, as a debt-free owner, that he owns equipment and livestock worth $10,000, and that he has $8,000 in the bank.

This farmer, having been brought up on a beef farm in a community producing both grass and grains, knows beef-production methods ranging from the cow-calf plan to drylot feeding. Further, inasmuch as he has been producing milk, hogs, and burley tobacco on his 110-acre farm, he is familiar with those enterprises.

This farmer's family includes his wife, a boy of high school age interested in farming and agriculture, and a 10-year-old girl. All are in good health. As both the farmer and his wife grew up on large stable farms in prosperous farming communities, both appreciate the scale of living which can be attained on a full-size commercial farm. Both, along with their children, are interested in establishing a larger farming operation. They prefer farm life and want to establish their scale of living at a high level.

QUESTIONS AND PROBLEMS

1. Present a lifetime financial plan for farm and family financing (a) as to kinds of actions, (b) as to relative quantities of money involved. Begin with your own personal situation as to age, finances, and opportunities, as:

Conditions	Actions	Time	Money Required	Source of Funds	Other
20 years old, single	Finish college	2 years	$1,600		
Single	Teach vocational agriculture	2 years	$1,500 for living	Salary	Save $1,500
Married	Marry	5 years	$500	Savings	
	Wife work		$1,500	Savings	Save $2,000 a year
	New car and child	9 years	$4,000	Savings	
	Buy farm		$4,000 down		Borrow

2. Do you know farmers who "started on a shoestring" and have developed good-sized farming businesses? If so, how did they do it? What were their associated family financial responsibilities? Are there reasons why conditions may not be as favorable for you?

3. Can a college graduate substitute earning capacity in the professional services for capital in getting started in farming? How much capital investment in
farming is required to earn an income equal to the salary of an assistant county
agricultural agent?

4. What are the opportunities in your home community to earn a living plus
$1,000 net a year doing contract work, and tenant operations? How much
capital would it require? Where could one get it? Where would one live?

5. Does money invested in operating capital and working capital earn more
than money invested in farm real estate? Why?

6. Is it easier for a merchant to borrow $50,000 on accounts receivable or for a
farmer to borrow $50,000 on a farm at your home town bank? Would you rather
loan a selected man $10,000 for 50 percent financing of a farm, or $10,000 for 80
percent financing of used cars, or $10,000 for 80 percent financing feeding cattle
(feed and cattle)?

PROBLEM EXERCISE 6
Selection of Farm Family for Case Studies

The Problem Exercises in this book provide for student analysis of individually
selected farm businesses. This one is the first in a related series. The description
contained in the last subheading should be used as a guide. The first decision
for the student to make concerns the selection of the specific individual farm
family which he will use for applying management analysis principles throughout the course. In most cases it will be found advisable to use the business and
family situations of the one currently existing. The point of view of the student
might be that of one acting in the capacity of a professional worker called in to
diagnose the long-time business problem of a farm family.

Using the last subheading of this chapter describing the class case farm and
family situation, make a similar analysis (and subsequent description) of the
farm business (including family) selected. Be sure to include the asset and net
worth situation, capacities, wants and preferences of the family, and family goals.

CHAPTER 7

Farm Selection and Evaluation of the Farm Resource

Introductory Statement

In organizing or reorganizing a farm business, the problem of selecting a farm or additional units of land may or may not arise. In either event the problems of evaluating land resources as a basis for organization and reorganization do arise. This chapter will consider, first, the problem of farm or land selection, and, second, the problem of evaluating land for an organizational basis. The amount of land which can be advantageously acquired, however, is limited by the considerations in the last chapter, namely: financial resources, personal (including family) capacities, and goals. Before proceeding with the problem of selecting a farm or a piece of land, several points of view deserve consideration.

Points of View

What Is the Value of a Farm? No one knows the value of a farm. Value depends upon the future, which is always a question mark in the present. Farms were worth less, much less, than they sold for in 1919 and 1920, and much more than they sold for in the 1930's.

When they were good buys in the 1930's it was all but impossible to obtain credit to buy them. Limited credit was one reason farms sold at low prices. Lending agencies were short on credit funds. Farms sell at low prices when products are selling at low prices, and the farms are, therefore, worth little as current income producers. When commodity prices are high, land prices are high, as farms have high current income productivity. A part of the difficulty in farm financing arises from the nature of farm production. Farming is a business of high fixed costs, uncertain prices, and uncertain yields. It often takes about 20 years for a farmer to realize a net income equal to his total capital investment, and many things, both good and bad pricewise, happen in 20 years. Wars, the attendant inflations, and consequent deflations are the principal causes of price fluctuations. Wars start and end with alarming quickness and with violent repercussions on farmers.

In buying farms the important problems center around resources, method, and timing. The problem differs according to financial resources, capacities, and goals; hence, it differs from individual to individual. A farm that sells for $30,000 may seem very cheap to one who has $30,000 or more in idle funds and whose primary object is to find a place to keep his capital. The same farm may seem very dear to one who has but a "shoestring," or maybe only the clip end of a shoestring. Such an individual takes great risk. If "fate" plays against the individual who purchases on a shoestring, he loses out. For most of us who are not plungers, a moderately conservative pattern of living and financing may ordinarily be expected to result in the acquirement of a good life and a good farm business of modest, but sufficient, size. Even some who are so unfortunate as to get in at the wrong time stay in through superior farm and family management until the break comes their way; and it usually comes. Timing is also important. Price levels rise and fall but debt commitments do not. Timing is, therefore, more important in connection with credit than with cash land purchases.

Farm Houses. A farm, whether purchased or rented, should have a house that will care for the family in a manner in keeping with its earnings. A good house with conveniences, including hot and cold water, electricity, and a central heating plant is highly desirable. Such conveniences are rapidly coming to be considered necessities by people with moderate incomes; hence, farms capable of producing moderate or better income should have them. Location on a good road, school bus service, and other community conveniences are also highly desirable. The comfort and welfare of the family is the main objective in farming. Good buildings and equipment can be paid for and kept up only on productive land or land that can be made productive. A conservative part of the investment, in most cases not more than 40 percent, in all the buildings and improvements can be justified by the farmer who is making a living at farming.

Good farm homes have economic as well as esthetic values. Well-planned homes save time for other productive work. Good homes also add to morale, give business confidence, and usually provide opportunity for learning. Learning is one of the steps in management. A leading county agent, W. B. Collins, once said, "Little improvement can come to farms until farmers get a good light to see by, and a good pair of eye glasses to see with." Days of drudgery are not conducive to learning modern farming. Modern homes, economically built, are productive tools.

Some Farm-Business Points of View on Barns. Barns are basically conservers of things produced and protectors of things being produced; they add time utility. A farm should have enough barns to care for the produce of the farm, and the cost of the care given to the produce should be carefully weighed against its value. Idle buildings are worth less than no buildings because they cost money to be kept idle. Probably, depreciation, obsolescence, insurance, taxes, and repairs are the nearest approach to perpetual motion. Depreciation is decline in value due to wear and age. Obsolescence is decline in value due to changes in needed types. D. Howard Doane, President of Doane Agricultural Service, Inc., considers the gambrel-roof type of dairy barns as "grandfather barns," i.e., obsolete. They have outlived their best use due to changing methods of handling hay and increased costs of laborers. In many European countries, barns on the better farms generally have outlasted methods of production. Changes in systems of farming, shifts in production areas for specific products because of shifts in population centers, and changes in consumer demand frequently render barns obsolete. Barns, therefore, need to be somewhat adaptable to change. A striking illustration of change in production practices on dairy farms is the change from stanchion-type barns with concrete floors and fixed equipment to rest-shed barns with milking parlors. Another is change from row-crop to sod-crop farming. Hay driers, pick-up balers, field choppers, mechanical elevators, and high labor costs are changing the demand from tall barns having loft mows with considerable depth for loose hay and hand feeding to mows on or near the ground for self-feeding.

Costs of Barns. A rough guide to justifiable investment in barns is that a year's gross production of the enterprise should pay for the barn. For example, cows earning a gross yearly income of $400 each justify being housed in barns costing about $400 per cow. The annual cost of a barn, expected to last for 50 years, is about 9 to 10 percent of the construction cost, made up as follows:

> Interest—4½ to 5 percent
> Depreciation (on original cost)—2 percent
> Repairs—1 to 1½ percent
> Insurance and taxes—1 to 1½ percent

Approached from another angle, the rough guide indicates that annual cost is excessive if it exceeds 10 percent of the annual income of the product housed. Thus, a hen producing $4.00 per year should be housed for 40 cents. Labor-extensive livestock such as beef cattle and sheep should be housed for less than 10 percent. The pole-type of barn construction greatly reduces cost of housing, as labor costs in construction are reduced to a minimum.

Fences. Fences are a necessary nuisance on typical commercial farms. Fences are made necessary by the use of livestock on pasture and in feed lots. Thus, the cost of use is chargeable to the livestock enterprises or to pasture. If one had no livestock, harvest-crop fields would not need fencing except to keep out the neighbor's livestock. In the highly productive cash grain areas of the midwest and on truck farms, fences are not necessary. To the individual owner the primary reason for fencing fields is to enable him to keep his livestock in the *pasture* fields where he puts them and to keep out his neighbor's livestock. It is axiomatic in livestock regions that "good fences make good neighbors." Perhaps the axiom should allude to keeping good neighbors. Barbed wire was a prime factor in settling the west as it helped to keep the "Cains" and the "Abels" from killing one another. The advantages of fences are:

1. They provide for use of grassland (sod crops) in farming.
2. They enable gleaning such crop by-products as hay aftermaths, shattered grain, pasturage along fence rows, etc.
3. They mark farm boundaries and keep one's livestock from troubling his neighbor (and the neighbor's from troubling him).
4. They may beautify a landscape (neglected, they make it unsightly).
5. They provide wildlife sanctuaries; particularly when neglected.

The disadvantages of fences are:

1. They are often in the way of contour cultivation.
2. They cost a lot of money.
3. They use land.
4. They are expensive to maintain and keep clean.
5. They injure animals.
6. They are predisposing causes of gulleys.
7. They make necessary expensive openings (gates).
8. They cause animals to make paths.
9. They cause additional travel.
10. They prevent easy shifts in crop boundaries.

Cost of Fencing—Kinds of Fences. Fences vary from brush piles to stone masonry and wrought iron grills of period design. Within the range of typical farm businesses, fences vary from a single strand of barbed wire stapled to trees or stakes to all-purpose fences of woven wire, stone, or rail. The major portion of all-purpose fences is woven wire. Present costs of number nine woven wire 48-inch fencing erected on six-inch or larger treated posts (or steel posts) are about $3.00 to $4.00 per rod. On rotation-crop and pasture-land farms about 700 rods of fence will be needed on a 100-acre farm, or some 7 rods per acre. A problem is provided in the Problem Exercises dealing with fencing costs of the individual case farm. The costs here given should be checked against those in local areas. A 160-acre quarter-section farm lying along a highway on two sides and fenced into four fields, and with the neighbors providing half of the interboundary fences, requires approximately 800 rods of fence. At a valuation of $2.00 per rod (average value) $1,600 are tied up in fences, equal to $10.00 per acre, or a total cost of about $160 per year (depreciation 4 percent; interest 4½ percent; repairs and taxes 1½ percent). Most of this cost must be charged to the use of pastures. Analyzing further, if one-fourth of the farm is used for pasture, i.e., 40 acres, the fencing costs are about $4.00 per acre of pasture per year. Thus, fixed fencing costs constitute an excellent economic reason for making pastures highly productive in order to justify the investment in fencing and return a profit.

Size of fields and size of farm influence fencing costs. A 1-acre square lot requires 50 rods of fence; a 10-acre square field requires 160 rods—16 rods per acre—whereas a 100-acre field of the same shape requires 1,265 rods or 12.65 rods per acre. What size of square field would have an acre in it for each rod of fence around it? In areas of low carrying capacity, such as some of the Great Plains and Rocky Mountains, it has been cheaper to use herdsmen than to use fences. However, the price of labor and the value of controlled grazing are pushing the use of more fencing in those areas. If the stocking rate of pasture is one cow per 20 acres and the cost of barbed wire fence $1.00 per rod, fields of 640 acres each would necessitate 640 rods (one-half the perimeter if square) or $640 in fencing investment—or some $70.40 in annual costs equal to $2.20 per cow per year.

Costs of Improvements. If one had 160 acres of bare land of a fair-to-good level of productivity but with no improvements, and which had to be improved at present (1953) building costs, the improvements would likely equal a conservative value of the farm as a whole when improved. Such costs could be itemized somewhat as follows:

7-room house with basement	$ 8,000 to $14,000
Feed barn for 50 units of livestock	6,000 to 8,000
Silo	1,000 to 1,500
1,600 rods fencing, all-purpose, good	3,000 to 4,800
Water systems	1,000 to 1,500
Outbuildings	1,000 to 2,000
Roads—miscellaneous	500 to 1,000
	$20,500 $32,800
Value per acre (no cost for land)	128 to 205

Water Management. Water management further complicates the problem of farm evaluation. *The objective of water management is to handle water so that it will do the most good and the least harm.* It involves land management, cropping practices, and agricultural engineering. On farms needing livestock, watering devices are involved also. The principal kinds of water management problems are:

1. Drainage.
2. Irrigation.
3. Rainfall with erosion vs. soil and water conservation.
4. Drinking water for livestock.
5. Water for household use.

All of these cost money but are worth the investments when prudently made and well used. Complete tile drainage costs $40 to $100 per acre, which should be recovered in increased net returns during the life of the tile and preferably sooner. Irrigating systems cost up to several hundred dollars, depending upon the type and cost of getting water. Portable sprinkler irrigation costs $50 to $200 per acre with modern methods using movable pipe fitted with quick coupling devices.[1] The cheapest method of handling water erosion from rainfall and at the same time of conserving both soil and soil moisture is to keep the land in sod. However, sod crops will not use labor resources fully or produce the largest gross returns per acre. Or will they? Some think they will. Water management on rolling land farms (Classes II to IV) with row cropping may call for diversion ditches, terraces, and sodded outlets with concrete or stone spillways. Contour cultivation can be had for little cost and will probably result in 10 to 20 percent higher yields. There is also a saving in tractor fuel in working.

Drinking water for livestock is another capital requirement. So are concrete feeding floors. Bulldozers have been a boon to farmers in

[1] For an interesting and valuable report on irrigation read "Portable Sprinkler Irrigation," *Fortune,* June, 1950.

helping to solve water problems. With them $200 to $500 builds dams on most farms that create a pond or lake, bringing comfort to livestock plus profit and enjoyment to the family. Complete water systems in which the water is pumped from wells into the house(s) and barns cost $1,000 and up. Farmers both deserve and need modern (i.e., modern 40 years ago) conveniences including water, lights, and central heating. Of course, the farmer may not be in a position to afford it.

The Problem of Selecting Farms and Land Occurs at All Tenure Levels

Renters, share tenants, croppers, even hired managers, as well as land buyers, face the task of selecting farms. Financial limitations also drive a man from cash renting to share-crop renting or from share-crop renting to cropping or hired-hand arrangements. Thus, in selecting farms both the farm and the tenure arrangement come up for consideration. *The proper tenure arrangement is one which permits a farmer to command a unit of land and improvements which will utilize economically his working capital, personal managerial and labor capacities, family labor, and such other assets as he may have.* It should not be forgotten that individual and family goals also partially determine the type of tenure arrangements which should be settled upon. In selecting tenure arrangements, it is well to keep in mind that small quantities of capital ordinarily return higher rates as working capital than when invested in land and fixed improvements.

Within a given tenure arrangement a range of farms are often available, i.e., small fertile farms, large rough farms, overbuilt farms, inadequately improved farms, grain farms, livestock farms, specialty farms, general farms, etc. Oftentimes one of the specific farms has some characteristic making it particularly attractive; it may have been in the family, the farmer may know it particularly well, or he may own a portion of it, etc. Even when a farmer owns a farm it may be well not to overlook the possibility of selling it and buying one better suited to the financial resources, capacities, and desires or goals of the farmer and his family. Now, what are the desirable characteristics of a farm?

1. It should be large enough to provide profitable employment for working capital which the farmer has or is willing and able to borrow.

2. It should be large enough to employ at least the fixed capacities of the farmer and his family at rates satisfactory to them.

3. It should have characteristics capable of satisfying the goals held by the farmer and his family.

Selection of the Class Case Study Farm

The financial resources, capacities, fixed assets, and goals of the class case study family were appraised in the last chapter. The present task is one of selecting a farm for the family which, it will be recalled, now owns one small farm and has inherited a one-third interest in a 335-acre farm. The farmer is apparently capable and has a son of high school age and a wife inclined towards farm living. He also has $18,000 worth of working capital. Both he and his family hold goals closely tied to successful operation of a fairly large farm.

It becomes apparent that the 335-acre farm has many advantages for the family. *First,* it offers full employment at probably profitable rates for the family labor, managerial capacity, and working capital ($8,000 of which is now nearly idle in the bank). On the larger farm the proportion of capital to labor inputs can be adjusted to use more capital, perhaps less labor, and perhaps more management. *Second,* the farmer can finance ownership of the larger tract and still have enough working capital and credit left over to operate the farm economically. *Third,* the larger farm will provide the means of satisfying many individual and family goals. Thus, the 335-acre farm is selected as the class case study farm for this family.

Once the farm is acquired, many formerly variable considerations become fixed and impose limitations on the kind of farming business which can be acquired. These additional fixed characteristics are tied in closely with land. Thus, the next step is to evaluate the land resource as a basis for organizing the farm business.

The Evaluation of Land As an Organizational Basis—The Land-Use or Land-Adaptation Approach

Let us again consider the logic of using the land (once it has been selected) as a basis for farm organization by studying the diagram in Figure 7.1. At the top of the diagram is a characterization of land—a central rectangle representing natural land with its attendant characteristics, location, topography, fertility, etc. At the bottom of the diagram is another rectangle representing a composition of some thousands of production and management practices, as rations for livestock, varieties of crops, and ways of doing things. Practices and costs and the things the land will produce, i.e., the parts of a farm, are mutually interrelated.

Beginning with the land selected for use, we can roughly determine the classes of crops it will produce advantageously over a period of

years. Class of crop means intertilled, small grain, sod, or trees. The
next step will be to select from these classes specific crops which throw
the highest comparative advantage to the business as described, or
which, in combination with one another, or with other enterprises, will
give the largest total advantage to the business. In selecting the crops

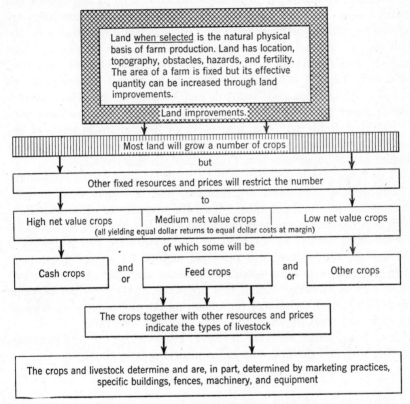

Fig. 7.1. The flow of organization problems.

and combinations of crops, use should be made of computations checking the additional costs of making changes against the resultant additional returns. These computations should also cover livestock products
produced from the crops produced. *If* the land is best suited (under
existing price relationships) to corn (an intertilled crop), oats (a small-
grain crop) and hay, a large proportion of feed will result. And, if
corn, oats and hay are the feeds produced, hogs and cattle are indicated as the kinds of livestock to use. Whether pork, dairy, or beef
production, taken singly, is engaged in will depend on (1) prices and

(2) preferences of the farmer. Suitable combinations of crops and livestock will also depend on the same two factors. The livestock market outlook and existing production facilities might determine whether wheat and soybeans in contrast to oats and hay should be grown. The crops and livestock selected also depend in part on the availability of particular farm improvements, such as hog houses and cattle barns. In some cases the advantages of certain enterprises are strong enough to justify construction of such facilities. Similarly, the selection of enterprises determines and is determined by pieces of machinery and equipment needed for the production of such crops and livestock. Finally, enterprise practices begin to fall into associations related to the crops and livestock and land uses. By this approach the "jig-saw puzzle" of the pieces of the farmers' resources have been transferred from confusion into a rough first approximation of organization through the use of a procedure which began with the proper choice of the important fixed factor, land, in this situation.

This procedure is properly called a modified *land-use or land-adaptation* approach to farm organization, and is widely used in both formal and informal planning. Since the majority of commerial family-farm businesses are best organized (for the planning spans faced by the farm family) on the basis of land adaptation and comparative advantage, as discussed, our principal method for roughing out farm organizations will be a modified *land-use approach to commercial family-farm farming*. Using this approach, the succeeding chapters deal with further techniques for answering the questions of what crops to grow and what livestock to produce on any such farm.

The first problem, however, is that of inventorying the land resources of the farm and the first step in inventorying is to classify.

Classifying Land

The organization of a farm business through the land-use approach begins with a land inventory based on a classification of the available land and soils. A farm may comprise one or several classes, subclasses, and operating units of land. For years farmers, agronomists, soil scientists, and others have recognized that land varies in types of usefulness. Farming practices indicating such recognition have been observed on many farms—particularly those including both hills and valleys. Farmers have recognized also that land of similar topography on their farms varies in soil and other factors, and have accordingly handled the various spots or units for somewhat different cropping or pasture practices. They have even recognized variations between directions of slope as constituting sufficient justification for separate practices. Southern and eastern slopes are warmer than northern and western exposures. Northern exposures may be well suited for the production of those crops which need to be retarded and less suited for those which need to be advanced as to season.

How to Apply the Land-Use Approach

The land-use approach for an individual farm recognizes:
1. Two land-use *suitability* classes.
    (a) Those suitable for production of crops to be harvested.
    (b) Those not suitable for harvested crops but suitable for pastures, woods, and other uses.
2. Land capability *classes* based upon *degrees* of limitation for intensive row cropping.
3. Land capability *subclasses* based upon the *kinds* of limitations, such as soil permeability, slope, or soil texture.
4. Land capability *units,* based upon a number of factors, such as land, soil, size of area, location of unit, and other practical management and organization problems. A unit is an area of land found to be practicable to handle as a separate piece(s) of a farm.

An outline of land capability classification as described by the Soil Conservation Service is presented in Table 7.1. The subclasses and capability units given are used as illustrations. A complete list of the subclasses and units would be too voluminous to reproduce here since many of them are applicable to restricted areas only. The instructors in each state or soil conservation district may secure literature giving a description of those pertaining to the area of their interests. The land-use capability classes are described:

Land Suitable for Cultivation [1]

I. Mapped solid light green—level, well-drained soils, where clean-tilled crops may be grown frequently without special conservation practices with good soil-management practices, including cover crops and fertilizer.

II. Mapped solid yellow—well-drained soils with gentle slopes, where cultivated crops require a limited amount or number of erosion-control practices. Example: rotations with contour cultivation and soil amendments.

III. Mapped solid red—usually rolling areas of variable soils which if cultivated are very susceptible to erosion. Require intensive erosion-control practices, such as long rotation, contour tillage with terraces, and the addition of soil amendments.

IV. Mapped solid blue—land characterized by steep slope, severe erosion, low productivity, stoniness, and/or other adverse physical conditions. May be used, if necessary, for occasional cultivation with adequate erosion-control measures, including soil amendments.

[1] The Soil Conservation Service, U. S. Department of Agriculture.

Table 7.1. Land Capability Classes

Major Land-Use Suitability Classes	Land-Capability Classes (Degree of Limitations)		Land-Capability Subclasses (Grouping of Units according to Kind of Limitation)		Land-Capability Unit (Land Management Groups Based on Permanent Physical Characteristics)
Suited for cultivation	I Green	Few limitations. Wide latitude for each use. Very good land from every standpoint			
	II Yellow	Moderate limitations or risks of damage. Good land from all-around standpoint			
	III Red	Severe limitations or risks of damage. Regular cultivation possible if limitations are observed	Red	Limited by hazard of water erosion; moderately sloping land	Moderately sloping, slightly acid soils on limestone
			Red	Limited by excess water; drainage needed for cultivation	Moderately sloping, highly acid soils on sandstone or shale
			Red	Limited by low moisture capacity; sand land	
	IV Blue	Very severe limitations. Suited for occasional cultivation or for some kind of limited cultivation			
Not suited for cultivation	V Dark Green	Not suited for cultivation because of wetness, stones, overflows, etc. Few limitations for grazing or forestry use			
	VI Orange	Too steep, stony, arid, wet, etc., for cultivation. Moderate limitations for grazing or forestry	Grouping of sites according to kind of limitation		Sites significant in management of ranges, pastures, forests, etc.
	VII Brown	Very steep, rough, arid, wet, etc. Severe limitations for grazing or forestry			
	VIII Purple	Extremely rough, arid, swampy, etc. Not suited for cultivation, grazing, or forestry. Suited for wildlife, watersheds or recreation			

Lands Not Suitable for Cultivation

V. Mapped dark green—poorly drained lands on flat or depressed topography which, because of inherently poor physical conditions, stoniness, overflow, would, if drained, produce only moderate returns as pasture or hay.

VI. Mapped solid orange—rolling to steep land, moderately susceptible to deterioration even under permanent vegetation. Suitable for forestry, grazing, or wildlife if managed to maintain adequate ground cover.

VII. Mapped solid brown—land having extremes of adverse physical conditions, such as shallow soils, very stony, steep slopes, and/or severe erosion. Highly susceptible to deterioration. Best suited for woodland or wildlife, protected from fire and grazing.

VIII. Mapped solid purple—extremely rough and swampy. Suited for wildlife, watershed, or recreation.

Solid colors are used to describe classes or degrees of usefulness; corresponding colors with hatchure (i.e., vertical, horizontal, or diagonal lines superimposed on the colors) are helpful in indicating kinds of limitations.

A capability map helps the farmer and the student to get a bird's-eye view of the kinds of crops suited to the farm physically. Within the physical limitations prescribed by the fixed conditions that he faces, the operator selects specific crops, labor, and capital resources on the basis of price relationships and personal preferences.

Further limitations on the operator's latitude in selecting crops become evident from further analysis of the land resources on the basis of past use, slope, soil type, and erosion. Symbols are useful in map descriptions to save writing space within the smaller divisions of the map. For example: (6), 6Ac, L_3, 64, B, 3, (7) when written on a map tells us that in unit 6 there are 6 acres; that the unit was in sod crops when the map was made (L_3), further that the soil is deep and derived from high-phosphate limestone (64), that the surface slope is 2 to 6 percent (B), and that from 75 percent of the topsoil to all the topsoil and 25 percent of the subsoil has been lost through removal by erosion (3), and finally that there is an occasional deep gully (7).

The complete crop-cover legend is:

A	Land removed from cultivation.	P_1	Good permanent pasture.
L_2	Close-growing, non-sod-forming crops.	P_2	Unimproved permanent pasture.
L_3	Sod crops, including hay, pasture, etc.	F_1	Forest trees.
L_1	Cultivated row crops.	F_2	Scrub forest and brush.
X	Idle land.	O	Orchard.

Slope Designation. Letters are used to designate slope. Slope is measured in vertical height per 100 feet of horizontal distance. A 5 percent slope means that the land surface rises (or drops) 5 feet per 100 feet in the direction of greatest slope. The SCS has moved in the direction of standardizing slope symbols somewhat as follows (the student should check the meaning of the different slope symbols for his own state):

A = 0 to 2 percent.   C = 7 to 9 percent.   E = 13 to 20 percent.
B = 2 to 6 percent.   D = 10 to 12 percent.   F = over 20 percent.

Erosion Designation. Erosion is described with the following symbols having the indicated meanings:

+ Recent accumulations.
1 From no apparent erosion to ¼ of the topsoil lost; occasional shallow gullies may or may not be present.
2 Between ¼ and ¾ of the topsoil lost; occasional shallow gullies may or may not be present.
3 Between ¾ of the topsoil and ¼ of the subsoil lost; occasional shallow gullies may or may not be present.
4 Between ¼ and ¾ of the subsoil lost; occasional shallow gullies may or may not be present.
5 More than ¾ of the subsoil lost to erosion of parent material; occasional shallow gullies may or may not be present.
(7) Occasional deep gullies.
8 Frequent shallow gullies.
(8) Frequent deep gullies.
9 Destructive gullying: shallow gullies.
(9) Destructive gullying: deep gullies.

Table 7.2 is a list of some of the soil-unit numbers together with description of the soil, the parent materials from which the soil was derived, a fertility rating, and the dominant soil-series names. Table 7.2 is not a complete list. Such lists as are pertinent to the state should be available at the state Experiment Station or SCS office.

The Land-Use Approach Results in a First
Approximation Reflecting Influences of Fixed Conditions

The preceding sections of this chapter have, in essence, outlined a procedure whereby land, as one of the most fixed assets on a given farm, can be

1. Inventoried.
2. Appraised as to the restrictions which its nature imposes upon the short- and intermediate-run operation of a farm business.

Table 7.2. The Soil Unit Numbers with Descriptions [1]

Soil Unit No.	Descriptive Titles	Underlying or Parent Material	Inherent Fertility	Dominant Soil Series
12	Moderately light or light textured, deep; water or wind deposits	Sand	Low	Bellevue, etc.
22	Rock outcrops	Bedrock	—	Rock outcrop
23	Very shallow, stony soils from sandstone and shale	Sandstone, shale (limestone)	Low	Stony Muskingum, etc.
24	Light-colored very cherty soils of low inherent fertility	Chert beds or gravels	Very low	Bodine
25	Shallow soils over marl or calc. shale; highly erodible	Marl or calcareous shales	Moderate	Otway
26	Soils shallow or very shallow to limestone, with numerous rock ledges	Limestone or limestone and calcareous shale	Moderate	Fairmount, Salvisa, etc.
30	Shallow or very stony or very gravelly bottoms	Alluvium or colluvial	Moderate	Stony bottom
32	Moderately deep soils from sandstone and shale (some limestone)	Sandstone and shale	Low to medium	Muskingum (nonstony)
33	Soils with very heavy subsoils from limestone with shale influence	Argillaceous limestone	Moderate	Talbott, Weon
34	Shallow to moderately deep soils with clay subsoils; limestone 15″–30″	Limestone and calcareous shale	Moderate	Mercer, Lowell, (shale phases)
35	Moderately deep soils over high-grade limestone	High-grade limestone	Moderate	Hagerstown (shale phases)
40	Light-textured, well-drained bottoms	Alluvium and colluvium	Low to medium	Pope (sandy)
41	Gravelly or cherty, well or excessively drained bottoms	Cherty alluvium or colluvium	Moderate	Ennis, Shannon, etc.
42	Highly erodible soils from thin-bedded sandstone or siltstones	Sandstone and siltstone	Low	Portland
43	Shallow loess over sands and gravels; droughty	Loess over gravel or sand	Moderate to low	Lexington, Brandon
44	Moderately deep to deep sandy loam uplands	Sandstone	Moderate	Hartsells, Hanceville
45	Very old leached terraces from mixed materials	Old alluvial deposits	Low	Bybee, Goodloe

[1] Descriptions of soil units pertinent to each state should be available at State SCS offices.

The restrictions imposed upon a farm business by the characteristics of the land under the businesses' control may be either narrow or broad. If the restrictions are narrow, we refer to the land use as *rigid*. If the restrictions are broad, we refer to the land use as *flexible*. The more flexible the use of a given tract of land is, the less important is the land-use approach in organizing and planning a farm. In any case, the land-use approach is a rough first approximation to be refined on the basis of marginal analysis, i.e., on the basis of computations matching additional costs against additional returns for each proposed modification in the first rough approximation.

Other Symbols for Land-Use Maps:

Roads	═══
Railroads	═╪═
Telegraph or telephone lines	T T T
Buildings in general	
Church	
Schoolhouse	
Permanent streams	
Itermittent streams	
Itermittent drainage without channel	
Lake, pond, or reservoir	
Wet spot	
Overflowed land	
Farm boundary	▬▬
Any located station or object (with explanatory note)	⊙
Rock outcrop	
Stone outcrops	
Gravel	
Chert fragments	
Made land	
Sand dune	
Permanent fence	×—×—×
Fence along highway	
Fence coinciding with land-use boundary	-×- - ×-
Gravel pits	
Sinkholes and depressions	
Bedrock escarpment	
Gully	
Alkali area	A

Appraisal of the Land Resources on the Class Case Farm

Let us now illustrate with the class case farm the technique of appraising land resources. On the 335-acre farm there are:

        120 acres Classes I and II land
        110 acres Class III land
        100 acres Class IV land
          5 acres roads, farmstead, etc.

The land of this farm is residual limestone upland, well drained and originally highly productive. The soils are somewhat shallow, ranging from 4 to 15 feet to bedrock. In topography the land varies from level ridges to 15 percent slopes. An occasional terrace or diversion ditch is needed on the Classes II and III land. The topography is representative of many rolling-land farms in the United States. Figure 7.2 shows 120 acres suitable for intensive row cropping (Classes I and

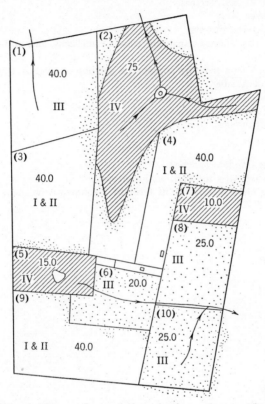

Fig. 7.2. A 335-acre farm of three land-use classes; $1'' = 660'$.

II), 110 acres suitable for rotation cropping (Class III), and 100 acres (Class IV) suitable for improved pastures. If necessary, Class IV land could be used for a row crop at some 10-to-12-year intervals.

PROBLEM EXERCISE 7
Land-Use-Capability Mapping

Make a land-use-capability map of the farm selected as your individual case farm on the basis of the methods described or as otherwise assigned.

1. Use drawing paper or plain white paper.
2. Select a desired scale: $1'' = 660'$ or $1'' = 330'$ is suggested.

3. Outline maps of most farms can be traced from aerial photographs, plotted from the metes and bounds given in deeds, or obtained from Soil Conservation Program plans, Bureau of Reclamation, Balanced Farming Programs or existing plots.

4. Let the map describe the farm as of the year drawn, showing

(*a*) Roads, fences, crop boundaries.

(*b*) Streams, drains, terraces.

(*c*) Land cover.

(*d*) Other physical objects.

5. Delineate the land-use-capability classes, subclasses, and units; color as described.

6. Within each field show by appropriate symbol as given in this chapter:

(*a*) Field unit number.

(*b*) Acreage.

(*c*) Crop or cover.

(*d*) Soil unit number.

(*e*) Slope.

(*f*) Erosion.

7. Submit on the date assigned.

8. Keep a rough copy for additional exercises.

9. Write a general description of farm to accompany the map.

CHAPTER 8

The Need for Economizing Principles in Developing Crop and Livestock Systems

Introductory Statement

Beginning with the inventory of the land resources of a specific farm within an area, a determination of the classes and proportions of different crops to use is of basic importance. As previously stated, the fixed characteristics of the land and distances to markets have probably helped to determine roughly the classes of crops which can be produced most profitably, i.e., intertilled, small grains, and sods. Within each class is a variety of crops, the greatest variation being in the intertilled class. Intertilled row crops vary in intensity from such crops as berries, using some 400 hours of labor per acre per year, through potatoes and truck crops, to corn or soybeans, using some 15 hours. On one point, however, there is little variation; they require plowing the land, intertilling, and subjecting sloping land to erosion. In this respect they are basically alike.

At the other extreme, the sod crops cover the nakedness of the land, thus protecting it from the rays of the sun, the lash of the wind, and the drive of moving water. Sods require little labor.

Sods are of two broad subclasses, hay and pasture, though the lines of demarcation and uses overlap. Such factors were considered in the previous chapter on land. We now face the problem of determining a cropping system within the restrictions imposed by the characteristics of the land.

The final specific cropping system is determined, within the above restrictions, by the prices of the different crops, the prices of products produced when the crops are fed, and by the prices of inputs.

This process of refining the rough first approximation to a farm organization derived from the land-use or labor-use approach involves matching of the additional costs against the additional gains derivable from each proposed modification.

Additional costs can be matched against additional gains by a wide variety of "common sense" computations. For years, the budgeting technique has been employed for this purpose. For an even longer period of time (over two hundred years) economists have been formulating the logical systems of thought behind such computations into a body of economic principles built around the concept of marginality (i.e., additional returns vs. additional cost)

Therefore, these principles should be examined at this point as a basis for further and more refined approaches to the problems of farm organization. This and the next four chapters will be devoted to these basic principles.

These principles will be used over and over again in connection with the problems of determining:

1. How much of each product to produce.
2. How much of each input to use.
3. How to combine enterprises.

This chapter is the first of five designed to give the student command of the formal principles of marginal analysis (additional returns vs. additional costs logic). These five chapters constitute a unit. Once mastered, they will provide the student with a form of reasoning useful in refining the first approximations derivable from the land-use approach. This form of reasoning deals mainly with variable or flexible inputs and, thus, will supplement the land-use approach for evaluating fixed inputs.

This chapter on production relationships involving one input will introduce the student to several important concepts. The student, in studying this chapter, will acquire a notation (set of symbols) for use in describing production relationships concisely. Furthermore, he will acquire rather precise notions of the different ways of expressing the law of diminishing returns. Also, the student will learn the general characteristics of total, average, and marginal physical production and value functions. These concepts are basic in the study of the economic aspects of operating individual farms and will be used repeatedly in subsequent chapters in dealing with both theoretical and applied subject matter.

Students of farm management and professional farm managers often ask the question, Why should a *practical* farm manager study and understand the fundamentals of production economics? The answer is that the knowledge so acquired serves two useful purposes. First, it gives the farm manager a system, a filing cabinet if you please, within which he can arrange information so that he can extract the maximum amount of help from it. Second, much farm management research deals with complicated production problems which can be handled only with the use of theoretical concepts; thus, if the practical farm manager is to utilize such research he must have some understanding of the principles upon which it is based.

The next few chapters must necessarily be somewhat more detailed than textbooks on economic principles. Most such books were written by people not closely associated with farm problems. Further, most cover such a wide variety of subject matter that adequate treatment, from the standpoint of farm management, cannot be given in them to the principles of production economics. Consequently, ordinary principles of economics cover the middle portion of production economics in an unrealistic and scanty way. The farm management student, in his thinking, has use for much more elementary, detailed, precise and, at the same time, more advanced concepts of production than are ordinarily presented in principles books. The aim of these chapters is to present such concepts so that they (the concepts) may contribute to the student's understanding of the existing information concerning agricultural production processes. The concepts can also be referred to as *theories, principles, frames of references, models,* etc. The student can take his choice as to the word or phrase that he desires to use in describing the economists' concepts of production. The authors will use the above terms interchangeably.

When one thinks about the production of any product, a long list of inputs or factors which affect the amount of product produced is brought to mind. In order to add preciseness to this discussion, these inputs or factors will be designated by X's. The first input will be designated X_1, the second X_2, etc., up to the last input which will be designated X_n, because, in general, the number of inputs usable varies between products.

When a physical scientist, such as an agronomist or an animal husbandryman, sets up an experiment to study the relationships between inputs and production, he ordinarily decides to study the influence of a certain number of inputs or outputs under fixed conditions. To the physical scientist the phrase "fixed conditions" means that he attempts to hold part of the inputs constant by experimental control.

If the experimenter cannot hold the required number of inputs constant and cannot study all of those which he permits to vary, the influence of those permitted to vary, but not studied, introduces errors into the experiment. These errors are ordinarily handled by the statistician who tries to "average them out." In summary, then, the physical scientist generally studies output as it depends upon certain designated inputs, given most of the remaining inputs fixed; any of the remaining inputs which may be permitted to vary introduce errors into the physical scientist's estimates of the input-output relationships.

Economists and professional farm managers do the same thing in setting up their concepts of production and costs. They have concepts of input-output relationships or, what are the same thing, production functions. These concepts deal with the relationships between product (or output) and the inputs which are used in its production. The economist refers to the cost of using those inputs permitted to vary as *variable costs*. The economist refers to the costs of the inputs which are held constant as *fixed costs*. The land-use and labor-use approaches, just examined, were concerned with appraisal of the fixed assets of a farm business. Any errors introduced by non-controlled inputs or factors such as weather are just as troublesome to the economist as they are to the physical scientist. In fact, such errors are probably more troublesome to the economist because, as was seen in Chapters 1 and 2, the existence of these errors makes it necessary to introduce management and its functions into theory. If all production, price, and consumption relationships were perfectly known, there would be no need for management and the science of farm management would be non-existent.

To add further precision to this discussion, let the product of a production process be designated by the symbol Y, and let the letter f before a parenthesis stand for the phrase "depends upon." The following expression can then be written and read as follows:

$$Y = f(X_1, X_2, \cdots, X_n)$$

The output of Y depends upon the variable inputs X_1 to X_n. It is also useful to have a symbol for separating the variable from the fixed inputs. A vertical bar, $|$, is used for this purpose. Y could stand for weight of hog, for example, with X_1 standing for corn, X_2 for protein supplement, X_3 for labor, etc. Thus, a production function can be expressed mathematically as follows:

$$Y = f(X_1, X_2, X_3, \mid X_4, X_5, \cdots, X_n)$$

In words the equation states that Y depends upon the variable inputs X_1, X_2, X_3, given the inputs X_4 to X_n fixed. It will also be helpful if X_1 is roughly conceived to be the input easiest to vary (such as feed in the production of meat) and X_n the variable most difficult to vary (such as land or family labor) with the variables X_1 to X_n arranged continuously more or less with respect to ease of variation.

Production Concepts Involving One Variable Input

Our study of marginal analysis will start with simple cases and gradually build up to the complexities of farming. A simple production relationship often studied by agronomists and animal husbandrymen and often considered by economists is the following:

$$Y = f(X_1, \mid X_2, \cdots, X_n)$$

This expression says that output of some product, say pork, depends upon input of some factor, say corn, with all other inputs held constant. Numerous research projects have been built around this concept. Production research scientists often make simplifying assumptions concerning the nature of the relationship between output and one input, given other inputs held constant. Such simplifying assumptions are often justified in the early stages of research on a problem, but generally, before the results can be put to their best practical use, the relationship between product and input must be conceived in terms of the law of diminishing returns. By "practical use" the authors mean "use in maximizing profits."

The law of diminishing returns holds that (except in very special instances) the addition of a variable input to fixed inputs results *first* in total returns which increase at an increasing rate, *second* in total returns which increase at a decreasing rate, and *third* in total returns which decrease with increases in the variable inputs. *Stop and reread the last sentence three or four times.* The range over which returns increase at an increasing rate is based upon the universal experience that proportions are important in the production process; i.e., returns from the variable input increase until some optimum proportion is approached and then decrease as the optimum proportion of the variable input to the fixed inputs is exceeded. The authors have looked for years for an exception to this law and have never found it. Many persons have attempted to demonstrate exceptions to the law of diminishing returns, but, in all instances known to the authors, these exceptions have proved to be special cases included in a proper statement of the law or have failed to conform to the specifications included in such a statement. The diminishing returns relationship between a product and *varying quantities of one input*, X_1, given other *inputs fixed* can be presented graphically as in Figure 8.1.

Another concept which must be developed at this point is that of *marginal product*. Marginal product is the addition to (or increment in) total production resulting from an increment in the variable input. When total product increases at an increasing rate, the marginal product is increasing. When total product is increasing at a decreasing

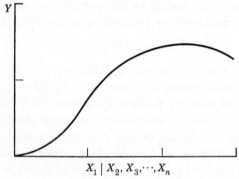

$$X_1 \mid X_2, X_3, \cdots, X_n$$

Fɪɢ. 8.1. The increasing and decreasing returns concept.

rate, marginal product is decreasing. When total product is decreasing, marginal product is less than zero.

The *average product* of an input is merely that portion of total product produced by the variable input divided by the amount of the variable input used.

We shall designate the total amount of Y produced as physical product. The line indicating the relationship between an output Y and an input X_1 is the *total physical product line*. The symbol for total physical product is *TPP*. The line showing how marginal physical product depends upon X_1 is designated the *marginal physical product line*. The symbol for marginal physical product is *MPP*. The line showing how average physical product depends upon X_1 is designated the *average physical product line*. The symbol for average physical product is *APP*. These three lines are graphically presented in Figure 8.2.

Figure 8.2 is divided into three stages. These three stages are important and should be carefully learned. In Stage I, marginal phys-

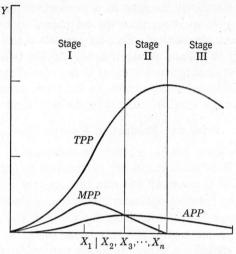

Fɪɢ. 8.2.   An input-output relationship showing average, marginal, and total physical productivity in Stages I, II, and III.

ical product is always greater than average physical product. Thus, it can easily be seen that, if it pays to produce any output in this stage, it pays to produce at least the maximum total output for this stage. As long as the marginal physical product is greater than the average, and the average physical product pays for itself, it pays to add more inputs. All that need be known is that it pays to produce any given quantity of the product. If it is known that it pays to produce any quantity, it follows that it pays to produce at least the maximum amount which can be produced in Stage I. Thus, a physical scientist without reference to prices can recommend that at least that quantity of X_1 be used by a competitive business which will drive the process to the edge of Stage I or into Stage II.

Stage III is the area in which marginal physical product is less than zero, i.e., in this area, additional input reduces total output. The physical scientist without reference to prices can flatly state that it does not pay a competitive business to use quantities of X_1 which would carry the production process into Stage III.

In Stage II, marginal physical product decreases continuously and is always less than average physical product. Here physical relationships alone are not sufficient to indicate the optimum rate of production. The economic question is: *At what point does the value of the marginal physical product become equal to the cost of the input used to secure it?* Obviously, as long as a production process pays more per additional unit of input than the additional unit of input costs, it pays to expand production. Equally obvious is the statement that it does not pay to expand production beyond the point at which the value of the marginal product is equal to the cost of the input because in this area additional expenditures for the input produce a quantity of product having a smaller value than the increment of input.

Price and Production Relationships

Physical scientists are in position to differentiate Stage II from Stages I and III as these stages are determined by physical relationships. However, if Stage II has any breadth, the physical scientist cannot select the point of optimum production without going through the economic processes of equalizing the value of the marginal physical product with the cost of the increments of input. Similarly, the farm manager should not expect to locate such optimum points without applying the economizing processes. In Stage II, any management recommendation as to the optimum amount of X_1 to use in the production of Y must depend upon the price of Y and the price of X_1, as well as on physical relationships. This means that, except in very special cases not often found in the real world, recommendations concerning optimum rates of input made under one set of price conditions are automatically wrong under a different set of price conditions. The implications of this statement for farm management budgeting cannot be rationally overlooked. Simply stated, the implications are that standard requirements data set up for one set of prices are automatically wrong for any other set of prices. The same is true (1) for the rations computed from the various feeding standards,[1] (2) for recommendations concerning the rates at which fertilizers should be applied, and (3) for much of the general requirements data usually presented. Who knows of a period in history in which prices have not been changing almost continuously? The student should think long and seriously concerning the implications of what he has just read. The subject will be discussed further in immediately succeeding pages.

The above discussion reveals a fundamental condition for the optimum use of the variable input X_1. That condition is that the *marginal value product* of X_1 (to be designated by MVP_{x_1}) must be equal

[1] John C. Redman, "Economic Aspects of Feeding for Milk Production," *Journal of Farm Economics,* XXXIV, August, 1952.

to the price of X_1 (to be designated by P_{x_1}).[1] This condition can be stated in equation form in two ways:

$$MVP = P_{x_1} \quad \text{or} \quad \frac{MVP}{P_{x_1}} = 1$$

These equations imply (1) that if the last unit of X_1 does not pay for itself less of X_1 should be used, (2) that if the last unit of X_1 more than pays for itself more of X_1 should be used, and (3) that use of X_1 should be stopped at the point at which X_1 just pays for itself.

At a later point, the student will probably raise the following question. If the feeding standards, fertilization recommendations, and requirements data are subject to the limitations indicated above, then what about the farm plans and budgets to be worked out on the basis of such information? Under typical price relationships, the forces of competition create typical or modal rates of usage among farmers for each input. In the long-run there is a close relationship between (1) such typical rates of usage and the feeding standards and fertilization recommendations, and (2) the optimum conditions specified above. Thus, the authors are relatively sure that a farm plan made up on the basis of the requirements will be approximately right in view of the (1) long-run price relationships, (2) the degree to which the typical farmer is informed concerning production processes, and (3) the efficiency of the free enterprise system in bringing about competitive adjustments. A moment's reflection will indicate that many inputs are fixed for considerable periods of time in setting up a farm business; hence, these inputs cannot be varied as prices change from time to time over certain ranges, and it is rather good strategy to fix them in the proportions indicated by experience to be about right under typical long-run price relationships. Further reflection will indicate that the inputs which remain variable can be easily adjusted to short-run shifts in price relationships; this permits short-run correction of the short-run mistakes arising from the use of standard requirements.

The concepts examined thus far in this chapter are basic to an understanding of much current and highly practical farm management research. *Without ability in the handling of these concepts, the prospective vocational agriculture teacher, county agent, professional farm manager, or modern scientific farmer cannot hope to use such research effectively.* It should also be realized that the nature of many prob-

---

[1] All economic principles and theory presented in this book will assume perfectly competitive firms (unless otherwise noted) in accordance with the general nature of the agricultural industry.

lems under examination by farm management researchers makes the use of these concepts and their ramifications mandatory if clear-cut practical results are to be secured.

These concepts and their ramifications provide a *conceptual framework* for (1) organizing production data to indicate how inputs of variable factors should be changed as price relationships shift and (2) indicating how inputs fixed for considerable periods of time should be organized when technological and long-run price changes occur. Under the first point, it should be noted that this conceptual framework is useful (1) to a farmer or extension man in adjusting the results of both research and farm experience to the conditions on a particular farm, and (2) to a researcher attacking an involved problem. Under the second point, it should be noted that this conceptual framework permits the implications of a change in technology or long-run price relationships for organization of the farm to be seen at once. *It is unnecessary to wait for the forces of competition to change the requirements data gathered by survey from actual farms.*

In subsequent chapters of this book, the results of research based upon these concepts will be presented in view of their significance to farm management. These presentations will deal with (1) feeding of dairy cattle, hogs, beef animals, and poultry, (2) cost of production as defined by these concepts, and (3) research dealing with the value productivity of different categories of inputs. In addition, the use of these concepts in visualizing the probable answers to problems upon which little or no research has been done will be illustrated from time to time. Such information will prove useful in both long-run budgeting and short-run adjustment problems.

Further Development of Price and Production Relationships

Earlier sections of this chapter have covered the general interrelationships between prices and physical production data in relation to the question of how much of a given product to produce. This section will re-examine these same relationships in more detail.

When the production relationships presented in Figure 8.2 are multiplied by the price of the product, they are converted to *value* productivity relationships. In Figure 8.3 the marginal physical product and the average physical product lines have been multiplied by the price of Y. Hence, they are labeled, respectively, MVP, standing for marginal value product, and AVP, standing for average value product. The total product curve remains in physical terms; hence, Figure 8.3 has two scales, one for dollars and the other for units of Y.

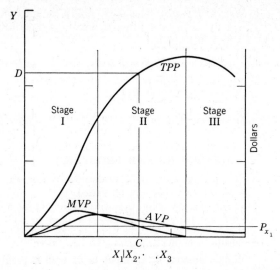

F<small>IG</small>. 8.3. Diagram showing relationships between value of marginal product, total physical product, average value product, and price of the variable input.

The accompanying diagram also shows the price of the variable input. This price is indicated by the horizontal line labeled P_{x1}. The optimum amount of X_1 to use is obviously C units. Beyond C, the dollar return to an additional unit of X_1 is less than the cost of X_1. Use of less than C units of X_1 would permit additional profits to be made by using the additional units of X_1 which would yield a dollar return in excess of their cost.

The *amount of Y* produced by C units of X_1 is found from the *TPP* curve at a point directly above C; i.e., in Figure 8.3, D units of Y would be produced by C units of X_1.

The following generalizations can be made from a study of Figure 8.3:

I. *A.* An increase in the price of X_1 would lower the amount of X_1 which it pays to use and, hence, the amount of Y it pays to produce.

    B. A decrease in the price of X_1 would increase the amount of X_1 which it pays to use and, hence, the amount of Y it pays to produce.

II. *A.* An increase in the price of Y would increase the amount of X_1 which it pays to use and, hence, the amount of Y it pays to produce.

    B. A decrease in the price of Y would decrease the amount of X_1 which it pays to use and, hence, the amount of Y it pays to produce.

III. All changes in the use of X_1 as a result of changes in prices are limited to Stage II in which $MVP < AVP$, in which $APP > MPP$, and in which

$MPP > 0$ and $MVP > 0.$[1] The most profitable rate of use within this area can only be located through the above-described economizing process which insures that:

$$MVP = P_{x_1}$$

$$\frac{MVP}{P_{x_1}} = 1$$

it being remembered that $MVP = (P_{x_1})(MPP_{x_1})$, under perfect competition.

QUESTIONS AND PROBLEMS

1. List as many of the inputs used in milk production as you can. Rank them according to the ease with which they can be varied.

2. If only one of these inputs, say labor, were variable, would the 5th, 20th, 60th, 100th or 150th hour per cow per year contribute the most to milk production? Could enough hours be devoted to each cow to eventually reduce her production of milk?

3. When is the optimum amount of an input being used if profit is accepted as the basis for judgment?

4. Suppose, on 1 acre of corn with a fixed amount of machinery and other inputs, that

    200 pounds of fertilizer produces 40 bu. ready to harvest.
    250 pounds of fertilizer produces 44 bu. ready to harvest.
    300 pounds of fertilizer produces 49 bu. ready to harvest.
    350 pounds of fertilizer produces 53 bu. ready to harvest.
    400 pounds of fertilizer produces 55.5 bu. ready to harvest.
    450 pounds of fertilizer produces 58 bu. ready to harvest.
    500 pounds of fertilizer produces 60 bu. ready to harvest.
    550 pounds of fertilizer produces 61 bu. ready to harvest.
    600 pounds of fertilizer produces 61 bu. ready to harvest.

How much fertilizer worth $2.50 a hundred should be used in producing corn worth $1.25 a bushel? How much fertilizer worth $5.00 a hundred should be used in producing corn worth $1.25 a bushel? How can prices affect the proper amount of fertilizer to use in producing corn?

5. Write a short essay on why the law of diminishing returns operates. List all exceptions to the law you can think of. How many of these exceptions are special cases?

[1] The symbol $>$ stands for "greater than"; the symbol $<$ stands for "less than."

CHAPTER 9

Multiple Production Relationships in Farming

Introductory Statement

This chapter in taking up the more complicated aspects of production functions is a continuation of Chapter 8. When output is conceived as depending upon two inputs, the manner in which the two inputs respond when jointly used becomes highly important. This chapter concentrates upon the usual relationships between two inputs used in the production of a given product. In studying the way in which two inputs are combined in producing a given product, two questions assume primary importance. The first has to do with the proportions in which the two inputs should be used. The second has to do with the amounts of the two inputs which should be used and, hence, with the amount of the product which should be produced. In the general case, these two questions cannot be answered without resort to economic principles. The latter portion of this chapter deals with similar problems involved in using more than two variable inputs in the production of one product.

Farm managers and students of farm management are quick (and justifiably so) to complain that the concepts of the last chapter are inadequate because their production problems involve more than one variable input. They say, for instance, that hogs consume both corn and protein supplement to say nothing about the different kinds of protein supplement. Thus, it is necessary to extend the concepts examined in the last chapter to concepts involving two variable inputs. In the last part of this chapter, the concepts for two variable functions will be extended to include any number of variable inputs appropriate for a given problem.

Output As Dependent on Two Variable Inputs

The general expression for a production relationship involving two variable inputs and an indefinite, but given, number of fixed inputs follows:

$$Y = f(X_1, X_2, \mid X_3, \cdots, X_n)$$

In words, this equation states that the output of Y depends jointly upon the inputs of X_1 and X_2 in some definite manner when the inputs X_3 to X_n are held constant. Because X_3 to X_n are fixed, any change in X_1 and X_2 or in either alone changes the proportions in which the inputs are used; hence, the law of diminishing returns applies when the use of X_1 and X_2 is expanded either individually or jointly. If the student desires an example at this point, he can let Y be pounds of pork, X_1 be corn, X_2 be protein supplement, while the fixed factors include such items as the number of hogs (to which X_1 and X_2 are fed), labor, buildings, land, management, mineral supplements, etc.

When one attempts to draw a figure representing the relationship between a product and two inputs, he is confronted with the necessity of drawing a three-dimensional diagram. Though different, this task is no more difficult than that faced by a mapmaker trying to show elevation on a piece of paper having only the two directions: (1) north-south and (2) east-west. The mapmaker resorts to contour lines to indicate elevation. Similarly, the economist resorts to contour lines indicating output of Y on a two-dimensional piece of paper showing the amount of X_1 used in one direction and the amount of X_2 used in the other direction. Such a product contour map is presented in Figure 9.1.

The number on each contour line indicates the amount of Y represented by that line. These product contours are oftentimes called *iso-product* curves because equal amounts of Y are produced by the various combinations of X_1 and X_2 represented by a given line. "Iso" means equal. The student should examine one of the product contour lines carefully at this point. Here again, the student may be able to aid himself by using the pork-corn-protein supplement example. Let the student consider the iso-product line indicated by the number 300. Still more definitely, let him consider the point A on this contour. As it would probably help to look at this contour separately, it is separately reproduced at this point as Figure 9.2. From this separate diagram, it is seen that a units of X_1 combined with a' units of X_2 produce 300 units of Y. Similarly, at point B, it is seen that b units

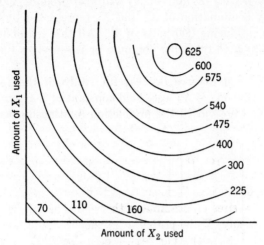

FIG. 9.1. Product contour map showing output as it depends on two inputs, used in connection with a set of fixed inputs.

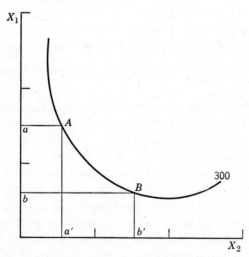

FIG. 9.2. Different combinations of X_1 and X_2 capable of producing 300 units of Y.

of X_1 combined with b' units of X_2 will also produce 300 units of Y. Similarly any combination of X_1 and X_2 represented by this contour is capable of producing 300 units of Y. All this reasoning applies in a parallel fashion to the other contours or iso-product lines in Figure 9.1.

The student can observe, by careful study of the following iso-product map, that (1) if X_2 were held constant at a given value C and then (2) if X_1 were varied the production relationship would be lim-

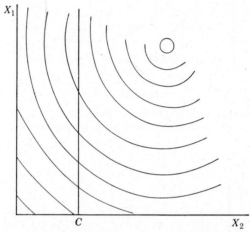

Fig. 9.3.   Line on a three-dimensional diagram, indicating origin of Figure 9.4.

ited to the case examined in the last chapter. That case was a two-dimensional cross section of the three-dimensional relationships now under consideration (see Figure 9.3). In terms of the pork-corn-protein supplement example, this cross section can be thought of as representing the relationship between pork production and varying quantities of corn inputs when a given number of hogs are fed only C units of tankage (X_2) under fixed conditions indicated by the constant inputs of the other factors. A two-dimensional cross section of the three-dimensional relationship between X_1, X_2, and Y is presented in Figure 9.4. This cross section assumes X_2 fixed at the value C and is the cross section located in Figure 9.3. The stages of a production relationship noted earlier are again evident. The end of Stage II occurs at the point at which the cross-sectional line touches the highest possible contour on the three-dimensional diagram (see Figure 9.3). The student is advised to spend some time relating Figures 9.3

and 9.4 to each other. Beyond the point at which the cross section touches its highest product contour, the marginal physical productivity of X_1 is less than zero. A little reflection will indicate to the student that, if X_2 were fixed at various levels other than C, each resulting cross section would touch one highest iso-product curve and beyond these points of contact the marginal physical product of X_1 would be less than zero.

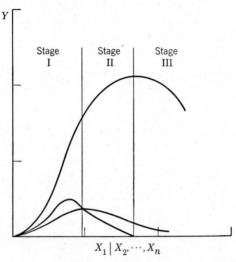

Fig. 9.4.   Two-dimensional diagram showing how Y depends on X_1, given C amount of X_2.

In terms of the pork-corn-protein supplement example, there is a given maximum amount of pork which can be produced by feeding additional amounts of corn with a fixed amount of protein supplement. This is graphically illustrated in Figure 9.5. Beyond the line of maximum production DO the marginal physical productivity of X_1 is less than zero.

In Figure 9.6, a second similar line EO has been derived by holding X_1 (corn in the example) fixed at different levels while varying x_2. In the example, X_2 is protein supplement. The diagram is thus divided into three areas. In one area, the marginal physical productivity of both X_1 (corn) and X_2 (protein supplement) is greater than zero while in each of the other two areas one of the marginal physical products is less than zero. Stop and study this diagram in detail! Spend as much time on it as you would on three or four pages of printing! It has just as much meaning!

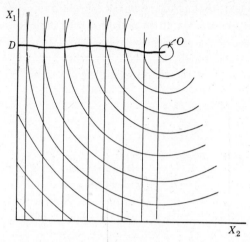

Diagram illustrating the method of locating the line DO beyond which more X_1 reduces the output of Y.

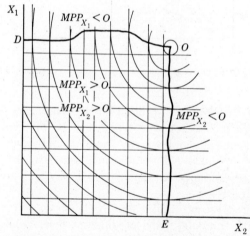

Fig. 9.6. Diagram illustrating method of locating the line DO (beyond which more X_1 reduces the output of Y) and the line EO (beyond which more X_2 reduces the output of Y).

Again, the question should be raised concerning what the physical agricultural scientist can say without reference to prices about the amounts of X_1 and X_2 which should be used in the production of Y. Obviously, if X_1 and X_2 have values, it rarely pays to produce Y with combinations of X_1 and X_2 for which either of their respective marginal physical products is less than zero. The physical scientist can make statements of this nature. In addition, he can ordinarily indicate that, if any Y is to be produced, both X_1 and X_2 should be used at least up to the point at which their average physical products are equal to their respective marginal physical products. This, however, leaves a wide range as to amount of Y to produce and amounts of X_1 and X_2 to use. *This range cannot be narrowed without resort to the use of price data in the economizing procedure.* This procedure requires the availability of (1) data on marginal physical productivity of X_1 and X_2 as well as (2) the prices under competitive conditions of X_1, X_2, and Y. The farm manager (or economist) and the physical agricultural scientist are mutually dependent upon each other at this point. The optimum rate of producing Y and of using X_1 and X_2 cannot be determined by the physical scientist without resort to prices and the economizing procedure. And, the economist cannot apply the economizing procedure without physical data in marginal form. Students of agriculture can hardly think too much concerning the importance of the foregoing statements.

Now, how can the economizing procedures be applied to locate the optimum amount of Y to produce and the optimum proportions in which X_1 and X_2 should be used to produce that output under a given set of prices? This question will be answered in two steps. *First,* the proportions in which X_1 and X_2 should be combined to produce any output will be determined. *Second,* the optimum level of output will be determined.

Proportions in Which to Use the Two Variable Inputs

It is obvious that the best way to spend a given amount of money on X_1 and X_2 in the production of Y is that way which will produce the most Y. This is the fundamental idea around which this portion of this chapter is developed. Read it again so that you see and understand this basic, simple, and fundamental idea.

In Figure 9.7, the line AB represents all possible combinations of X_1 and X_2 which can be purchased for $10.00 when $P_{x_1} = 1.00$ and $P_{x_2} = 5.00$; point C on this line indicates the highest iso-product curve which can be reached with any combination of X_1 and X_2 worth

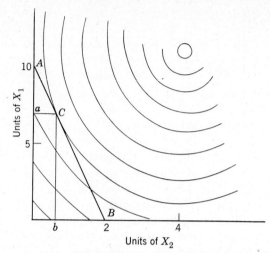

Fig. 9.7. Diagram showing iso-cost line and highest production, C, attainable at the cost represented by the iso-cost line.

$10.00. The line AB is known as an *iso-cost line* because all combinations of X_1 and X_2 represented by it have equal total costs. That the line AB covers all combinations of X_1 and X_2 worth $10.00 can be demonstrated as follows: How much X_1 can be purchased for $10.00? The answer is obviously 10 units of X_1. How much X_2 can be purchased for $10.00? Two units of X_2, obviously. How much X_1 and how much X_2 can be purchased if the $10.00 is split equally between the two inputs? The answer is 5 units of X_1 and 1 unit of X_2. A continuation of this process locates every point in the line AB.

In this case, it is obvious that a units of X_1 and b units of X_2 should be purchased and used as this combination will yield more Y than any other.

If this procedure is repeated for a sufficient number of different levels of expenditure, a series of iso-cost lines, each indicating an optimum way to combine X_1 and X_2 to produce a different amount of Y, can be located. This has been done in Figure 9.8. The line connecting the optimum points on the iso-cost lines is called *the scale line* or *line of optimum proportions*. It indicates the optimum proportions in which to combine X_1 and X_2 to produce any given output. At all points along the scale line, the following relationship holds

$$\frac{MPP_{x_2}}{MPP_{x_1}} = \frac{P_{x_2}}{P_{x_1}}$$

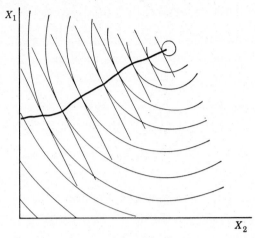

X_1

X_2

FIG. 9.8.   Diagram illustrating procedure for locating the scale line or line of optimum proportions.

If the student will stop to reason a moment, he will see that this relationship does specify the conditions under which an expenditure of a given amount of money on the use of X_1 and X_2 would yield the greatest amount of Y. Suppose that MPP_{x_2}/MPP_{x_1} were greater than P_{x_2}/P_{x_1}; obviously, under these conditions it would pay to use relatively less of X_1 and relatively more of X_2. Suppose that MPP_{x_2}/MPP_{x_1} were less than P_{x_2}/P_{x_1}; obviously, under these conditions it would pay to use relatively more of X_1 and relatively less of X_2. Only when MPP_{x_2}/MPP_{x_1} is exactly equal to P_{x_2}/P_{x_1} is it impossible to expand the output of Y from a given expenditure by transferring expenditures between the two inputs.[1]   It is mathematically true that MPP_{x_2}/MPP_{x_1} is the

[1] That the slope of an iso-cost line is $-P_{x_2}/P_{x_1}$ when X_1 is plotted on the vertical axis and X_2 on the horizontal axis is proved as follows: By definition, the equation of the iso-cost line for a given cost C is:

$$C = P_{x_1}X_1 + P_{x_2}X_2$$

Transposing,

$$X_1 = \frac{C}{P_{x_1}} - \frac{P_{x_2}X_2}{P_{x_1}}$$

Differentiating,

$$\frac{dx_1}{dx_2} = -\frac{P_{x_2}}{P_{x_1}} = \text{slope of iso-cost line}$$

Also, it is easy to prove that the slope of an iso-product line on the same diagram is $-MPP_{x_2}/MPP_{x_1}$. Consider a positive change in X_2 (designated by ΔX_2) and a negative change in X_1 (designated by $-\Delta X_1$) such that the positive change in Y

slope of an iso-product line and that P_{x_2}/P_{x_1} is the slope of an iso-cost line. The most Y is secured along a given iso-cost line at the point at which the iso-cost line just touches the highest possible iso-product line. By observation, the slopes of the two lines (in the X_1, X_2 plane) are equal at such a point. The question posed earlier as to the most profitable proportions in which X_1 and X_2 should be combined to produce any given amount of Y has been answered. Further, the condition under which X_1 and X_2 are properly combined to produce a given amount of Y has been expressed in equation form.

The question concerning the most profitable amount of Y to produce is still to be answered, and the discussion is now redirected to that end.

Amount to Produce

The scale line indicates the optimum proportions in which X_1 and X_2 (for example, corn and protein supplement) should be combined to produce varying amounts of Y (in our example, pork) with a given amount of the fixed inputs such as number of hogs, amount of labor, etc. At every point along the scale line,

$$\frac{MPP_{x_2}}{MPP_{x_1}} = \frac{P_{x_2}}{P_{x_1}}$$

which after transposing can be expressed as:

$$\frac{MPP_{x_1}}{P_{x_1}} = \frac{MPP_{x_2}}{P_{x_2}}$$

(designated by ΔY) resulting from ΔX_2 is equal to the negative change in Y (designated by $-\Delta Y$) resulting from $-\Delta X_1$. It follows that:

$$MPP_{x_1}(-\Delta X_1) = -\Delta Y$$

and that

$$MPP_{x_2}(\Delta X_2) = \Delta Y$$

But, as $-\Delta Y$ is equal to ΔY except for sign, $MPP_{x_1}(-\Delta X_1)$ is equal to $MPP_{x_2}(\Delta X_2)$ except for the sign. Hence,

$$\frac{MPP_{x_2}(\Delta X_2)}{MPP_{x_1}(-\Delta X_1)} = \frac{\Delta Y}{-\Delta Y} = -1$$

Dropping $\Delta Y/-\Delta Y$ and transposing yields

$$-\frac{MPP_{x_2}}{MPP_{x_1}} = -\frac{\Delta X_1}{\Delta X_2}$$

Let $\Delta X_2 \to 0$ and $MPP_{x_2}/MPP_{x_1} \to dX_1/dX_2 = $ slope of iso-product line.

The symbol MVP_{x_1} has been used before; it stands for marginal value product and is $MPP_{x_1} \cdot P_y$ under perfect competition and homogeneous products. Hence, if each side of the above equation is multiplied by P_y the following equation is secured: $MVP_{x_1}/P_{x_2} = MVP_{x_2}/P_{x_2}$ Previous discussion indicated that the optimum amount of one input was being used and the optimum amount of product was being produced when

$$MVP_{x_1} = P_{x_1}$$

or, stated alternatively, when

$$\frac{MVP_{x_1}}{P_{x_1}} = 1$$

The optimum amount of Y is being produced when this condition holds, simultaneously, for both inputs or when $MVP_{x_1}/P_{x_1} = MVP_{x_2}/P_{x_2} = 1$. A tight mathematical proof of this is given in the footnote.[1] In words this equation implies the following: (1) as long as the marginal value product of any variable input (say, corn or protein supplement in this chapter's usual example) exceeds its price (cost), it pays to expand its use and, hence, the production of Y (in this case, pork), (2) when the marginal value product of a variable input (say, corn or protein supplement) is less than its price (cost), it pays to reduce its use and, hence, the production Y (in this case, pork), and (3) when the marginal value products of all variable inputs used in the production of

---

[1] When Π = profit, the equation for profit is:

$$\Pi = YP_y - X_1 P_{x_1} - X_2 P_{x_2} - \text{fixed cost}$$

Partial differentiation with respect to X_1 and X_2 yields:

$$\frac{\partial \Pi}{\partial X_1} = MPP_{x_1} \cdot P_y - P_{x_1}$$

$$\frac{\partial \Pi}{\partial X_2} = MPP_{x_2} \cdot P_y - P_{x_2}$$

Setting the two partial derivatives equal to zero which is the mathematical condition for maximum profit (under the assumption of perfect competition, perfect knowledge, and law of diminishing returns) and transposing yields:

$$MVP_{x_1} = P_{x_1} \quad \text{and} \quad MVP_{x_2} = P_{x_2}$$

or alternatively stated:

$$\frac{MVP_{x_1}}{P_{x_1}} = \frac{MVP_{x_2}}{P_{x_2}} = 1$$

Y are exactly equal to their respective prices (costs), the most profitable amount of each input is being used and, hence, the most profitable amount of Y is being produced.

Production Concepts Involving More Than Two Inputs

Many of the production processes in agriculture involve a dozen or more inputs. Considerable difficulty was experienced at the beginning of the chapter in devising a method for presenting graphic illustrations of production concepts involving the variable inputs. As a matter of fact, the method of handling two variable inputs moved away from graphic toward algebraic presentation. For problems and concepts involving more than two variable inputs, algebraic presentation is the only alternative open.

If five inputs, for instance, were variable in the production of one product any geometric representation of the production relationship would involve six dimensions. The human mind simply cannot handle six dimensions geometrically. However, six dimensions can be handled algebraically and logically. Both mathematics (either geometry or algebra) and economic logic give similar results in the two-variable input case. Both mathematics and economic logic indicate that more than two variable inputs are properly used when the following equation holds:

$$\frac{MPP_{x_1}}{P_{x_1}} = \frac{MPP_{x_2}}{P_{x_2}} = \frac{MPP_{x_3}}{P_{x_3}} = \cdots = \frac{MPP_{x_d}}{P_{x_d}}$$

where the letter d stands for the last input which happens to be variable in the particular planning span under consideration. In words, this equation states that the variable inputs are being used in their optimum proportions if the product of the last unit of any input used bears the same relationship to the price of the input as exists for all other variable inputs.

The law of diminishing returns is conceived to hold regardless of the number of variables involved. This means that marginal returns to single variable inputs or to groups of variable inputs ordinarily first increase, then decrease and, finally, probably become negative. As long as this law holds, it follows that the optimum proportions can be reached which are defined above.

The optimum amount of Y to produce is defined by the following equation:

$$\frac{MVP_{x_1}}{P_{x_1}} = \frac{MVP_{x_2}}{P_{x_2}} = \cdots = \frac{MVP_{x_d}}{P_{x_d}} = 1$$

Read in words, the above equation indicates that the use of any input should be expanded as long as its marginal value product is greater than its cost, that the use of an input should be contracted if its marginal value product is less than its cost, and that all inputs are properly used when their respective marginal value products are precisely equal to their costs. Read in farmers' terms, the equation says that additional quantities of anything used in production should be used as long as they pay for themselves and no longer.

Appropriate Production Function Concepts

The appropriate production function concept—single, two-variable, etc.—for a given situation depends on the number of inputs which a manager is trying to manipulate. In general, a manager is concerned only with inputs presently earning either more than replacement cost or less than opportunity cost.

If an asset is capable of earning an income making it worth more than replacement cost, it pays to use more of it. If an asset is not capable of earning an income making it worth its opportunity cost, it pays to vary it, i.e., to divert it from its present to an alternative either within or outside the business. In either event, the asset is variable, not fixed.

If, on the other hand, an asset is presently earning an income making it worth *not more* than replacement cost and *not less* than opportunity cost, then no reason exists for varying it and it remains a *fixed asset*. In those rare instances in which replacement and opportunity costs are equal, an asset remains fixed only so long as its earning power in a particular enterprise makes it worth that cost at the margin.

The difference between replacement and opportunity cost depends on the cost of shifting the asset between uses. Thus, land is often a variable asset between enterprises on a farm but a fixed asset for the farm as a whole because of brokerage and legal fees and personal subjective costs involved in its sale and purchase. Pasturage, once produced, tends to be a fixed asset, owing to the costs of harvesting and hauling it or of bringing livestock to it.

The list of assets which a manager wants to vary and the list which he desires to leave fixed determines the relevant length of run or planning span. And, of course, the relevant length of run is related to the appropriate subproduction function, as each subproduction function assumes a list of inputs fixed at stated levels. In a later chapter on cost of production concepts it will be seen that variable and fixed costs refer to the cost of using these same two groups of inputs. Thus, the distinction between fixed and variable assets is basic in farm management. It determines what kind of plans are being made, i.e., long, short, or any of an infinite number of plans of intermediate length of run. It determines the make-up of marginal, average, and fixed costs.

The fact that fixed assets are worth what they produce is the source of two fundamental difficulties. The first difficulty occurs in accounting whenever an attempt is made to price such assets. The second occurs in empirical cost of production work aimed at securing fixed costs either for use as such or as components of other cost figures.

The first difficulty was encountered in Chapter 4 in figuring (by the method of residuals) returns to various inputs. A way of pricing such inputs on the basis of their earning power is presented in the last pages of the next chapter. The difficulty in connection with cost of production concepts will be discussed further in Chapter 12 on cost of production concepts.

Output As It Depends upon Units of Joint Variable Inputs

This section is based upon concepts derived from an iso-product contour map; hence, such a map is presented as Figure 9.9. In the above contour map, a series of iso-cost curves have been superimposed on the iso-product lines. The points of tangency between the iso-cost

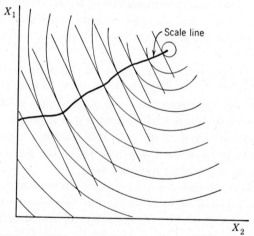

Fig. 9.9. Product contour lines with iso-cost lines superimposed to locate scale line.

curves and the iso-product curves define the scale line. The student should recall from earlier portions of this chapter that the location of a scale line depends in part upon the slope of the iso-cost curve; this slope, in turn, is determined by relative prices of the two inputs. Hence, the student should observe that the location of a scale line is determined partly by the relative prices of the two inputs and, in a joint way, partly by the nature of the production function. The

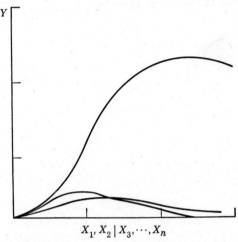

$$X_1, X_2 \mid X_3, \cdots, X_n$$

Fig. 9.10. Output as it depends on joint inputs of X_1 and X_2 (combined according to the scale line) with fixed amounts of $X_3, \cdots, X_n$.

student should also recall that the scale line indicates the optimum or most profitable proportions in which to combine the two inputs to produce various amounts of the product.

If output is plotted in a two-dimensional diagram as a function of the two fixed inputs (combined in proportions dictated by the scale line as shown in Figures 9.8 and 9.9), Figure 9.10 is secured. The joint inputs of X_1 and X_2 along the horizontal axis can be measured in terms of money, i.e., a unit of X_1 and X_2 being a dollar's worth of the two inputs combined in the proportion dictated by the scale line. In the above diagram the law of diminishing returns holds because other inputs remain fixed. The usual example (for this chapter) can be used in connection with the above diagram. Let Y be output of pork and let X_1 and X_2 stand for corn and protein supplement, respectively, with the fixed variables being labor, number of hogs, buildings, equipment, management, etc.   The phrase "combined according to scale line" is highly important.   Students are urged to ask themselves why this is so.

In a succeeding chapter dealing with cost of production in agriculture, much attention will be given to output as it depends upon the input of joint variable factors of production.   Cost of production is highly important in all aspects of farm management.   An understanding of cost concepts depends on understanding how output depends, in the length of run for which costs are being computed, on the joint use of the variable factors of production.

CHAPTER 10

Multiple Production Relationships in Farming (continued)

Substitutability and Complementarity among Inputs

It is important that we consider the extreme cases of nearly perfect substitutability among inputs and nearly perfect complementarity among inputs because important "rules of thumb" can be derived from a study of these cases. It should be stressed that both perfect substitutability and perfect complementarity are extreme cases not often occurring in the real world. It can, however, be pointed out in passing that many feeding recommendations are based upon the assumptions of perfect complementarity and perfect substitutability. More will be said about this at a later point.

Pairs of inputs such as (1) barley and corn and (2) tankage and soybean meal are fairly good substitutes for each other in the production of pork. Corn substitutes for barley as a source of carbohydrates. Tankage substitutes for soybean meal as a source of protein. Other pairs of inputs such as corn and tankage, or barley and semi-solid buttermilk tend to complement each other in the production of pork, i.e., one serves as a source of protein and the other as a source of starch, each of which complements the other by making the production process more efficient. Almost any two common inputs used in producing almost any common farm product can be classed as to substitutability or complementarity by a fairly competent agriculturalist.

The important "rules of thumb" referred to above can be clearly seen if some time is spent studying hypothetical product contour maps for (1) pairs of substitutes and (2) pairs of complements.

Substitutes

Figure 10.1 is a map which shows how output of some product, say Y, depends on two inputs, X_1 and X_2, which are nearly perfect substitutes for each other. It is assumed that the remaining inputs are fixed and that, hence, the law of diminishing returns applies. Examination of Figure 10.1 will indicate that 10 units of either X_1 or X_2 alone will produce 20 units of product. It will also indicate that something less than 5 units of X_1 combined with something less than 5 units of X_2 will produce 20 units of product; the fact that the joint use of the two inputs does not result in a substantial increase in efficiency,

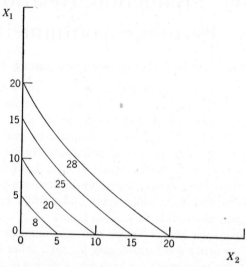

FIG. 10.1. Product contour map showing how the production of Y depends on X_1 and X_2 which are good substitutes when other inputs are fixed.

indicates that the two inputs are good substitutes for each other. Substitutability is also indicated by the straightness of the iso-product lines and by the fact that either input alone is about as efficient in the production of Y as when they are used together.

In Figure 10.2, one iso-product line from the above diagram is reproduced for detailed study. On this detailed diagram two iso-cost curves have been superimposed. The difference between the two iso-cost curves results from a small difference in the price of X_1 relative to the price of X_2. The important point to notice is that, as a result of a very small change in the price of X_1 relative to the price of X_2, it becomes profitable to substitute one input almost completely for the other. The two iso-cost curves represent the same expenditure of cash.

The "rule of thumb" derivable from the above follows: *when prices of good substitutes change only slightly relative to each other, it pays to adjust production plans quickly so as to utilize the cheaper of the two.* As a corollary, *it pays to keep a business so organized that it is easy to shift between the use of good substitutes when small changes occur in their relative prices.*

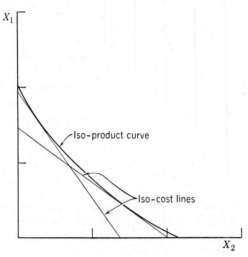

Fɪɢ. 10.2.   Iso-product curve or product contour and two iso-cost lines.

Complements

Figure 10.3 shows how output of a product, say Y_2, depends upon two inputs which are nearly perfect complements for each other. Again it is assumed that remaining inputs are fixed and that, hence, the law of diminishing returns holds.   In the case of nearly perfect complements, the technical conditions of production are such that inputs make their maximum contribution to production when they are combined in rather definite proportions.   In the product contour diagram of Figure 10.3, neither of the inputs used alone will produce anything, but in the proportions of about 1 unit of X_1 to 1 unit of X_2 they are effective in the production of Y.   In Figure 10.4, one iso-product contour from the above product contour map has been reproduced. Two iso-cost curves having equal values have been drawn tangent to this iso-product curve.   One of these iso-cost curves assumes the price of X_1 to be very high relative to the price of X_2.   The other iso-cost curve assumes the price of X_2 to be very high relative to the price of X_1.   The point to be observed here is that, despite the large change in

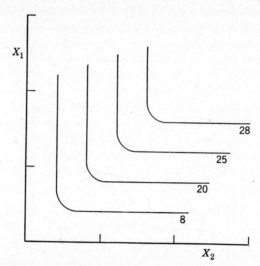

FIG. 10.3. Product contour map showing how the production of Y depends on X_1 and X_2, which are good complements when other inputs are fixed.

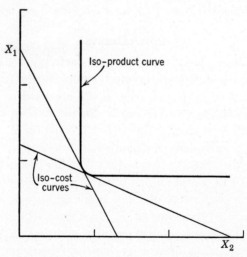

FIG. 10.4. Iso-product or product contour and two iso-cost lines.

the price of X_1 relative to the price of X_2, the most profitable proportion in which to use X_1 and X_2 is changed only very slightly.

The following "rule of thumb" is derived from the above discussion: *Even when prices of two nearly perfect complements change widely relative to each other, it is not desirable to make large changes in the proportions in which the two inputs are used in order to utilize the inputs in their most profitable proportions.* The following may also be stated as a corollary "rule of thumb": *When a production process utilizes two nearly perfect complements it is unnecessary to keep the production process flexible with respect to the proportions of X_1 and X_2 which can be handled,* as changes in relative price will not have large effects on the most profitable proportions in which such inputs should be combined.

Pairs of Perfect Substitutes and Pairs of Perfect Complements Are Really Single Inputs

If the student will stop and reflect a moment he will see that, when two inputs begin to substitute perfectly for each other in some such ratio as 1 to 4, 1 to 2, or 1 to 1, they lose their separate identities. For instance, if one source of carbohydrate material contains 50 percent carbohydrates and another source contains 25 percent carbohydrates, the two substitute for each other, as a source of carbohydrates in the ratio of 2 to 1. As far as production processes requiring carbohydrates are concerned, the two inputs are essentially one input, carbohydrate. In such cases, a producer more or less forgets about the two inputs and concentrates upon their carbohydrate content as a single input.

When two inputs are so complementary that they have to be combined in given proportions, say 1 to 1, or 1 to 5, they, too, lose their identity as single inputs and the manager is likely to start talking about the two, combined in the necessary proportions, as a single input. As an extreme example, we might consider left shoes and right shoes. Left shoes and right shoes are perfect complements for the ordinary individual possessing two usable feet. Yet we rarely speak of left shoes and right shoes as separate commodities; instead, we speak of a pair of shoes. The two commodities merge into a single commodity. Many of the input relationships in livestock production are quite complementary. In these cases, we find one kind of protein mixed, in given proportions, with another kind of protein and regarded as a single input. The farmer, in such cases, begins to think about "so and so's" feed supplement rather than about different kinds of protein as separate inputs.

Perfect Substitutability and Complementarity Not Often Found in the Real World

The above discussions have dealt with the cases of (1) nearly perfect substitutes, (2) nearly perfect complements. In the real world, most pairs of inputs tend to be complements or substitutes but few pairs tend to be either perfect substitutes or perfect complements. In fact, the usual relationship appears to be as follows: generally inputs substitute for each other over a given range and then tend to be complementary over a wider range. The student can observe this from the "typical" product contour map usually drawn (see Figure 9.1).

Despite the truth of this generalization many feeding and fertilization standards assume pairs of inputs to be either perfect complements or perfect substitutes. It is usual to say that proteins and carbohydrates need to be combined in fixed proportions in a ration for a given animal. Yet, the experience of farmers yields untold numbers of cases in which the protein content of hog rations has been successfully adjusted in response to changes in relative prices (see Chapter 16). This indicates that there is a range in which protein and carbohydrates substitute for each other. The experience of farmers also indicates that protein and carbohydrates cannot be substituted for each other over a wider range which, in turn, indicates that carbohydrates and protein are complements over such ranges. All these facts are in accord with the above generalizations. Further examples could be drawn from almost any number of feed and fertilization problems.

On the other hand, many feeding standards often assume that inputs are perfect substitutes for each other; i.e., that carbohydrates from barley substitute in a one to one ratio for carbohydrates from oats in a feeder pig ration. Conceptually, the feeding standards tend to make the extreme assumptions that inputs are either perfect substitutes or perfect complements. The unrealism of these assumptions is indicated by the fact that the feeding standards become continuously more and more voluminous as exception after exception to their obscure assumptions of nearly perfect substitutability and complementarity make it necessary to add discussion after discussion, page after page, and even extra tables to the standards. An overall result of these additions to the standards is a greater and greater recognition of the partial complementarity and partial substitutability of the real world.

Output as It Depends upon Categories of Inputs

Farmers, bankers, farm-management men, and agricultural economists often speak about the income-producing capacity of groups of inputs. It is very common to hear members of these groups discuss the advisability of investing more money in land, as contrasted with working capital; or livestock, as contrasted with machinery; or machinery, as contrasted with labor. When a person talks about investing in machinery he is often talking about investment in a wide variety of inputs, ranging from corn planters through tractors to self-propelled combines and bulldozers. Similarly, when one speaks about investments in livestock, he may be referring to a wide variety of inputs ranging from sheep and goats through hogs, dairy cattle, etc., to high-quality purebred cattle.

Economic theory contains corresponding concepts. Classical economists have long talked about the earnings of land, labor, capital, and, less accurately, management. Similarly, farm-management men have spent a considerable amount of time trying to isolate and determine the income-producing capacities of various assets. One finds in the usual farm account book a method of computing returns from various factors and combinations of factors such as *operator's labor and management* or *operator's and family's labor and management,* etc. Inaccurate as such computations are, they do indicate interest in the dollar productivity of groups or categories of inputs.

Several general economists have attempted to estimate the productivity of categories of inputs, by countries, by industries, and by individual businesses. The first major piece of work done in farm management, along the lines outlined by general economists, was that done at Iowa State College by O. Brownlee, G. Tintner and Earl Heady. Heady was concerned with the value productivity of five input categories:

1. Real estate.
2. Labor.
3. Machinery and equipment.
4. Livestock.
5. Cash operating expenses.

If we let $Z_1, \cdots, Z_5$ stand for each of the above categories of inputs, and W stand for the dollar value (gross income) of all the products produced, we can write

$$W = f(Z_1, \cdots, Z_5)$$

This expression indicates that gross income depends upon inputs of the five different categories. The law of diminishing returns should be expected to hold for

$$W = f(Z_1, \cdots, Z_i \mid Z_{i+1}, \cdots, Z_N)$$

because of the influence of the fixed amounts of $Z_{i+1}, \cdots, Z_N$. In Heady's work, management, as an input, was not included in any category; its absence was probably partially responsible for the diminishing marginal value productivity of all inputs which appears in Heady's estimates.[1]

For the relationship between gross income and categories of inputs to be meaningful, it is desirable that certain conditions be true. These conditions are:

1. That the inputs within a category be as nearly perfect substitutes or perfect complements as possible.

2. That categories, made up of substitutes (a) be measured according to the least common denominator (often physical) causing them to be good substitutes and (b) be priced on the basis of the dollar value of the least-common-denominator unit.

3. That categories made up of complements (a) be measured in terms of units made up of the inputs combined in the proper proportions (which are relatively unaffected by price relationships) and (b) be priced on an index basis with constant weights assigned to each complementary input.

4. That the categories of inputs be neither perfect complements nor substitutes relative to each other.

5. That investments and expenses be kept in separate categories.

6. That maintenance expenditures and depreciation be eliminated from the expense categories because of the difficulty encountered in

---

[1] The specific equation fitted by Heady was:

$$W = aZ_1{}^iZ_2{}^jZ_3{}^kZ_4{}^lZ_5{}^m$$

This equation was fitted by ordinary least-squares procedures in linear logarithmic form. As such, it permitted any tendency toward diminishing returns present in the raw data to be reflected in the estimates. When the sum of i through $m > 1$, increasing marginal returns to all inputs used jointly are evidenced; when the same sum < 1, decreasing marginal returns to all inputs used jointly are evidenced; and, when the sum $= 1$, constant marginal returns are indicated. The same is true concerning any one of the input categories and its coefficient.

preventing duplication. (This means that the earnings of the investment categories must be large enough to cover maintenance and/or depreciation.)

The first three of the above conditions are desirable in order to insure that the inputs, within each category, are combined in the proportions dictated by the scale line in the uncategorized production function:

$$Y = f(X_1, \cdots, X_n)$$

Perfectly adjusted competitive firms of varying size would tend to yield data not properly reflecting the degree of diminishing returns experienced by the firms. To be more specific, estimates from such data are likely to underestimate the marginal value productivity of small amounts of the inputs, considered both singly and jointly, and overestimate their productivity, also considered both singly and jointly, for large amounts of the inputs. Care in the selection of data and in the interpretation of such estimates can offset these shortcomings to a considerable degree. Data should be selected over a fairly wide range and from imperfectly adjusted firms. As the fitting technique is not simultaneously capable of covering two of the three stages of production, care should be taken to secure data primarily from firms (and enterprises) in Stage II (see Chapter 8 for a discussion of the stages).

It is possible to construct estimates from farm account records and survey data which are very useful to agencies setting up lending programs for farmers, professional farm managers, research workers in agricultural economics, and a wide variety of other persons. As indicated above, a great variety of people feel the need in discussing, planning, and studying farm management problems to speak about general input categories. Such estimates are useful as a basis for evaluating the dollar or value productivity of assets fixed at different levels on individual farms (see the discussion dealing with the problem of pricing fixed assets in Chapters 4, 12, and 20).

An illustration of the use of this procedure and of its value is given in the following section.

The Earning Power of Input Categories on Upland Farms, Marshall County, Kentucky, 1951

Survey records and records kept in connection with T.V.A. test demonstration farms in Marshall County, Kentucky, were analyzed by the procedures outlined above. In all, thirty records were analyzed.

Seven figures were obtained for each farm as follows:

1. *Gross Income*. This figure included the sales of crops, livestock, and seeds plus the value of products used in the home plus or minus changes in certain inventories. As both beginning and ending inventory values were figured at the same prices, gross income did not include changes in inventory values due to price increases. Further, changes in inventory values due to depreciation of machinery and buildings were left out (for the most part) from gross income. Hence, gross income, as reported, should be sufficiently large to cover maintenance of the machinery and building investment. Gross income left out the rental value of the farm dwellings.

2. *Land Was Measured in Acres Only*. The dollar value of land was not used because the value of land for building sites along the main highways was not related to its income-producing capacity for farm purposes. As Marshall County farm buildings tend to be poorly adapted to the newer types of agriculture, the value of farm buildings was not included. This explains why the rental value of the farm dwelling was left out of gross income.

3. *Labor Was Measured in Terms of Months Only*. An attempt was made to find out for each farm the number of man-months devoted to or spent on the farm.

4. *Machinery Investment*. This figure, designed to measure the total machinery investment for the farm, was the beginning inventory value of machinery, plus proportional charges for new machinery purchased during the year, less proportional charges for machinery sold off the farm during the year. Farmers should expect to earn returns on this investment at least high enough to cover an interest charge, plus maintenance and/or depreciation charges.

5. *Breeding and Workstock Investment*. This figure, designed to measure the investment in livestock for the year as a whole, is essentially the beginning inventory value of breeding and workstock, plus proportional charges for breeding and workstock purchased during the year, less proportional deductions for those sold off the farm during the year. Feeder animals were treated as current expense items because, by and large, farmers expect to get back dollar for dollar each year for expenditures on feeder animals, whereas they expect to cover only interest on their investment and depreciation in connection with breeding livestock.

6. *Forage Production Investment*. This figure was designed to measure the investment in forage production. It is essentially the replacement value of the hay and pasture stands on the farm, in-

cluding the residual values of fertilizer applied, in establishing such forage crops, plus investments in mechanical structures or land-clearing necessary in order to establish such forage crops. An acre of good, well-established fescue and ladino was valued at between $35 and $40; an acre of Korean lespedeza in condition to reseed itself was valued at about $2. Other forage and hay stands were assigned corresponding appropriate values.

7. *Other Expenses.* This figure was designed to include all current expenditures on the farm expected to yield dollar for dollar returns in a given year except expenditures on hired labor, taxes, insurance, and maintenance of building and machinery investments. It includes expenditures on gas and oil used in the tractor and in the automobile (for farm purposes), annual seeds, feeder stock, the beginning feeder-stock inventory, miscellaneous supplies, fertilizer nutrients whose values are consumed in 1 year, the value of perennial forages plowed down for row crops, custom charges for machinery, breeding fees, etc.

When the relationship between gross income and the six input categories was estimated statistically, certain difficulties were encountered. For instance, it proved impossible to secure reliable estimates of the influence of forage investment on gross income as distinguished from the influence of livestock on gross income. When it was realized that the forage and livestock investments were complementary, they were combined in accordance with condition 1 (see the above section), and usable estimates resulted.

For the "usual" (geometric average) amount of each input category used on the thirty farms, the estimates indicate that the following marginal value products were being earned: land—less than nothing per acre;[1] labor—$55 a month; machinery—4 percent on the investment; livestock and forage—56 percent on the investment; and current expenditures—86 cents on the dollar spent. These estimates were very much in line with what would be reasonably expected. Marshall County land, in a raw state, is virtually non-productive but is very responsive to fertilizer and forage-seed investments. Marshall County farms are small, the usual size being 103 acres, on which the usual amount of labor used was 9.4 months per year. With the usual total

[1] Though the estimates show *land* earning a negative marginal value product, the estimates are not significantly different from zero and are regarded to be such; however, when the equation is used for predictive purposes the negative value is used.

product worth $3,846 and the usual investment in machinery running at $1,420, it is not surprising to find the marginal value product of machinery and labor, especially, and, for that matter, of other expenditures, somewhat low. The marginal value products are the net earning powers of the different inputs; i.e., $100 invested in forage and livestock returns $56 annually to cover interest, depreciation, and maintenance. The $56, unlike a measure such as gross returns per animal unit, does not have to cover feeds, breeding fees, veterinary fees, etc. Those expenditures are covered by the category labeled other expenditures, which, in this case, were returning 86 cents per dollar spent.

The equation from which the above marginal value productivities were derived follows:

$$\text{Gross income} = 26.1(\text{Land})^{-0.0245}(\text{Labor})^{0.135}(\text{Mach.})^{0.015}(\text{Forage})^{0.440}(\text{Exp.})^{0.174}$$

Analysis of a Specific Farm Business

With the aid of an algebra book and a table of logarithms, the "expected" gross income can be quickly computed for a given specific farm, using the quantities of resources indicated in column (2) below.

(1) Input Category	(2) Amount Used	(3) Logarithm of Amount Used	(4) Coefficient	(5) (3) × (4)
Land	50 acres	1.70	−0.0245	−0.042
Labor	14.2 months	1.152	.135	.156
Machinery	2,657 dollars	3.42	.015	.051
Livestock & forage	2,465 dollars	3.392	.440	1.494
Other expenses	577 dollars	2.76	.174	.481
Constant				1.418
Total				3.558

The antilog of 3.558 is $3,622, the estimated gross income.

Estimated gross income is what is expected, on the basis of the experience of the entire group of farmers, from what was used on this farm. The actual gross income of this farmer was $3,790—he earned $168 more than expected from what he used.

The study also made it possible to estimate the earning power of the inputs and, hence, to compute various earning figures directly rather than as residuals resulting from arbitrary deductions, as was done in Chapter 4.

The marginal value products earned by the different input categories (in the amounts used on this farm) are estimated to be as follows:

Labor	$34.43 per month [1]
Forage and livestock	$0.6462 per dollar invested
Land	−$1.77 per acre
Machinery	$0.0204 per dollar invested
Other expenditures	$1.096 per dollar spent

Here again the above rates of return are net to the last unit of each input; i.e., the last $100 invested in forage and livestock was returning 64.62 cents on the dollar invested, with feed, breeding, and veterinary expenses covered by returns to the other expenditures' category at a rate of almost $1.10 per dollar spent.

These estimates, combined with the data on amounts used, make it possible to estimate the earning power of each category of inputs directly. For example, 14.2 months at $34.43 per month earned $488.97. Nine months of operator's labor at the same rate earned $409.87, while 5.2 months of family labor at the same rate was earning a total of $179.10. The $2,657 investment in machinery earned 2.04 percent or $54.33, while the investment in 50 acres of land lost an estimated $1.77 per acre or $88.73 and the investment in forage and livestock of $2,465 earned 64.65 percent or $1,593.68, for a total *return to these investments of $1,559.28*, inclusive of maintenance and/or depreciation. In addition to returns to labor and investments, an extra sum of money amounting to $1,653.72 above other expenditures was received—this additional amount includes profits, managerial returns, and, perhaps, returns on certain investment items not included above. *Operator's net earnings* then amounted to the earnings of his 9 months of labor $309.87, plus the sum of profits, etc., $1,653.72, totaling $2,063.59. Gross income less cash expenses is, in this case, $3,213. If a charge for depreciation and/or maintenance expenses is subtracted from cash farm earnings, an estimate of *farm earnings* (as previously defined) results.

Reorganization on the Basis of the Analysis

Now let us look at this man's business from an analytical standpoint. His land, it is estimated, was earning nothing or less than nothing, his labor an estimated $34.43 per month at the margin, his machinery only 2.04 percent with maintenance and depreciation unchanged. On the brighter side, his investments in forage and livestock

[1] In general, $MVP_{Z_i} = \dfrac{b_i E(G)}{Z_i}$, where b_i equals the Z_i coefficient, $E(G)$ is expected gross income, and Z_i is the input used. In case of labor, $MVP_{\text{labor}} = \dfrac{(0.135)(3,622)}{14.3} = \dfrac{488.96}{14.2} = \$34.43$.

were paying an estimated 64.65 percent and his current expenditures were paying about $1.10 on the dollar. The rates of return are badly out of line—a return of between 10 and 20 percent is needed on machinery and more than $34 is needed per month for labor. The low rates of return obviously result from trying in a grassland county to utilize $2,657 worth of machinery and 14.2 months of labor on only 50 acres and in connection with but $2,466 worth of forage and live-stock and $577 of other expenditures.

One course which appears open involves an expansion in forage and livestock and a contraction in labor and machinery use.

First, $1,200 worth of machinery could be sold. In addition, 6 months off-farm employment paying, say, $300 a month could be secured. This would provide up to $2,500 for investment in forage and livestock, paying a high rate of return. In addition, an extra $1,500 could be borrowed, and other expenditures could be upped to $1,200 annually, mainly for feed concentrates, from current receipts. Thus, the reorganized picture would be as indicated in column (2) below.

(1)	(2)	(3)	(4)	(5)
Input Category	Amount Used	Logarithm of Amount Used	Coeffi-cient	(3) × (4)
Land	50 acres	1.70	−0.0245	−0.042
Labor	8.2 months	0.914	0.135	0.123
Machinery	1,457 dollars	3.153	0.015	0.047
Livestock and forage	7,500 dollars	3.875	0.410	1.705
Other expenses	1,200 dollars	3.079	0.174	0.536
Constant				1.418
Total				3.767

The antilog of 3.767 is $5,848, the expected gross income, under 1951 conditions, from the reorganized farm, an amount a little less than $400 for each of the 15 cows which could be supported under this investment and expenditure pattern. The rates which, it is estimated, such a farm organization would earn are as follows: labor, $96 a month; machinery investment, 6.02 cents on the dollar invested; livestock and forage investment, 34.3 cents on the dollar; land, less than nothing; and, other expenditures, 84.8 cents per dollar spent. Not bad—certainly an improvement—but still weak on machinery earnings and now low on the earning power of other expenditures.

Returns for the investment include $2,573 on the livestock and forage investment, $88 on the machinery investment, less $29 lost on the land, for a total of $2,632 inclusive of maintenance and/or depreciation. Labor earnings would amount to $789. In addition to returns to labor and investments, an extra sum of money would be left over after covering other expenses which amount to $2,427. This additional amount includes profit, managerial returns, and returns on certain other expenses and expenditures not covered above.

For greater investments in forage and livestock (still the high-paying portion of the business even after reorganization) land and the forage-livestock investment are not independent; i.e., land is necessary in order to expand the forage and livestock investment and the two are somewhat complementary. As not much more than $40 per acre can be invested in forage production, the $7,500 invested on 50 acres of land and in 15 cows (including young stock) have about exhausted the possibilities for investments in forage and livestock without buying more land.

If, then, after the farm was put on the above better-paying basis, 100 more acres were acquired, 50 acres more were seeded down, 15 more cows were purchased, the machinery investment expanded to $2,500 (for milking machines, coolers, and haying equipment), $1,300 were devoted to other expenditures, and 14.2 months' labor were again used, what would be the picture? Expected gross income would be $8,376.

Under these conditions, labor would be earning about $80 a month, machinery investments about 5 percent, livestock and forage investments about 28.3 percent, land nothing or less than nothing, and other expenditures $1.12 per dollar spent. At the margin, machinery returns are still low, labor earnings are lower than before the land was purchased, forage and livestock returns are falling nearly to the sum of interest and maintenance costs, and returns to other expenditures are high. Further, the business, as a total, is experiencing diminishing returns to all inputs.

The organization could be further improved through the use of more current expenditures. Such a reorganization would be profitable and would increase the earning power of labor and machinery. This process of reorganization would continue until

$$\frac{MVP_{(\text{labor})}}{P_{(\text{labor})}} = \cdots = \frac{MVP_{(\text{other exp.})}}{P_{(\text{other exp.})}} = 1$$

in accordance with economic principles previously expounded. If the complication due to the complementarity between land and livestock-forage investments is ignored, the ultimate organization would be determined by the reservation price placed on labor, the rates of return deemed necessary on machinery, and livestock-forage investments. In the process of expanding the farm business, the law of diminishing returns (as reflected in the equation) would insure that returns would eventually fall to a point for each input category which would prevent further expansions.

The importance of personal reservation prices for labor, etc., as a limit to size of business will again become evident in connection with Chapter 21 on budgeting.

CHAPTER 11

How Many Enterprises?

An enterprise in a farming business is usually defined as the production of a single crop or kind of livestock. Production of beef cattle, sheep, hogs, chickens, corn, wheat, sorghum, cotton, cherries, celery, oranges, cranberries, and popcorn are sufficient examples. For some enterprises, such as dairying, one may sell several products, such as milk, calves, cows, and purebred breeding stock. This definition of a farm enterprise is incomplete because:

1. A line of production may result in a single product such as potatoes, or a number of products as described above under dairying.
2. The primary product may be sold directly or converted into other products before selling.
3. No limitations have been placed on quantities.
4. Relative importance of different lines of production is ignored.
5. Disposition of products (sale off the farm or use in the household) is ignored.

The authors of this book define a farm enterprise as a line of production necessitating individual and distinct production treatment. Thus, size, relative importance, number of products, and disposition of products, are eliminated from the definition. For example, a farmer growing potatoes as a separate unit either for home use or for sale, and for which he is required to assemble equipment for plowing the land, planting the crop, spraying, and harvesting, has a potato enterprise. By the same definition, one using his resources in producing wholesale milk, calves, cows, and purebred breeding stock has a dairy enterprise unless a separate set or handling of resources is involved for each component. Similarly, the individual vegetables in a garden are parts of a single enterprise until an individual allocation of resources must be used for one of them. Enterprises are thus defined in terms of inputs rather than outputs.

153

Multiple-Enterprise Farming and Diversification

In street language diversification consists of doing a number of things, whereas specialization is confined to doing largely one thing. The U. S. Census defines specialization as a system of production receiving 50 percent or more of the income from a single source. Income is sales plus produce used. Source is product sold, not primary origin.

Thus, according to the Census definition, one receiving 50 percent of his income from sales of beef cattle is an animal specialty farmer even though (1) he produced on the farm the animals and all hay, pasturage, and other feed entering into them, and (2) he used a larger quantity of resources in producing other products.

The Census defines generalized farming as the sale of a number of items none of which is equal to 50 percent of total sales. The term "vertical diversification" has a special meaning. An example of vertical diversification is dairy farming from which milk is sold in the form of pasteurized fluid milk, sweet cream, ice cream, and candy bars.

Diversification Widely Advocated. Perhaps no single farming practice has been so widely advocated as diversification. If one should ask the first ten men he met on the street for a definition of a good farm manager he would probably be told by many of them that a good farmer is one who diversifies—"one who does not put all his eggs in one basket," "one who rotates his crops." If one should ask the same ten men for a definition of a good city business or professional man, he would probably be told that a successful city man is one who specializes. For example, they would point to steel, railroad, or banking magnates; or mention the names of such men as Henry Ford, or Walter P. Chrysler, as being successful men in the specialized field of auto manufacturing. "America has become great," we are reminded constantly, "because, for one thing, we specialize." Jim is an expert accountant, John a master mechanic, Joe an architect, Bill a minister, George an anthropologist. Tom is a heart specialist, whereas Robert is an orthodontist, which are illustrations of specialties within a field of specialization. In merchandising we have special stores for men's clothing, women's shoes, electrical appliances, and television. Even in football some teams specialize in the T-formation; others prefer the single wing. "America is built on specialization," they say, and yet farmers should diversify.

The attitudes appear inconsistent, do they not? The inconsistency lies in the confusion of concepts regarding diversification. The term has been widely used to advocate two distinct lines of action.

1. The need to add enterprises in order to use resources more completely.

2. The need to scatter or divide the use of resources for the sake of distributing risk.

The typical farmer's first need is to use his resources fully. This he accomplishes through the device of conducting a number of enterprises; he follows *multiple-enterprise* farming. With this practice his business takes on the nature of a "drug store" which sells not only drugs but other things, including sodas and lunches; or of a coal merchant who sells ice in summer. In contrast there are those who scatter their investments for the purpose of spreading risk. The authors will use the term multiple-enterprise farming to denote the former and diversification to denote the latter.

The Theory of Combining Enterprises

The preceding chapters have dealt with the economics of single enterprises within a farm business. This chapter opens the question of multiple-enterprise farming. The next portion of this chapter employs the notation used in the three theoretical chapters dealing with single enterprises. It attempts to present the theory of enterprise combination in a concise manner. Because of its conciseness, a considerable amount of study will be required if the student is to grasp its full meaning. It is important that a student grasp the meaning of this chapter (1) if he is to understand thoroughly the problems of combining enterprises as farm sizes change and as progress is made in the accumulation of fixed assets, (2) if he is to grasp the full meaning of the problem of diversification, and (3) if he is to understand a succeeding chapter on cost of production concepts.

Production Functions for Two Enterprises within a Firm

The authors have defined a farm enterprise as a line of production necessitating individual and distinct production treatment. This definition will be rigidly adhered to in this chapter. Let us label the products of the two enterprises, Y_1 and Y_2. The two enterprises are separate and distinct because the inputs $X_{d+1}, \cdots, X_g$ are fixed in the production of Y_1 whereas the inputs $X_{g+1}, \cdots, X_n$ are fixed in the production of Y_2. The inputs $X_1, \cdots, X_d$ are variable inputs which can be devoted to the production of either Y_1 or Y_2. Figure 11.1 presents the two production functions. The first diagram in Figure 11.1 shows how the production of Y_1 depends upon the joint inputs of X_1,

$\cdots$, X_d (combined according to the scale line) with X_{d+1}, $\cdots$, X_g fixed. The second diagram in Figure 11.1 shows how the production of Y_2 depends upon the amount of X_1, $\cdots$, X_d (combined according to the scale line) used in conjunction with the fixed quantities of X_{g+1}, $\cdots$, X_n.

An example will help the student to interpret the symbols in the above paragraph. Y_1 could be alfalfa, and Y_2 could be corn. The fixed inputs X_{d+1}, $\cdots$, X_g for the production of alfalfa, or Y_1, would be such items as mowers, hay rakes, loaders, hay mows, etc. The fixed

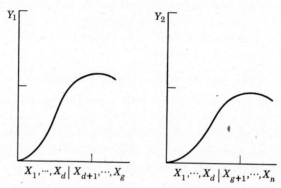

Fig. 11.1. Production functions for Y_1 and Y_2, both products of a single firm.

inputs for the production of corn, or Y_2, would be such items as corn pickers, corn cultivators, elevators, and cribs. The variable items X_1, $\cdots$, X_d, which are useful in the production of both products, would be such items as labor, tractor power, horse power, land, etc. It is helpful, and realistic, to assume that the variable items are not fixed item by item. For instance, in transferring land, labor, and tractor power from the production of corn to the production of hay, it might be desirable to sell some of the tractor power and hire additional labor.

Figure 11.2 represents a considerable change in procedures for graphing output. Therefore, it is necessary that the student re-read this section several times and consider it very carefully if confusion is to be avoided. Figure 11.2 is a diagram involving two enterprises producing two products, Y_1 and Y_2. The amount of product Y_1 produced is plotted on the vertical axis. The amount of product Y_2 produced is plotted on the horizontal axis. The curve plotted between the two axes represents the various combinations of the two products Y_1 and Y_2 *which can be produced at a given total cost.* The curve thus meas-

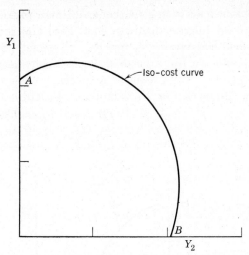

Fɪɢ. 11.2.   Iso-cost curve for production of Y_1 and Y_2.

ures both product and costs because all points along it represent equal
costs.   It may, therefore, be referred to as an iso-cost curve.   That
given cost is made up of three items:

    1. The cost of using X_{d+1}, $\cdots$, X_g, the items of production fixed
in the production of Y_1.
    2. The cost of using X_{g+1}, $\cdots$, X_n, the items of production fixed
in the production of Y_2.
    3. A given expenditure for X_1, $\cdots$, X_d, the items of production
which can be used in the production of either Y_1 or Y_2.

A higher or lower iso-cost curve would involve greater or lesser amounts
of the variable inputs X_1, $\cdots$, X_d only, because all other inputs are
fixed.   Because a certain set of inputs is fixed in the production of Y_1
and another set of inputs is fixed in the production of Y_2, the proportions in which the two are produced can be changed only by shifting
the variable inputs, X_1, $\cdots$, X_d, between the two products.   Point A
in Figure 11.2 results when all the variable inputs are devoted to the
production of Y_1.   Point B in Figure 11.2 results when all the variable
inputs are devoted to the production of Y_2.   The rest of the points
along the iso-cost curve are found by devoting different proportions
of the variable inputs, X_1, $\cdots$, X_d, to the production of the two different products.   This process is illustrated more specifically in Figure
11.3.

Figure 11.3 contains: first, a diagram, A, of the production function for Y_1; second, the iso-cost diagram, B, of Figure 11.2; and third, the production-function diagram, C, for Y_2.

The student can see from the diagram in Figure 11.3 (A) that, if 100 units of $X_1, \cdots, X_d$ (combined according to the scale line) are devoted to the production of Y_1, B units of Y_1 will be produced and that, if no units of $X_1, \cdots, X_d$ are applied to the production of Y_2, zero units of Y_2 will be produced. The result is B units of Y_1 and zero units of Y_2 or point B on the iso-cost diagram. A similar procedure will

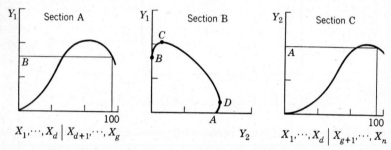

FIG. 11.3. Production functions for Y_1 and Y_2 and resultant iso-cost curve for production of Y_1 and Y_2.

locate point A on the diagram. The student is asked to follow this procedure for locating point A himself in order to be sure that he understands the reasoning presented here.

The production functions for Y_1 and Y_2 are of such a nature that use of 100 units of the variable inputs causes production of either product to be carried into Stage III, the area of negative marginal returns. This is true for both products. As a result, when the firm is producing only Y_1 it is possible to divert part of the variable inputs from the production of Y_1 to the production of Y_2 *and increase the production of both products* up to the point C on the iso-cost line. Similarly, if the firm were producing Y_2 alone, it would be possible to divert part of the variable inputs from the production of Y_2 to the production of Y_1 *and* increase the production of both. When either or both of these two situations exist on an iso-cost curve, we say that the enterprises are *complementary*. Between points C and D the two enterprises are *competitive* even though they are complementary over the ranges BC and DA. Such enterprises are commonly referred to as complementary even though they are produced in the competitive range. In this case, complementarity results from (1) the fixed inputs for each enterprise and (2) the nature of the production function. These two conditions are such that, if the variable inputs are devoted to either product alone, negative marginal returns are yielded in Stage III.

From point C to point D the two products are *competitive*. Between these two points, the production of Y_2 can be expanded only by reducing the production of Y_1. Similarly the production of Y_1 cannot be expanded without reducing the production of Y_2. On the individual production functions both products are being produced in Stage II. Stage II, the student will recall, is the logical area for producing each product on their respective production functions. It is perfectly obvious that it is not logical to produce two products in an area of complementarity because complementarity implies production of one of the products at negative marginal returns. The existence of complementarity results in multiple-enterprise firms producing products which are *competitive in the proportions in which produced*. Thus, two enterprises which are said to complement each other, in the sense of this chapter, ordinarily compete for the use of the variable inputs under actual production conditions.

Combinations in Which to Produce Two or More Products with a Given Amount of Money

The question concerning the proper proportions in which to produce Y_1 and Y_2 has not yet been answered. On the basis of physical production data, we have indicated that it is uneconomic to produce the products in the two areas of complementarity, BC and DA. The way to determine the proportions in which to produce the two is to ask the question: What proportion, for the given cost represented by the iso-cost curve, will produce the most revenue? Obviously, *the proportion which will yield the greatest revenue at a given cost is the best proportion*. Lines, each representing an equal amount of revenue throughout its length, can be superimposed upon the middle diagram in Figure 11.3. Figure 11.4 presents an iso-cost curve as in Figures 11.2 and 11.3 with superimposed iso-revenue lines. Each one of these lines represents a given amount of revenue. *The slopes of the whole set of iso-revenue lines are determined by the price of Y_1 relative to the price of Y_2.* Each line gives all the quantities of Y_1 and Y_2 which at a given set of prices would produce a given amount of revenue. Iso-revenue line (b) is worth more than line (a); similarly (c) is worth more than (b), and (d) more than (c). Obviously, point E in Figure 11.4 represents the most profitable proportions in which to produce the two products. Point E represents the only proportion in which Y_1 and Y_2 can be

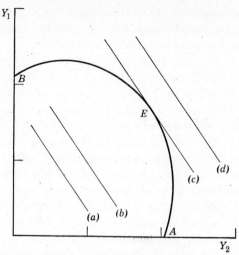

FIG. 11.4. Iso-cost curves with superimposed iso-revenue curves.

produced (at the given cost) to secure the revenue represented by iso-revenue line (c). All other proportions produce less revenue. At this point the given expenditure of money on the production of Y_1 and Y_2 returns the greatest possible revenue derivable from the two physical production functions we have been considering under the cost limitation imposed by the iso-cost line BEA.

Thus far, the optimum proportions in which to produce Y_1 and Y_2 at a given cost level have been determined graphically. Algebraically, these conditions can be stated as follows:

$$\frac{MPP_{(x_1, \cdots, x_d)y_1}}{MPP_{(x_1, \cdots, x_d)y_2}} = \frac{P_{y_2}}{P_{y_1}}$$

or, by transposition and division by $P_{(x_1, \cdots, x_d)}$ with $X_1 \cdots X_d$ combined according to the scale lines,

$$\frac{P_{y_2} \cdot MPP_{(x_1, \cdots, x_d)y_1}}{P_{(x_1, \cdots, x_d)}} = \frac{P_{y_1} \cdot MPP_{(x_1, \cdots, x_d)y_2}}{P_{(x_1, \cdots, x_d)}}$$

Read in words, the first equation written above states that Y_1 and Y_2 are being produced in the proper proportions, for a given cost, when the marginal physical productivity of the variable inputs applied to the production of Y_1 bears the same relationship to the marginal physical productivity of the variable inputs applied in the production of Y_2 as the ratio between the prices of Y_1 and Y_2. The second equation is in a form which can be easily extended to cover any number of enterprises or products. The extension of this equation to cover any number, i, of products is accomplished by adding additional terms to the equation as follows:

$$\frac{P_{y_1} \cdot MPP_{(x_1, \cdots, x_d)y_1}}{P_{x_1, \cdots, x_d}} = \frac{P_{y_2} \cdot MPP_{(x_1, \cdots, x_d)y_2}}{P_{x_1, \cdots, x_d}} =$$

$$\cdots = \frac{P_{y_i} MPP_{(x_1, \cdots, x_d)y_i}}{P_{x_1, \cdots, x_d}}$$

Read in words, this equation states that the ratio between the value of the marginal physical product of the variable inputs devoted to the production of one product must bear the same relationship to the price of those inputs as exists for all other products produced with the inputs if the products are being produced in the proper proportions. It is assumed that the variable inputs $X_1, \cdots, X_d$ are combined in accordance with the scale line in producing each product.

None of the foregoing discussion has determined, conceptually, the *amounts* of the products to be produced. It has determined only the *proper proportions* in which to produce the products when a given amount of money is to be spent on the totality.

Determination of the Amounts of Two or More Products to Be Produced in a Given Planning Span or Length of Run

In this section, the discussion will continue to be confined to a given planning span or length of run. That planning span is defined by (1) the fixed factors of production for each enterprise and (2) the quantities at which these factors of production are fixed. For purpose of simplification, discussion in the early paragraphs of this section will again be confined to a business having only two enterprises. This section contrasts with the preceding section because a whole series of iso-cost curves will be considered. *Selection of the proper iso-cost curve will determine the proper amount of each product to be produced.* This selection is the important second problem to be solved.

This discussion will be based on an iso-cost diagram derived from two production functions of the nature presented in Fig. 11.1. A series of iso-cost curves are plotted in Figure 11.5. Each of these iso-cost curves has associated with it a different amount of variable inputs. These iso-cost curves were each derived by changing variable inputs between production functions by the same procedure followed in deriving the iso-cost curve plotted in Figures 11.2 and 11.3. Some of the lower iso-cost curves are concave. This concavity arises from the fact that the cost limitations, for each of these lower curves, limits the use of variable inputs on both production functions to Stage I, or the area of increasing marginal physical productivity. The highest iso-cost curves exhibit convexity throughout but not areas of complementarity as previously defined. Areas of complementarity would result if the amount of variable inputs were such that production of

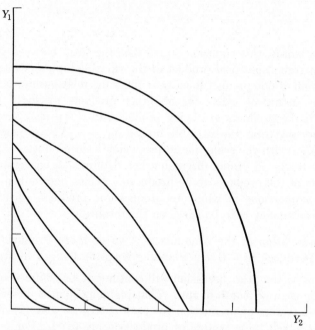

FIG. 11.5. Iso-cost curves for production of Y_1 and Y_2.

one or both of the products could be carried into Stage III, the area of negative marginal returns.

Figure 11.6 superimposes a series of iso-revenue curves on the iso-cost curves of Figure 11.5. Within Figure 11.6 an expansion line has been traced and is so labeled. This line represents the optimum proportions in which Y_1 and Y_2 should be produced at any level of expenditure. Graphically, the line passes through the points at which the iso-cost curves and iso-revenue curves are exactly tangent to each other.

As expenditures on the two products, Y_1 and Y_2, are expanded along this expansion line, a point is reached beyond which additional expenditures do not yield a corresponding increase in revenue. The point at which additional costs equal additional revenues is the point which

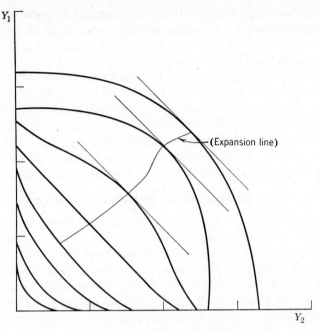

Y_1

(Expansion line)

Y_2

Fig. 11.6.   Iso-cost curve diagram with superimposed iso-revenue curves.

defines the optimum amounts of Y_1 and Y_2 to produce. This point always falls in an area of competitiveness as previously defined. Algebraically, the equation which defines this point of optimum output is as follows:

$$\frac{MPP_{(x_1, \cdots, x_d)y_1} \cdot P_{y_1}}{P_{(x_1, \cdots, x_d)}} = \frac{MPP_{(x_1, \cdots, x_d)y_2} \cdot P_{y_2}}{P_{(x_1, \cdots, x_d)}} = 1$$

Because we have specified, for each individual production function, that the variable inputs be combined according to the scale line, the above equation can be expanded to the following:

$$\frac{MPP_{x_1(y_1)}P_{y_1}}{P_{x_1}} = \cdots = \frac{MPP_{x_d(y_1)}P_{y_1}}{P_{x_d}} = \frac{MPP_{x_1(y_2)}P_{y_2}}{P_{x_1}}$$

$$= \cdots = \frac{MPP_{x_d(y_2)}P_{y_2}}{P_{x_d}}$$

The student should recall that marginal physical product of an input multiplied by the price of the product (for instance, $MPP_{x_1(y_1)} \cdot P_{y_1}$) is the marginal value product under competitive conditions. Read in words, the last equation states that the optimum amount of each product is being produced if the marginal value products of all variable inputs are equal to their respective prices in the production of the two products being produced.

The above reasoning concerning two products can be easily expanded on an intuitive basis to include more than two products. The last equation presented need merely be extended to include any given number of products. The interpretation of such an extended equation will be the same as that given for the preceding equation. The student should not forget that each enterprise, in the length of run or planning span under consideration, is defined by the fixed factors invested in it.

Some Implications of the Above Reasoning

The concave iso-cost curves plotted in Figure 11.6 are of considerable interest as a source of ideas concerning two types of farms. The *first* type of farm is the small undercapitalized farm which does not have enough purchasing power to command the variable inputs needed. Because of this limitation on purchasing power, such farms cannot operate in the profitable Stage II area on either of its production functions. Even if such a farm produced only one product, it would not have enough capital to buy enough of the variable inputs to put the production of that product on a paying commercial basis. Under these conditions, income may fall so low that the farm will be forced to add additional products or enterprises, not for the sake of economic efficiency in a commercial sense but in order to produce a more balanced subsistence diet. For instance, on a farm unable to enter commercial hog or dairy production because of capital limitation, both the hog and dairy enterprises may be maintained in the inefficient Stage I area and, in addition, poultry and sorghum enterprises may be added in order to balance the family diet. The *second* type of farm having concave iso-cost curves may be in such a position as a result of overinvesting in fixed assets for each of the enterprises. By overinvesting in fixed assets, such farmers may have impaired their credit position so much that they are unable to secure enough of the variable inputs to get into the profitable Stage II area in the production of either enterprise. Such farm businesses are often referred to as "land poor," "machinery poor," or "over-built."

It now becomes apparent that the nature of the iso-cost curves depends, in major part, on the nature of the fixed investments. Large fixed investments (proportionally) prevent complementarity because such large investments increase the capacity of the enterprise in which the investments are made to absorb units of the variable factors at positive marginal returns. In contrast to the effect of the quantity of fixed investments, an increase in the number or proportion of the inputs which are fixed increases complementarity. As a higher and higher proportion of the inputs involved in the production processes become fixed the marginal physical productivity of the remaining variable inputs becomes steeper and steeper and of shorter duration. As a result it becomes more and more imperative that the two products be produced in increasingly fixed proportions.

The longer the length of run, the smaller is the proportion of inputs which are fixed in the production of any one product. Hence, the longer the length of run or planning span encountered, the less complementarity one expects to find.

(1) "Pseudo" or "By-Product" Complementarity and (2) Supplementarity Due to Need to More Fully Utilize Inputs Fixed for the Whole Farm

Traditional farm management stressed one type of complementarity and supplementarity in examining enterprise combinations. For example, by-product nitrogen, by-product soil structure, by-product erosion control, etc., are emphasized in studying the problem of combining legumes with grain-crop enterprises. The need to have more than one enterprise in order to more fully utilize buildings, labor, and power machinery is also stressed; similarly, it is pointed out that seasonality often prevents full use of labor, buildings, and power machinery on one enterprise.

The nature of land restricts employment of labor and equipment resources in the same manner as seasons. Frontier farmers, having virgin soils enriched by the accumulation of centuries, used land for one crop rather continuously. Wheat, then wheat and corn were grown to the full capacity of farmers to "handle the crop." Much of the sloping land of the eastern states was cropped continuously. When the slopes were first cleared of trees little attention was paid to erosion and declining productivity. English farmers encountered the problem of declining productivity and added turnips and clover to other crops centuries ago. Gradually, farmers have found that it pays to change crops or grow them in systematic crop rotations. The advantages of crop rotations from a fertility standpoint are generally so well understood that a single enumeration of them should be sufficient without further explanation.

1. Legumes in rotations are useful in restoring nitrogen.

2. Sod crops, the root systems of which (a) contribute soil structure and humus and (b) slacken the rate of erosion are advantageous.

3. Rotations upset the life cycles of insects and diseases, thereby reducing injury from these handicaps.

4. Cultivated crops contribute to soil aeration.

Seasonality in crop growth restricts the number of acres that a given unit, or set of resources, can plant and harvest; or, what is more important, it restricts the number of days in the year in which the set of resources can be used. As a first illustration let us use corn growing. If one could plant and harvest corn every month within the year, present restrictions in the use of labor and machinery resources would not apply and a given farmer could produce corn somewhat on an "assembly line" basis, using both labor and corn-growing equipment throughout the year. (That is, he could if he had a sufficient acreage of land for growing corn.) Since this cannot be done, the farmer is forced to elect one of two choices.

1. He may grow what corn he can plant and harvest within the time allotted by nature and do nothing the remainder of the time.

2. He may supplement his own resources during planting and harvest with outside aid and find other things to do with his labor (and other adaptable resources) when not used for growing corn.

In the foregoing, the corn crop was used for illustrative purposes. However, the same limitations in the use of labor and equipment apply to other crops, and to a large degree to the production of livestock. Full-time farmers find it advantageous to use outside aid at seedtime and harvest in order to expand production of their main-crop enterprises, and yet they are forced by competition to find additional enterprises if nature and economic advantages offer such additions. Such additional enterprises are supplementary, and thus multiple-product farms become more efficient than a single-enterprise farm in the same situation. Two enterprises are supplementary when they jointly permit a fuller utilization of resources than when the farm is operated singly.

By-product complementarity is also referred to, here, as "pseudo" *complementarity* because the apparent iso-cost curves are not true iso-cost curves. Consider, for example, row-crop and legume enterprises. In a given rotation and at a given cash outlay, corn and alfalfa might be produced in different proportions as indicated in Figure 11.7.

Figure 11.7 illustrates the commonly known fact that inclusion of a legume in a row-crop rotation often increases the amount of row crop produced in the rotation as well as results in the production of additional leguminous roughages.   These joint events occur in the area *AB* which is an area of complementarity similar in appearance to the line segment *BC* in Figure 11.2 of this chapter.   The curved line *ABC* in Figure 11.7 is an iso-cost curve in the sense that equal expenditures

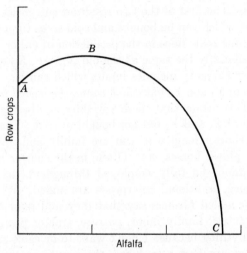

Fig. 11.7.   Iso-cost curve illustrating "pseudo" or by-product supplementarity in the case of row-crops and alfalfa enterprises.

on the items *ordinarily* considered costs are made at all points along the line.   In fact, however, the line *ABC* is not an iso-cost line as legume crops produce nitrogen, humus, and soil structure as by-products.   These by-products become inputs for the corn enterprise.   These by-products are productive; thus, they have value and should be (1) credited to the legume enterprise and (2) charged to the corn enterprise, a procedure which would make it difficult to consider the line *ABC* a true iso-cost curve.   By-product or "pseudo" complementarity is very important in agriculture.   Complementarity between the hog-fattening and beef-fattening enterprise is another important example not previously mentioned.

Supplementarity due to the need to fully utilize inputs fixed as far as the farm is concerned but variable between enterprises is also very important in farming.   This type of supplementarity arises when an additional category of inputs is added to the three categories considered at the beginning of this chapter. Those categories were: (1) the variable inputs $X_1, \cdots, X_d$ which could be used in the production of either Y_1 or Y_2 under the assumption that they could be bought and sold so as to permit combination in the proportions dictated by the scale line, (2) the inputs $X_{d+1}, \cdots, X_g$ which are fixed in the production of Y_1 and (3) the inputs $X_{g+1}, \cdots, X_n$ which are fixed in the production of Y_2. The additional category to be considered at this point is secured by dividing the first category, made up of $X_1, \cdots, X_d$, into two categories. The first of the two resultant categories contains only those variables which can be bought and sold so as to permit combination according the scale lines in the production of either Y_1 or Y_2; this category is essentially the same as the old $X_1, \cdots, X_d$ category. The second and new category includes inputs which can be varied between the production of Y_1 and Y_2 but *which cannot be varied for the business as a whole.* This means that these variables can be transferred from the production of Y_1 and Y_2 but not bought or sold. Examples of such inputs in the shorter lengths of run are family and operator's labor, land, tractors, plows, horses, etc. Often, in the shorter lengths of run, these items cannot be fully employed throughout the year on one enterprise; hence, additional enterprises are added. When a new enterprise is first added farmers say that they add it in order to make use of some "extra" family labor, pasture, tractor power, etc., which "isn't worth anything because I don't want to or can't sell it." When such enterprises are first introduced, the inputs are valued at practically nothing, principally because such inputs are not producing anything of value if employed on the old enterprise. However, if the new enterprise is successful and, for this reason, is expanded, the point is eventually reached at which the following question must be asked: Does it pay to curtail the old enterprise further in order to expand the new one? In terms of the principle presented earlier in this chapter this question can be phrased as follows: Is the MVP (of the inputs fixed for the business but variable between enterprises) in the new enterprise still greater than in the old enterprise? If it is, the new enterprise is expanded further. If it is smaller, the new enterprise is contracted. If the two MVP's are equal, the enterprises are properly combined. The student should turn back to the beginning of this chapter at this point and re-examine the equations presented there. The idea here is essentially the same as the idea there:

$$\frac{P_{y_1} \cdot MPP_{x_c}}{P_{x_c}} = \frac{P_{y_2} \cdot MPP_{x_c}}{P_{x_c}}$$

X_c is one of the inputs fixed for the business as a whole but variable between enterprises Y_1 and Y_2. The price of C, designated by P_{x_c}, is rather meaningless as C is not being bought or sold; hence, it can be canceled in the above equation which yields:

$$P_{y_1} \cdot MPP_{x_c} = P_{y_2} \cdot MPP_{x_c}$$

The price of C in the production of Y_1 is really its MVP in the production of Y_2, and vice versa. In other words C has an "opportunity cost" equal to its MVP in alternative enterprises in the farm business under consideration here. This cost is determined by (1) the price of the alternative products and (2) the marginal physical productivity of C in the alternative employments.

What is stated above, with respect to inputs fixed for the business as a whole but not for particular enterprises, is also true for the "by-product" inputs considered earlier. The economizing rules presented earlier apply with the logical modification that: *the inputs are priced within the business* according to the principle of opportunity costs *instead of in the market place*. The extension of the above reasoning for two products to cases involving an indefinite number of products is a straightforward task of adding products and inputs without changing the application of the economizing principles.

Multiple-Enterprise Farming and Size of Business. Farmers in the humid areas and to some extent in semi-arid regions have physical conditions providing opportunity to grow a large number of crops when truck, garden, and fruit crops are included. (Most garden and fruit crops are grown as field crops in those places having a high degree of comparative advantage for each of them.) This advantage, composed of physical and economic factors, was discussed at some length in Chapter 5 as a basis for choosing a method of approaching organization. Those doing subsistence farming produce and process a large number of farm products and provide themselves with other services, as they have insufficient quantities of products to sell for cash to buy services. Thus, they "grow" their own feather beds, dry their fruits, swap nursing, build their own improvements, and process their own meats, etc. Highly multified farming is often subsistence farming. Many lines of action are pursued, efficiency is low, and soil fertility is not too well preserved.

In contrast, many commercial farmers—those who produce primarily to sell—concentrate on production of few products, the number depending on the physical relationship. Some commercial farmers produce but few or no subsistence items, relying upon the open market for most of their food requirements. On such farms gardening becomes of minor importance, home slaughtering of meat is frequently reduced to locker capacity or discontinued entirely. The Thanksgiving turkey is bought at the store, and in many cases bottled milk is secured through a milk route. Such farmers direct their resources to the production of one to a few enterprises so as to produce them in a somewhat efficient manner. If but one line of production is carried, the business is said to be highly specialized. Examples of highly specialized farms are the large wheat farms, the cattle ranches, sheep ranches, and large cotton or tobacco farms. Commercial poultry farms provide another illustration. Because other enterprises do not or may not employ resources efficiently, these farms are specialized. Large scale permits such farms to employ their resources completely on one enterprise. The grower producing 10,000 broilers each 10 weeks probably has full use of all fixed resources and does not need to add other enterprises to the extent of a farmer (a) producing but 1,000 per batch or (b) one producing but one batch. In any case the farmer's problem is to secure optimum returns from the combined resources used (marginal value product equal to marginal factor cost). This may be done with one or many enterprises. The marginal concept applies to the variable factor(s) when added to a fixed quantity of other factors. Obviously, the larger the quantity of the fixed factor, the more units of the variable can be associated with the fixed factor at the margin.

Between the small-scale, highly multified subsistence farms and the large-scale businesses (which tend to be but are not necessarily specialized) are some 2.5 million commercial family-sized farm businesses producing two to maybe five kinds of crops, and/or one to three types of livestock in order to use resources fully and to equate marginal returns approximately with marginal factor costs for all enterprises.

On small farms multification is probably a necessity, if the operators expect to live on the returns from such small-scale farming. On some farms multiple production may not be desirable. For example, overflow river-bottom farms are annual crops farms and thus must produce but one or two crops. Corn, soybeans, cowpeas, or cotton are grown as a single crop, depending upon the latitude. Many western plains wheat farms and cattle ranches are one-crop or one-enterprise livestock farms because of climatic, market, and soil conditions. These farmers must be big enough to stand one, two, or maybe several years of adverse conditions to stay in business.

In humid areas blessed with favorable weather and soil conditions, commercial upland farms often have several crops and several kinds of livestock to choose from and their businesses vary from moderate multification to semispecialization. Farmers who are limited on capital investment and who are driving for high net earnings multify, as needed, to the point of keeping each enterprise big enough to make it relatively worth while and to fully utilize the various inputs. They will not go beyond the point of "what pays" according to their judgments except to avoid risk. A certain number of farmers who own "large" farms and who are less limited in funds with which to operate multify less because they value leisure and free time rather highly at their income levels. Many of this group who have passed into semiretirement let out harvested crops to a renter and keep the remaining acreage in permanent pasture harvested with beef cattle. Such farmers receive a higher degree of satisfaction by using more of their assets as sources of leisure and less of their assets as sources of income.

As long as one can use his resources on a single enterprise and earn more for the units at the margin than he could obtain from alternative new uses, he will continue to do so in preference to starting new enterprises (unless he wishes to diversify to spread risk). This means that where it is biologically possible, as in broiler production or dry-lot dairying, to practice continuous production on a modified assembly-line basis at a high rate of marginal return one will devote his resources to one enterprise up to the limit of making marginal returns equal to marginal factor cost as determined by the physical limitations of seasons, space, other fixed factors (including managerial capacity), or a diminished desire for gain.

Limitations of capital restrict the use of large acreages of arable land to a limited few. Thus, most farmers choose as their principal or main enterprise—around which to develop farming programs—an enterprise which has high and sustained marginal returns; they then produce this product with their fixed investment as long as marginal returns to the variable inputs exceed those obtainable from other enterprises. They add to such a crop (or livestock) other enterprises which will employ unused resources equally advantageously at the margin. If they are interested only in monetary returns, this process of expansion is continued until marginal returns are equal for all enterprises. If they are interested in other values, new enterprises may be added and old enterprises expanded until the marginal satisfaction derived from equal additional expenditures on all enterprises and in the various leisure and community pursuits are equal.

From the above discussion, it is obvious that the existence of complementarity (and, hence, multified farms) depends upon the production relationships existing for the variable factors of production, given the fixed investments in each enterprise. If the fixed investments are large in relation to the money available for the variable factors of production, complementarity is not likely to exist. If the fixed investments are small in relation to the money available for the variable factors, complementarity is likely to exist. Both conditions can exist on small farms. Both conditions can exist on large farms. Both can be changed when the opportunity for changing the fixed factor organization presents itself. On the other hand, if a high proportion of the inputs used in the production of the various products is fixed, complementarity is likely to exist. If a small proportion of the inputs used in the production of the various products is fixed, then complementarity is less likely to exist. The proportions of the inputs fixed depend upon the length of run or planning span being considered. In general, the longer the planning span, the larger is the proportion of the inputs which are variable. Both small and large farms operate in both the long and the short run. Again, the relationship between size of business or scale of operation and complementarity is obscure. Complementarity determines multification; hence the relationship between multification and size of operation is obscure.

The Fuller Use of Available Resources Illustrated

We are now ready to illustrate how to determine the number of enterprises a farmer should carry in terms of the marginal principles applicable to all farmers.

A farmer should select for his leading enterprise one that will yield high and sustained marginal value products. He should then add other enterprises to use his fixed resources when they are not used on the leading one to the point that he will salvage from their use a return equal to what he would get if they were put to the next best alternative use (marginal returns equal to marginal opportunity cost). For example, if a man has the following opportunities to use his labor or other resources and can net:

An average of $2.00 per hour for 100 hours on corn (60 cents at margin).

An average of $1.00 per hour for the next 110 hours on wheat (60 cents at margin).

An average of $0.60 per hour for the next 90 hours on hogs (60 cents at margin).

An average of $0.40 per hour for the next 60 hours on cattle (20 cents at margin).

An average of $0.30 per hour for the next 50 hours on poultry (20 cents at margin).

An average of $0.20 per hour for the next 40 hours on "subsistence" (20 cents at margin).

he will produce corn, wheat, and hogs if he refuses to take less than 60 cents per hour for his time. He will continue using his resources through "subsistence" if he considers 20 cents per hour "worth his while" (he will in this case, however, expand the production of corn, wheat, hogs, cattle, and poultry until they too earn only 20 cents at the margin). If the number of hours he could devote to the most profitable enterprise were not limited by seasonality and other factors (i.e., if constant returns existed in the corn enterprise, a highly unlikely situation) he would:

1. Devote all his resources to growing corn all of the time as it would be unbusinesslike to grow anything else.

2. Grow enough corn to meet his standard of living and be content to remain idle the remainder of the time.

Let us now examine or diagram an illustration of the employment of resources through the use of complementary enterprises. (For the value of another view of the same principle.)

In Figure 11.8 marginal revenue curves AM, $A'M'$, and $A''M''$ and average revenue curves EX, $E'X'$, and $E''X''$ are drawn for the three enterprises: A, "corn," B, "wheat," and C, "hogs," returning an average of $2.00, $1.00, and 60 cents per hour when ON, $O'N'$, and $O''N''$ quantities of labor are used, respectively. Let the reservation price for the farmers' services be 60 cents per hour or just below as represented by the line RS across the figures.

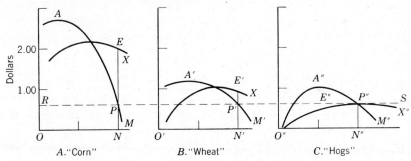

Fig. 11.8. Marginal and average returns from resources on three enterprises.

Our producer can get 60 cents per hour at the margin, using any of the three enterprises, but on enterprise *A* he can get an average of $2.00 per hour where the margin is 60 cents at an input of 100 hours. He is prevented from using further inputs at a marginal return equal to or greater than 60 cents an hour on *A* by season and/or acreage, and has the opportunity to get larger returns than 60 cents on a second enterprise. Thus, on *A* he will net $1.40 per hour or the difference between *NE* ($2.00) and *NP* (.60) or *PE* (1.40). Having additional resources which may be used in a different way and at a different time, he elects *B* "wheat." Through the employment of 110 hours of resources on *B* he can get 60 cents per hour at the margin as shown in Figure 11.8 *B* and $1.00 per hour average for the 110 hours by putting in *O'N'* resources. At this point 40 cents per hour is netted or the difference between *N'P'* and *N'E'* equal to *P'E'*. Having yet additional resources without use, he turns to the production of *C* "hogs." On *C* he can get 60 cents per hour at both the margin and the average as shown in Figure 11.8 *C*.

These principles are well illustrated in the management practices of 39 Illinois farmers examined by the Department of Agricultural Economics of the Illinois Station. Both farmers and research workers have long recognized the principle of comparative advantage, and farmers have selected enterprises and scope of enterprises on the basis of it to the best of their abilities. Enterprise cost studies have not always shown that the advantage lies with those enterprises generally believed to hold it. The comparative returns of the various enterprises appear to rank the enterprises in about the same order that farmers do. Let us compare the average dollar outputs per $100 inputs for the various enterprises. They are:

Average Returns Per $100 of Total Inputs

	Good Conditions	Fair Conditions
Corn	$323	$318
Soybeans	197	183
Oats	186	181
Alfalfa hay	124	111
Clover hay	90	94
Mixed hay	86	80
Hogs	116	95
Milk cows	103	90
Feeder cattle	101	
Beef cattle	91	
Poultry	93	66

Both the authors of this book and the Illinois department staff recognize: (1) the limitations of one year's data, (2) the limitations of computational methods employed, and (3) that the year studied was a good corn year. The corn yields could be one-third lower, however, and the average comparative advantage of corn would still be indicated. These farmers apparently use as much of their resources for corn as they can, then turn to soybeans, then to oats, hay, and finally pasture. With feed as a resource and "time on their hands" during certain hours of the day, days of the week, and months of the year, they add livestock to use these resources to some advantage even though average returns to resources spent on them are not in a class with returns spent on the main enterprises. The marginal returns per dollar input, however, would be equal for all enterprises if the farms were perfectly adjusted from the profit standpoint.

The Reduction of Risk

One of the problems encountered in business management is that of risk. Prices and yields are two of the important sources of risk in farming. Multiple-enterprise farming would be practiced whether or not risks existed. Diversification as defined in this book is practiced to meet risks. Diversification reduces risk from failure of one harvested crop because of drouth, insects, diseases, etc. Diversification spreads risk from changes in the relative prices of products produced. It does not protect against changes in the overall price level to a significant degree, since prices of farm products generally tend to move together under these conditions. This subject will be discussed in more detail in a later chapter.

QUESTIONS AND PROBLEMS

1. Why do individual farmers contend so vigorously for increased allotments of adapted crops when under government restrictions?

2. What did restrictions in corn acreage have to do with the use of grass for silage? Why did one affect the other?

3. Is multification practiced on overflow river-bottom farms? Why? Is risk high or low on such farms?

4. Show that farmers try to use resources on production opportunities to the extent of equimarginal returns.

5. Explain the actions of drug store management in using soda fountains and in serving plate lunches.

CHAPTER 12

Cost of Production Concepts
and Farm Management

Introductory Statement

This chapter is a conceptual chapter, i.e., it deals with concepts instead of data and specific applications. These concepts are useful in thinking about cost problems; they are also useful in checking the meaning attached to cost data continually being presented to farmers by academic and commercial sources. Cost concepts are difficult concepts. It behooves the student to study this chapter with considerable care. For students interested in some of the more complicated aspects of cost concepts an appendix is presented at the close of this chapter.

Some of the pertinent questions concerning costs are: What does it cost to produce a unit of product in terms of out-of-pocket or variable costs? In terms of total costs? How are the costs of fixed inputs charged? How is the list of variable or out-of-pocket costs related to the planning span under consideration? If one input increases the productive efficiency of a second input, how are costs of production computed? Must fixed costs be covered if a product is to be produced? What is a fixed input? If the cost of using a fixed input is a fixed cost, why does it vary with the price of the product produced?

The preceding chapters in this book dealing with production relationships provide a groundwork for understanding many of the difficulties encountered in cost of production work. They also indicate in part (1) some considerations to keep in mind in doing and using cost of production work and (2) the limitations which must necessarily be attached to cost of production computations. In these chapters, it was stressed that a different subproduction function exists for every length of run considered and for every different set of fixed factors within any length of run. It was also stressed that on each subproduction function a separate scale line exists for every possible set of relative prices of the inputs. Actually there are at least seven cost schedules for every possible production function and scale line. These schedules are:

1. The total cost schedule.
2. The total variable cost schedule.
3. The total fixed cost schedule.
4. The marginal cost schedule.
5. The average variable cost schedule.
6. The average fixed cost schedule.
7. The average total cost schedule.

Each of these schedules has a separate and distinct use which will be discussed in the section of this chapter entitled "The Seven Cost of Production Concepts and Their Uses."

This chapter, which attempts to present clear cost concepts to the students, is predicated on the assumption that "good" cost figures and concepts are highly useful. This chapter should help students, as future farm managers, to understand the cost of production data presented to them by farm-management researchers. It should also help students, as future farm management researchers, to grasp the important concepts underlying cost of production. And, lastly, this chapter should help students, as future extension workers, to envision the cost of production problems faced by the farmers that they are obligated to help.

One concept that has to be be driven out of a student's mind is that one cost of production figure exists. It is imperative that the student understand that there are at least the seven different cost concepts enumerated above. It is also imperative for the student to realize that these concepts are *schedules* of costs or cost structures for a series of different outputs.

In order to make meaningful cost computations the following information is required. *First*, the nature of the production relationship, for the length of run under consideration, must be known. This implies that the fixed inputs are known in *quantity* as well as by quality or name. This also implies that the method of production to be employed is known. The *second* requirement is that the prices of the variable inputs be known. This price requirement is necessary in order to meet the third requirement. The *third* requirement is that the location of the scale line be known for the set of fixed inputs and the existing set of relative prices for the variable inputs. From the pertinent scale line, it is possible to compute *total variable costs, average variable costs* and *marginal costs*. Knowledge of the fixed factors and their prices (or the product price) make it possible to compute *average fixed costs* per unit of output and *total fixed costs* for any level of output. Total fixed costs can be added to total variable costs for the same level of output to arrive at *total costs* and *average total costs* for any level of output.

Selection of the Relevant Subproduction Function on the Basis of Length of Run and Appropriate Sets of Fixed Factors of Production

Much of what needs to be written under this heading has been written in earlier chapters. Therefore, it will not be repeated here. Instead the following reassignments within this book are given to the student.

1. The portion of Chapter 8 dealing with production relationships involving one input. This section should be reread carefully in order to see that when studying any cost of production problem one studies output as it depends upon a set of controllable variable inputs and another set of fixed (and hence uncontrollable) inputs. The student should also become very aware of the danger of inaccuracies resulting from inputs which are neither studied nor held fixed.

2. The two sections in Chapter 9 dealing with
   (*a*) Production concepts involving more than two variable inputs.
   (*b*) Appropriate production function concepts. These sections should be restudied so that the student may more clearly grasp the fact that a different subproduction function exists for every length of run or planning span in which production decisions are made.

It cannot be overemphasized that a different list of inputs is fixed for each planning span or length of run. And, it cannot be overemphasized that the quantities of the fixed inputs on hand in any given length of run or planning span determine the nature of the subproduction function. For example, for the length of run in which it is not advantageous to rebuild or tear down a dairy barn, to buy or sell additional land, and to sell or install dairy equipment, the relevant subproduction function is very different from that in the longer length of run or planning span in which it is advantageous to tear down, build, and remodel barns, buy and install equipment, or buy and sell land. In the first length of run the variable inputs are, primarily, labor, management, feed (within limits), small supply items, and both the number and quality of animals which can be housed in the existing barn and handled with the existing dairy equipment. In this short length of run, the low point in the average total cost schedule probably occurs at about the stanchion capacity of the barn, if a stanchion barn is used, assuming an appropriate rate of feeding. If the dairyman attempts to expand production by adding cows beyond the capacity of the barn, he probably runs into increasing marginal and average total costs. These increases probably occur as the result of reduced efficiency in the use of labor, crowding of animals, etc. If the manager restricts the production of milk by milking, say, only one-half the number of cows which the barn and equipment will handle, he probably encounters increased average total costs and, in extreme cases, even increased marginal costs because of inefficiencies in the use of certain variable inputs. It takes a certain length of time to set up the equipment for (1) milking, (2) cleaning the stable area, and (3) feeding, regardless of whether 10 or 20 cows are handled. This illustration should stimulate the student to think about the effects of length of run (planning span) and fixed inputs on cost of production. Succeeding sections of this chapter will further develop the student's thinking on this subject.

Relative Prices of Inputs and the Location of the Scale Line on the Relevant Subproduction Function

The section in Chapter 9 dealing with *the proportions in which to use two variable inputs* outlined the procedure for locating a scale line on a two-variable-input production function. The section entitled "Production Concepts Involving More Than Two Inputs," in the same chapter, gives the algebraic condition for locating the scale line in production functions involving more than two variable inputs. The student should refer to these sections and reread them carefully. He should strive particularly to gain an understanding of how relative prices among inputs determine the location of scale lines. It is important to know that relative, not absolute, prices of inputs locate the scale lines. It might also be advisable for the student to reread the section in Chapter 10 on substitutability because that chapter emphasizes the way complementarity and substitutability among inputs affect the degree to which relative prices locate scale lines. The readings to which the student has been referred will impress on his mind again that different scale lines exist for every set of relative prices. In the next section of this chapter, it will be seen that a different, definite production relationship exists between product and variable inputs for each different scale line. And, in the section following that, it will be seen that a different set of seven different cost schedules exists for each set of production relationships.

Relative prices of variable inputs change almost continuously in the real world. It follows that the location of scale lines, the nature of the relevant joint production relationships, and the nature of cost structures change almost continuously. In order for cost of production computations to have much long-run significance, therefore, it is desirable that "normal" relationships among the prices of the variable inputs be used in computing cost schedules. This procedure involves a slight inconsistency. In computing cost functions for short-run periods, the normal price relationships for longer periods of time cannnot be expected to exist. This inconsistency, however, is reconcilable. If "normal" price relationships are used, even for short-run cost of production computations, the computer will be assured that his computations will be as near to those existing in actuality as if he had used any single set of short-run price relatives.

Production Relationships between Output and Joint Variable Inputs

In the section of Chapter 9 entitled "Output As It Depends upon Units of Joint Variable Inputs," the overall relationship between joint inputs of variable factors of production (combined according to the scale line) and production was examined. The student should re-examine that section of Chapter 9 at this point. It will be recalled that output can be plotted as a function of the joint variable inputs (combined according to the scale line) as in Figure 12.1.

The production relationships plotted in Figure 12.1 are: (1) total physical productivity, (2) average physical productivity, and (3) mar-

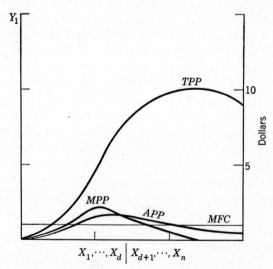

Fig. 12.1. Output of Y_1 as dependent on joint variable inputs of $X_1, \cdots, X_d$ combined in proportions dictated by scale line.

ginal physical productivity. These productivities are the joint result of all the variable inputs used simultaneously (in the combinations dictated by the scale line appropriate for the existing relative prices of the variable inputs).

It is difficult to devise a unit for measuring joint inputs of a number of variable factors of production. One unit, which is usable, is provided by our monetary system. Therefore, *the units of* $X_1, \cdots, X_d$ plotted along the horizontal axis of Figure 12.1 *are one dollar's worth of the variable inputs*. The cost, then, of an additional unit of the variable factors of production is automatically one dollar. This cost is superimposed upon the production relationships plotted in Figure 12.1 as the horizontal line, labeled marginal factor cost, *MFC*, which intersects the right-hand scale at one dollar.

Variable Cost Schedules

Figure 12.1 contains all the information necessary to derive the total variable cost schedule, the marginal variable cost schedule, and the average variable cost schedule. The cost schedules are ordinarily and traditionally plotted on a diagram which has output along the horizontal axis with a dollar scale of costs on the vertical axis. Figure 12.2 is such a diagram, it contains a total variable cost curve, a marginal

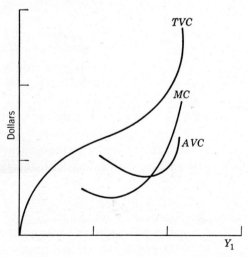

FIG. 12.2. Total variable cost, marginal cost, and average variable cost curves for producing Y in a given length of run. (Total cost curve on different scale.)

cost curve, and an average variable cost curve plotted from the respective cost schedules.

The total variable cost curves plotted in Figure 12.2 are derived from Figure 12.1 as follows. The vertical axis on Figure 12.1 indicates output which is plotted on the horizontal axis of Figure 12.2. Similarly, the horizontal axis of Figure 12.1 gives total variable cost which is plotted against the vertical axis in Figure 12.2.

The average variable cost curve plotted in Figure 12.2 is derived from Figure 12.1 by the following method. Total variable cost, secured as indicated in the above paragraph, is divided by the output of Y. The result is the average variable cost of producing a unit of Y. This is repeated for each output of Y, and the results are plotted in Figure 12.2 above the corresponding output of Y.

The marginal variable cost curve is computed from Figure 12.1 by the following method. Each additional unit of the variable inputs used costs one dollar. Each additional unit of the variable inputs used produces the marginal physical product indicated in Figure 12.1. Thus, the cost of producing an additional unit of Y, at any level of output, is found by dividing the marginal factor cost of one dollar by the marginal physical product of a unit of the variable inputs at that level of output. When this is repeated for each level of output, a schedule of the marginal cost of producing different quantities of Y is produced, which, in turn, can be plotted to yield the marginal cost curve appearing in Figure 12.2.

How to derive total variable, average variable, and marginal cost schedules geometrically has been explained; the schedules are for a given set of relative prices, for a given set of variable inputs, for given production methods, and for a given set and constant quantities of the fixed inputs. The set of cost curves plotted in Figure 12.2 involves variable costs only and can be identified only by specifying the conditions under which it was derived. If the product Y is regarded, for example, to be milk, it should be obvious to the student that there are at least $(\text{infinity})^2 \times 4$ cost curves dealing with the variable factors of production used in producing milk. An infinite number of ways exist in which the fixed factors involved in any firm in any length of run may be combined. There are an infinite number of sets of relative prices for the variable inputs; each set determines a different scale line. And there are four different cost functions involving the variable factors of production. Thus, as stated above, the number of cost curves involving variable inputs which it is possible to derive in the production of milk is infinity × infinity × 4. In making cost of production computations the conditions to which the computations apply should be selected very carefully. The conditions selected should cause the computations to apply to concrete important situations in the real world.

Fixed Cost Schedules

Throughout this chapter, it has been emphasized that a set of cost computations can be identified only in terms of the fixed factors involved, the relative prices of the variable inputs involved, and, to a lesser extent, the price of the product produced. The fixed factors determine the nature of the average fixed cost schedule or curve, the nature of the total fixed cost schedule or curve, and the nature of the total cost schedule or curve which is made up in part of fixed cost items. It is easy to know the quantities of the fixed factors involved;

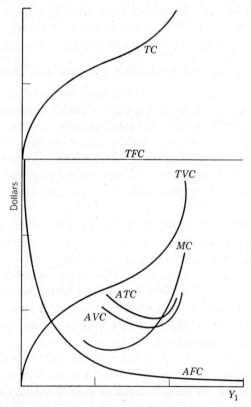

Fig. 12.3. The seven cost concepts presented graphically.

it is, however, almost impossible to price them accurately. Because these factors are fixed in the production of the product under consideration for the time span being studied, market prices are often poor measures of their values (see the discussion of total fixed costs in a later section of this chapter). Within the period in which they are fixed, they are worth an amount determined by their earning power. The price of the product determines the earning power of the fixed inputs. When prices are assigned by some means to the fixed factors, the total fixed cost schedule or curve becomes a constant equal to the sum of the price-quantity products for each factor. If the fixed factor services are priced on the basis of their earning power, total fixed costs are equal to total revenue less total variable costs. Average fixed cost, of course, is equal to total fixed cost divided by the amount of the product produced. The total cost curve for the whole operation is, of course, the sum of the total fixed cost and the total variable cost curves. Average total cost can also be computed by dividing total cost by amount of the product produced. All seven of the cost curves, including the fixed cost curves discussed herein, are plotted in Figure 12.3.

The Seven Cost of Production Concepts and Their Uses

Thus far in this chapter heavy emphasis has been placed upon the division of costs into two major groups, variable costs and fixed costs. Under variable costs are included total variable, average variable, and marginal cost concepts. Under fixed costs are included the concepts of total fixed and average fixed costs. Two hybrid cost concepts involve both fixed and variable costs; these concepts are total and average total costs. This section will discuss the meaning and uses of each of the above seven cost concepts.

Total Variable Costs. The businessman often refers to total variable costs as total out-of-pocket costs. Total variable costs represent the sum total of expenditures on the variable inputs for any level of output. They are short-run costs. The inputs included are those inputs which are variable in the length of run under consideration. Because the manager has control of all the variable inputs, total variable costs must be covered in their entirety in the short run or the manager will not incur the expenditure.

Average Variable Costs. Average variable costs, of course, are total variable costs divided by the amount of the product produced. If a manager is to cover his out-of-pocket or total variable costs, the price which he receives for the product must be at least equal to average variable costs. If the price falls below average variable costs, the enterprise cannot be operated without incurring a loss even on an out-of-pocket basis, not to mention the fixed costs over which the manager has no control. If average variable costs are not covered nothing will be returned to the fixed assets.

Marginal Costs. In terms of business decisions, the marginal cost concept is the most important of all the concepts considered herein. Marginal costs deal only with variable costs; no fixed costs enter into marginal costs. Marginal cost is the cost of producing an additional unit of output at a given level of output. The marginal cost schedule is the series of marginal costs for the entire range of outputs. In any given length of run a manager is willing to produce additional units of product as long as the units produced bring in enough to pay for (1) the additional costs involved in producing the additional units and (2) average variable costs. Marginal cost is the additional cost involved in producing additional units. Fixed costs are not included in marginal costs because they are fixed and hence are neither increased nor decreased by additional production. When farm economists speak about necessary costs they are talking about marginal costs. Necessary or marginal costs are the costs, in a given length of run, which must be covered in order to get a given level of output. The inputs included in figuring marginal or necessary costs are determined by the length of run under consideration. The necessary costs for producing dairy cows in a one-year planning span need not cover the costs of providing buildings and other fixed equipment. In the five- or ten-year planning span, however, necessary and marginal costs include the cost of all items which a farmer can take control of in such a planning span. Marginal costs, as can be seen from Figure 12.3, can exceed average total costs even though no fixed costs are included in marginal costs.

Total Fixed Costs. Total fixed costs are meaningful only in the length of run which fixes the components of such costs. In a given length of run the components or inputs making up total fixed costs are committed to the production of the product under consideration. These items remain fixed (1) as long as they are not worth their replacement cost in their present use and (2) as long as they are worth more in this use than in the next highest alternative; in fact, this is a fair definition of a fixed input. The services of such inputs are worth, in their fixed position, exactly what they will produce. The historical cost of these items is unimportant in the particular length of run under consideration. If the income produced by the fixed inputs is greater than would have been anticipated from their historical costs, the fixed items are worth more than their cost, historically. The reverse is true if what they produce now does not justify the historical cost. The difficulties involved in handling fixed cost items do not arise within any given length of run. Instead the difficulties arise when confusion exists concerning the length of run for which fixed cost data are being made.

Average Fixed Costs. Average fixed cost, as a concept, is subject to all limitations of total fixed costs as a concept. This follows because average fixed cost is nothing more or less than total fixed costs divided by output.

Total Cost. Total cost is a hybrid concept in a sense that it is the sum of total fixed and total variable costs. The difference between total revenue and total cost is, of course, profits as defined by accountants and many economists. The main use of the total cost concept is that of figuring net profits. As a concept, total cost is subject to all the limitations of its components. Total fixed cost is the component cost subject to the greatest number of and most important limitations.

Average Total Cost. Average total costs are total costs divided by output and, as such, are subject to all the limitations of the total cost concept. The statement is often made that, in the long run, average total costs must be covered but that in the short run only average variable costs must be covered. The truth is that the only costs which need to be covered in any length of run are average variable costs. In the ultimate long run, all costs become variable costs and thus fixed costs become unimportant because they cease to exist. In the ultimate long run, average variable costs are not necessarily the sum of average variable costs and average fixed costs in any of the shorter lengths of run. Hence, average total costs for the shorter lengths of run are not of great conceptual importance.

APPENDIX TO CHAPTER 12

Complications in Cost of Production Computations

DUE TO COMPLEMENTARITY AND SUBSTITUTABILITY AMONG INPUTS

Discussion of the complications introduced into cost of production computations by complementarity and substitutability among inputs logically falls into three parts. The first part deals with such relationships among variable inputs, the second with such relationships among fixed inputs, and the third with such relationships among both fixed and variable inputs. The discussion will be confined, for the sake of simplicity, to the case of two inputs. It should be recalled, from Chapter 10, that perfect substitutes are really the same input for purposes of producing the product under consideration and that perfect complements are really one input made up of two component inputs combined in constant proportions.

When *two inputs* which are *good substitutes* are both variable, the concepts presented above are perfectly valid as a basis for computation. A difficulty, however, arises as a result of price instability. Small changes in relative prices cause great changes in the relative amounts of the two inputs used; these changes upset the physical components of costs. However, such changes in the physical makeup of costs have little effect on the totality of costs. When *two inputs* which are *good complements* are both variable, the concepts presented above are also valid. As the degree of complementarity becomes increasingly greater it becomes increasingly difficult to determine the separate productivities of the inputs. The saving consideration is that as complementarity increases it becomes increasingly unnecessary to differentiate the separate productivities—the two inputs become one input and can be easily treated as such in cost computations.

When two inputs which are good substitutes are both fixed, the validity of the above cost concepts is not affected. Fixed cost concepts are never precise at any rate. The quantities fixed in the production of the product must be charged to the product. The price to be used in charging these inputs is determined by the price of the product as long as the inputs are fixed, as the fixed inputs are not varied as long as what they are worth does not exceed what it costs to get more of them or fall below what could be realized from them if they were sold or used elsewhere. This argument with respect to fixed pairs of substitute inputs applies equally well to fixed pairs of complementary inputs.

Similarly, the complications which arise when one of two substitutes or one of two complements are fixed and the other is variable are unimportant. In such cases, substitutability causes returns to be more sustained while complementarity causes the law of diminishing returns to operate more abruptly. Apparently, no new computational problems arise with respect to substitutability and complementarity which cannot be handled with the concepts presented earlier in this chapter. Apparently, most of the difficulties attributed to complementarity and substitutability result from confusion concerning the length of run to which a given set of cost computations apply. If one of two complementary inputs is first considered fixed and then considered variable, little sense can be made of the resultant cost figures. The same is true concerning complements. In fixed positions, the total value of *all* fixed inputs is determined by the price of what they produce. In variable positions, the value of a *single* input is determined by its market price or its earning power in alternative uses. Confusion as to whether an input is fixed or variable results in dangerous inconsistencies which make it virtually impossible to make cost computations, let alone handle complicated interactions among inputs.

Due to Complementarity and Competitiveness among Products

It should be recalled from Chapter 11 that two perfectly complementary products are really *one product* made up of two component products produced in fixed proportions. Complementarity, it was noted in that chapter, results primarily from (1) the nature of the production process and of the inputs fixed in the production of the two products, (2) the possibility of utilizing by-products from the production of one product as inputs in the production of the other product, and (3) the possibility of using inputs fixed for the business as a whole more fully by producing more than one product.

Competitiveness and complementarity among products arising from the nature of the production process and fixed factors does not appear to present problems which the above cost of production concepts cannot handle.

Complementarity arising from by-products in the production of one product which are useful in the production of the other creates several important problems. First, if the one product and its by-product are produced in fixed proportions, they are perfect complements and, hence, are really a single product. Because of this, an increase in the price or value of the product decreases the cost of producing the by-product and vice versa. The value of the by-product depends in part on its marginal value product in producing a second main product. If two products are complementary because production of one results in a by-product useful in producing the second, two things must be done. First, the value of the by-product must be credited to the process producing the first product. Second, the by-product must be charged to the second product.

Before this can be done, the by-product must be valued. The value of the by-product depends, in part, on the cost of producing it within the firm. If the by- and main-products are complements the above discussion applies in computing their costs. Once the marginal cost of producing the by-product is known, its value is determined between limits by its marginal value product in the production of the second main product. The limits are (1) the sales value of the by-product and (2) the cost of buying more of the by-product. As many by-products are coarse, bulky, low-value items, these limits tend to be far apart. Hence by-products tend to be used within the firm and except in the extreme cases should be priced at their *MVP* in producing the second product. To price by-products at sales price (except when some of the by-product is being sold) would underestimate costs. To price at purchase price (except when some of the by-product is being purchased) would overestimate costs.

Supplementarity arising from using inputs (fixed for the business as a whole) more fully by producing additional products creates some difficulties. These difficulties, however, tend to be less troublesome when subjected to rigorous conceptual examination. Definite production functions exist for each product; each of these functions regard the input fixed for the business as variable. Definite scale lines exist on each of these production functions. The problem is that of distributing the input (fixed for the business as a whole) between the production of each product in such a way that it returns marginal value products having equal values in both enterprises. As for all fixed inputs, the pricing problem cannot be satisfactorily handled except when the prices of the products are known. In this case, the price of the factor for any level of input in the production of one product is the value of its marginal product in the production of the other product. The value of the marginal products depends on (1) the prices of the two products and (2) the amount of the input used, which, in turn, determines the size of the marginal *physical* product of the input. The solution is complicated but the problem can be solved. Again, it should be stressed that the solutions make conceptual sense only for specific lengths of run and for specific quantities of the inputs necessarily fixed in these lengths of run.

PROBLEM EXERCISE 8

Costs and Cost Curves

The student is to compute the data required to fill in the blanks in the eight vacant columns below. Following this, he is to use the data to plot graphs similar to Figures 12.1 and 12.3.

(1) Batches of Variable Inputs	(2) Fixed Inputs	(3) Marginal Factor Cost	(4) Total Product	(5) Marginal Physical Product	(6) Average Physical Product	(7) Total Variable Costs	(8) Total Fixed Cost	(9) Total Cost	(10) Average Variable Cost	(11) Average Fixed Cost	(12) Average Total Cost	(13) Marginal Cost
0	20	$ 0	0	—	—	$—	$20	$—	$—	$—	$—	$—
1	20	10	3	—	—	—	20	—	—	—	—	—
2	20	10	7	—	—	—	20	—	—	—	—	—
3	20	10	12	—	—	—	20	—	—	—	—	—
4	20	10	19	—	—	—	20	—	—	—	—	—
5	20	10	27	—	—	—	20	—	—	—	—	—
6	20	10	34	—	—	—	20	—	—	—	—	—
7	20	10	40	—	—	—	20	—	—	—	—	—
8	20	10	45	—	—	—	20	—	—	—	—	—
9	20	10	48	—	—	—	20	—	—	—	—	—
10	20	10	50	—	—	—	20	—	—	—	—	—
11	20	10	51	—	—	—	20	—	—	—	—	—
12	20	10	51	—	—	—	20	—	—	—	—	—

CHAPTER 13

Fitting Crops into a Crops Program

Introductory Statement

At the beginning of Chapter 8, dealing with the need for economizing principles in developing crop and livestock systems, an introductory statement demonstrated the need for such principles in selecting and adjusting crop and livestock systems. Chapters 8 through 12 were devoted to the exposition of these principles. As we now return to the actual selection of crops, the student may find it profitable to reread the introductory statement for Chapter 8.

Selecting Specific Crops

The specific crops that will contribute most to the individual family farm business in the long run are those that:

1. Use labor resources of operator's family efficiently when such labor is equipped with economic quantities of machines and other capital.

2. Complement one another in the use of land, equipment, and all labor used to the point of maximizing total returns and equating returns at the margin.

3. Provide an economic basis for the maintenance or increase of soil productivity.

4. Are in market demand as such, or economically form the basis of abundant, palatable, nutritious rations for livestock.

In the choice of specific crops each farmer has some latitude within each class of crops. Within the row-crop or intertilled class are the highly intensive cash crops (much labor in relation to land) as: celery, tobacco, potatoes, truck, strawberries, peanuts, cotton, beets, beans, and tree fruits.

Other intertilled crops of less labor intensity are: corn, soybeans, and sorghum.

Within the small-grain classification are: wheat, barley, rye, rice, and oats.

Within the sod-crop division are: hay and pasture. Even hays and pastures can be made more intensive, or extensive, through selection from a wide variety of plants, each having their own particular advantages and disadvantages, such as alfalfa or lespedeza, and through production practices.

It is a singular, yet pronounced, practice that farmers in the harvested-crops-producing section of the United States have sought to find at least one crop that can be marketed directly for cash.[1]

Points of View on Rotations

Each unit of land should be made to earn an income through production of harvested crops, improved pasture, or timber each year. The unit may be farmed with a crop rotation, or be used continuously for one crop.

Rotations, both long and short, have many things to recommend them and have had many recommendations. They have limitations as well—some very serious, particularly on small farming units. Rotations have generally followed a pattern. Perhaps the most widely used pattern is composed of:

> 1st year—a plow-land crop (intertilled—row).
> 2nd year—a small grain.
> 3rd year—a hay crop.
> 4th year—a pasture.

Modifications are, of course, very numerous.

1. The plow crop may be used more than one year.
2. The hay crop may be used one to several years.
3. On the more level lands pasture is frequently omitted.
4. On the steeper lands pasture is used for two to several years.

The pattern, however, is that land is plowed for row crops, row crops are followed by small grains, and small grains by sods. The reasons are clear.

---

[1] Some of the livestock areas of the midwest and some of the dairying areas of the northeast are important exceptions.

1. Such a sequence conserves labor and machinery, as the small grain is planted without replowing.

2. Sod crops are seeded in the growing small grain—with little or no additional land preparation—the small grain crop acting as a "nurse" as well as a "robber" crop.

3. Such a sequence distributes labor and balances production.

4. Such a sequence "mines" the soil less rapidly, but, more importantly, produces and utilizes the by-products (nitrogen, humus, soil structure, etc.).

5. Such a sequence provides both summer and winter feeds.

Rotations of crops have particular advantages from a labor point of view on commercial family farms if the scope of the individual crop enterprise is large enough to produce it with at least a fair degree of efficiency in the use of machinery and labor. The crops may have complementary advantages, also.

A Rotation Should Contribute to Efficiency in the Use of Labor Resources. Within an area, class of crops—row, small-grain, sod, tree-fruits—largely depends on classes of land and prices, with land generally the more important. The use of individual crops within the class depends on prices, on quantity of land (and labor) available to the operator, or on a high degree of adaptation to such specialized cash crops as cotton, vegetables, cranberries, fruit crops, potatoes, or tobacco. Operators of "small" farms—who have a choice—use their lands for more intensive cropping than those having "large" ones. Farmers of the Appalachian Mountains region serve as excellent illustrations. Even though the land is not well suited, they grow corn on hillsides frequently as steep as 65 percent slope. Farmers who have an opportunity to produce highly intensive cash crops are in a very fortunate position, particularly if they operate small farms.

One of the objectives of good management is the full economic use of all the physical agents of production or units of these agents. Often, the farmer's own labor is the most important of these factors to the individual farmer on a family farm because:

1. It may be a fixed factor in "his" business.

2. It is often the principal physical resource of farm families.

One of the objectives of the crops program, therefore, is to provide appreciable quantities of productive work, at acceptable rates of return for at least the members of the operator's family on family-financed farming units. Corn offers more employment than wheat per acre; row crops than sod crops; hay than pasture; tobacco, potatoes, strawberries, peas, beans, and cotton than corn; alfalfa than red clover, etc. The most intensive crop in an area is likely to be the cash crop if there is one, and if the intensity is greater than that of corn the crop will most likely be sold for cash. These will generally be found in areas of specialized farming.

Intensity of crops have historically been measured by the days or hours required on the average by a number of farmers within an area to produce and harvest an acre of them. The labor requirements of crops per acre have been undergoing significant reductions since the advent of power machines—especially the row-crop tractor, the all-purpose combine, the pick-up baler, and the cotton picker. Reductions have made possible the handling of larger acreages and thus larger farming units.

These changes in labor requirements, plus the wide variations in efficiencies and in practices from area to area, make any list of labor requirements on crops inaccurate for wide use. The following list is given, therefore, to present a technique for making general comparisons between crops, and for weighing, estimating, or making first approximations of labor requirements per farm or per man. Each instructor should provide a list or lists for the areas represented by his students, and should discuss additional costs vs. additional returns for changes in the amount of labor used.

Table 13.1. Comparisons of Labor Requirements per Acre of Crops

Crops	Approximate Days per Acre
Apples	3 to 15
Corn (tractor)	
cut, shocked, stored	3 to 7
picked, stored	0.7 to 1.2
Celery	30 to 45
Cotton	6 to 12
Hay (one cutting)	0.3 to 1
Potatoes	6 to 10
Small grain	0.6 to 1
Strawberries	12 to 30
Tobacco	
Burley	20 to 40
dark fired	20 to 30
flue cured	30 to 40
Pasture	0.5

Crops in a Rotation Should Supplement One Another. In multiple crop systems, the various individual crops in the cropping system are near optimum adjustment when labor and equipment can be:

1. "Comfortably" employed at all seasons.
2. Used to earn returns equal to cost at the margin in all uses.

Crops which will accomplish the first tend to be supplementary; those requiring resources at the same time tend to be competitive. Corn, small grains and hay tend to supplement each other with respect to the use of labor and other resources as seeding the hay crop in or with small grain is followed by:

Plowing for corn.
Preparation of land and planting corn.
Cultivation of corn.
Harvest of hay or small grain (depending upon the variety of hay and the kind of small grain).
Harvesting corn.
Seeding small grain (if fall seeding is practiced).

Supplementarity may be increased through use of varieties, time of planting, and methods of handling. For example, corn intended for the silo may be planted later or earlier, alfalfa hay may be cut two or three or four times (depending upon the area), thus shifting harvest dates. Large acreages of single crops may be planted with varieties that vary in the number of days required for maturity.

Not all the labor resources, however, need to be absorbed by crops. Livestock can be used with the same type of advantage as additional crops. Provisions for developing the livestock program will be discussed later, but it is not amiss at this time to point out some of the common devices used by farmers to provide full employment.

1. As crops require most attention in the summer, livestock may be used for winter employment.
2. Within a day, dairy cows and other types of livestock may be cared for in the early morning and evening hours, whereas crops are cared for in the late morning and afternoon hours.

Rotation Provides a Basis for Increasing Soil Productivity. Soil productivity is increased or maintained through:

1. Avoiding excessive erosion.
2. Increasing organic matter and nitrogen content.
3. Replenishing or increasing minerals.
4. Maintaining pH balance.
5. Water control.

Erosion control on rolling land is largely a matter of sod-crop cover and mechanical practices for row crops. Fitting good rotations to land capability Classes II and III together with contour cultivation, strip cropping, and terracing as needed will usually avoid excessive erosion. Building up productivity through fertilizing, liming, and use of adapted plants also helps to avoid erosion. Productive land erodes less than poor land. "To him that hath shall be given, and to him that hath not shall be taken away" applies forcibly to land as well as to people. An old adage runs:

> More crops—more cattle.
> More cattle—more manure.
> More manure—more crops.

This can be extended to include: More crops—more organic matter— more cover, easier-to-get covers of sod crops—less rain splashing—less run-off—less erosion; more moisture retention, less leaching, better drainage, less sunburning, faster germination of seed; thus, more winter cover with small grains, etc.

The kernels of soil-productivity programs on farms used for harvested crops and rotation pasture are roughly:

1. Two tons of ground limestone for humid areas once about each 10 years.

2. The addition of 20 pounds of P_2O_5 per acre per year to maintain phosphorus on soils of a productivity equivalent to 50 bushels of corn or more per acre. Increase this amount on poorer soils until a good level is attained. Any system of farming removes phosphorus from the land. About three-fourths of the removal is regained in the manure when the crops are fed. More phosphorus is removed than will be supplied by 20 pounds of P_2O_5 per acre per year if good crops are produced and sold directly.

3. The returns of manure produced which should equal at least 2 tons per tillable acre per year. (A part may be dropped on pasture.)

4. The use of legumes or commercial nitrogen to help maintain the nitrogen content.

5. Cover crops on sloping land, for erosion control and green-manure production, on every class of land where such can be squeezed in.

6. Potash when available supply is low.

About one-third of the organic matter of feed fed to livestock is regained in the manure. One ton of dry matter, therefore, in crops plowed under is equal to the organic matter in 3 tons of the same crop if fed. Manure is about 80 percent water. Thus a ton of dry matter in a crop is worth 5 tons of manure. A full growth òf sweet cloveŗ may equal an application of 25 tons of manure per acre, with no labor and machinery costs involved in application.

Organic matter is valuable to soils. It functions through: supplying and releasing nitrogen, aiding tilth, holding water, checking erosion, providing plant food, and other ways. It is lost through: oxidation—which is accelerated through row cropping—erosion, careless handling.

The older civilizations have learned the value of organic matter the hard way. They resort to painful extremes in modern days to preserve it, following such practices as collecting the "night soil" from the people in cities. Nature doubtless required thousands of years to stock the virgin soil with organic matter. Consider the following approximations:

1 acre, 7 inches of soil = 2,000,000 pounds.

Highly productive soils (5 percent humus) = 100,000 pounds humus.

100,000 pounds humus = 200,000 pounds raw OM per acre in such soil.

1 ton manure = 400 pounds dry OM.

200,000 pounds dry OM = 1,000,000 pounds manure.

1,000,000 pounds manure = 500 tons.

Five hundred tons of manure to enrich an acre of soil! When one does a fairly good job of crop and livestock farming he produces about 2 tons per acre per year; therefore, the addition of 500 tons would require 250 years—plus the losses en route to the addition. Fortunately, good yields can be produced on soils of less than 5 percent humus.

These figures can be questioned for accuracy. If they are a half or a fourth or even a tenth true they point to a sobering conclusion.

The writer put 2 tons of stable manure on a garden of 1,500 square feet (about 0.03 of an acre) each year for 13 years before he was able to change a spot of yellow, sticky clay to a friable clay, and the soil was of 60-bushel corn productivity at the beginning. This application was equal to about 765 tons per acre in 13 years, or at the rate of 60 tons per acre per year.

Generally farmers apply enormous applications of manure to their gardens annually and know that productivity is but slowly increased under continuous cultivation. A program for increasing or maintaining organic matter is mandatory for most soils.

Crops should be fertilized in addition to the above with nitrogen, phosphorus, potash, and the trace elements according to:

A. Productivity level and need.
B. Prices of the products.
C. Costs of the materials.
D. Other demands for the money needed on the basis of returns per dollar spent.

Inventorying the land and the soils of a farm, the characteristics of plants, the economy of crops, and rotation of crops is accompanied by setting up a specific cropping system.

A Simplified Crops Program

Determination of cropping systems is easy for some farms, such as overflow river bottoms, because:

1. Erosion is not a problem.
2. Only annual plow crops can be grown because of overflow.

Many such farms are found along the Ohio, Missouri, and Mississippi rivers. The problems of farming such lands are numerous, but the problem of deciding what crops to grow is a simple one as the conditions imposed by nature effectively narrow the choices.

In other areas, such as on many of the farms of the Great Plains, the lack of moisture restricts the economic use of land to grazing livestock. Solutions for both of these areas arise out of situations causing all the acreage of the farm to be classed in one land class, because of conditions outside the control of the individual farmer. If one has a farm of winter overflow land it is usually put to corn, soybeans, or cotton year after year.

A 320-acre, level-land farm which does not overflow and which is made up of good or excellent grades of land has little or no erosion problems. Assuming the land to be well drained either naturally or artificially, a number of crops could be grown. Prices of the various crops, yields, complementary and competitive influences among crops would demand consideration in developing a cropping system or deciding upon what crops to grow.

Let us assume, for the sake of simplicity, at this point in the learning process, that the farm is to be operated by a renter and that a livestock program is not deemed desirable. The crops to be grown will be determined by a desire to secure the largest net income for the year's work, with some consideration for retaining a part of the fertility. If 8 acres are reserved for the farmstead and an additional 7 acres counted as wasteland for boundaries and turning rows, there would be 305 acres available for crops. What crops would return the highest net income? For additional simplicity, let us assume that the choices must be made from among corn, wheat, oats, soybeans, grass and legume hay, and grass and legume pasture. All these crops are complementary or supplementary over a range, and all are competitive over a range. Over the competitive range they all compete for use of land; corn and soybeans compete for use of machinery and labor in the spring and fall, the small grains compete with the grasses and legumes for moisture and plant food in late spring and early summer.

Over the ranges of complementarity and supplementarity, the different crops use some of the labor and machinery resources at different times; the legumes and grasses complement the grains with fertility, humus, and soil tilth, and restrict disease and insect troubles.

On the gross-income side we may expect corn to rank highest, followed by soybeans, wheat, oats, hay, and pasture. A renter (and owner), having no provisions for livestock, would have no opportunity to secure gain from pasturage. If the largest gross income per acre can be obtained from corn, why not put all the land in corn? The discussion of enterprise combinations in previous chapters shows that to follow such a course a given outlay on resources would produce less—by-products would not be produced and used—than if divided. Soybeans are the next highest producer of income, both from the gross and net points of view. Soybeans demand labor and equipment somewhat later than corn for planting and are less extractive of plant nutrients. Corn-belt farmers have experienced, and Experiment Station data has proved, that some acreage should be devoted to legumes other than soybeans. Perhaps 25 percent of the cropland is best used for green manure or such hay crops as red clover, alfalfa, or combinations of these with some grass. Labor distribution further indicates the wisdom of such a cropping system. The 320-acre farm is large enough to use efficiently hay-producing machinery if 25 percent of the land is devoted to hay. Thus our first approximation to a cropping system for this farm would be 150 to 160 acres in corn, 75 to 80 acres in soybeans, and 75 to 80 acres in wheat (or oats) and clover. Corn and soybeans, and also wheat and oats, offer opportunities for partial or complete substitution as weather demands.

Crops Program for Farms with Level and Rolling Lands
THE CLASS CASE FARM

Let us now project our attention to a farm having more complex problems in developing a cropping system because of the rolling topography of a portion of the land. A 335-acre farm described in Chapter 7 is used for this illustration.

There are:

    120 acres Classes I and II land.
    110 acres Class III land.
    100 acres Class IV land.
      5 acres roads, farmstead, etc.

Figure 7.2, on p. 107, portrays a 335-acre farm of three land-use classes (Class IV, pasture). The unshaded portions of the map are portrayals of Classes I and II lands (green and yellow if colored), the cross-hatched portions portray Class IV lands (blue if colored), and the dotted portions of the map Class III lands (red if colored).

The Classes I and II lands are located on the farm so that the three fields of 40 acres each can be permanently fenced to separate them from neighboring farms and from other fields to be used for grazing on this farm. The Class I units, "green" land, can be used somewhat more intensively than the Class II units or "yellow" land, and, thus, a rotation of (1) corn (rye cover), (2) corn, and (3) wheat (sweet clover, Korean lespedeza with a grass or grain) may be tentatively considered. Corn being an intensive crop uses the variable inputs to high capacity; thus, two years of the three are used for it. Within the same three fields are Class II lands which should be less intensively cropped than the Class I land but which need not be separately fenced, as temporary fence can be used. Terraces are used between the Classes

I and II units to catch run-off from the higher land, particularly when the higher land is in wheat and the surrounding lower land is in row crops. The main enterprise of the farm is tobacco, which has the choice of all land, because of price and its capacity to use variable factors intensively. It will be grown on the Class II land because:

1. Tobacco requires rapid drainage of water through the soil for high quality.
2. The level Class I land is deeper and more retentive of moisture in August, when less moisture is desired for tobacco than for corn.

The Class II land rotation, therefore, is tentatively set as: tobacco, followed the second year by barley and the third year by red clover. Tobacco is harvested early (usually in August) in ample time for seeding winter barley.

The Class III or "red" land has been delineated in four areas of gentle slopes on the farm and may be used for either a 4- or 5-year rotation, or longer, according to relation of prices and needs. The rotation temporarily selected and illustrated is for 5 years as follows:

1. Barley seeded in late August or early September (wheat or spring oats could be substituted) is preferable as a feed. It is seeded to advantage earlier as a cover crop. (Mixed hay with alfalfa as the base seeded in the spring.)
2. Mixed hay (largely alfalfa).
3. Pasture.
4. Pasture.
5. Pasture.

The hay and pasture mixture could consist of 10 pounds alfalfa, 3 pounds fescue, 2 pounds timothy. This mixture has several economic advantages, (1) it produces its own nitrogen, (2) the fescue produces forage in the late fall and early spring, (3) the alfalfa is a heavy producer in the spring, summer, and fall months. The forage is to be cut for hay or silage the first year (two cuttings taken off in "dry" summers and three in average ones), and used for pasture the second year.

The steeper Class IV units of land, "blue" land, are used as permanent pasture, and are reseeded only as needed. The pasture mixture consists of Kentucky bluegrass, ladino clover, trefoil, and Korean lespedeza. Here again the pasture plants complement one another, and, in addition, the lespedeza furnishes insurance against dry late summer weather.

Table 13.2 shows how the three rotations and permanent pasture combine to form a tentative cropping system for this farm. Table 13.3 is a cross section of the cropping system, showing the budgeted 1952 land uses, production, gross product values, and direct sales.

Table 13.2. Illustration of Rotations and Cropping System for a 335-Acre Farm of Level and Rolling Upland

Land and Crops	Slope Percent	Acres	1951	1952	1953	1954
Class I II						
Field						
9–I	0–3	23	Wheat (g.m.)	Corn (rye)	Corn (W)	
9–II	4–6	17	Barley	Clover	Tobacco	
3–I	0–3	23	Corn (W)	Wheat (g.m.)	Corn (rye)	
3–II	4–6	17	Tobacco (B)	Barley	Clover	
4–I	0–3	23	Corn (rye)	Corn (W)	Wheat (g.m.)	
4–II	4–6	17	Clover	Tobacco (B)		
Class III						
Field						
1a	7–9	20	Barley	M. hay	Pasture	Pasture
1b	7–10	20	M. hay	Pasture	Pasture	Pasture
6	7–9	20	Pasture	Pasture	Pasture	Barley
8	7–9	25	Pasture	Pasture	Barley	M. hay
10	7–9	25	Pasture	Barley	M. hay	Pasture
Class IV						
Field						
2	10–15	75	Permanent pasture			
7	10–15	10	Permanent pasture			
5	10–15	15	Permanent pasture			

QUESTIONS AND PROBLEMS

1. Messers. Nevens, Touchberry, and Prescott [1] of the Dairy Department of the University of Illinois expressed the opinion that corn belt land produces as much gross cash income when the land is put to pasture as when put to corn. Measured in terms of value of milk produced, each acre of pasture was said by them to be worth about $169 (1948). These returns were compared to the value of 75 bushels of corn. Do you find any basis for disagreeing with their opinions as stated?

[1] W. B. Nevens, R. W. Touchberry, and J. A. Prescott, Jr., "How Much Is Pasture Worth?" *Hoard's Dairyman,* October 25, 1949.

Table 13.3. An Illustration of a Crops Production Budget for the 335-Acre Farm for the Year 1952

	Crop	Acres	Yield	Prod.	$GPV [1]	Sales	Remarks
Class I							
Field							
9–I	Corn	23	80	1,840	3,220	xx	Seeded in fall to rye cover
4–I	Corn	23	80	1,840	3,220	xx	Seeded in fall to wheat
3–I	Wheat	23	26	589	1,316	1,205	75 bu. for seed. Seeded to S. Clo. and Korean. Turned under next year as green manure
Class II							
Field							
4–II	Tobacco	17	1,800	30,600	15,300	15,300	Seeded to barley
3–II	Barley	17	30	510	586	xx	Seeded to clover
9–II	Clover	17	2	34	850	xx	Cut for hay—2nd crop green manure
Class III							
Field							
Ia	M. hay	20	2.5	50	1,250	xx	
Ib	R. past.	20	1	20	500	xx	
6	R. past.	20	1	20	500	xx	
8	R. past.	25	0.6	15	375	xx	
10	Barley	25	30	750	862	xx	
Class IV							
Field							
2	P. past.	75	0.5	37.5	938	xx	Bluegrass, Korean
7	P. past.	10	0.5	5	125	xx	ladino, fescue, and
5	P. past.	15	0.5	7.5	188	xx	trefoil
Lots, Roads, and Waste		5	xx	xx	xx		
Totals		335	xx	xx	29,230	16,505	

[1] 1950 prices.
Estimated production would total:

Corn, 3,680 bushels.	Clover hay, 34 tons.
Corn stalks, 46 acres.	Alfalfa, mixed hay, 50 tons.
Barley, 1,260 bushels, straw 42 tons.	Pasturage, 105 season units.

2. What is the relative importance nationally of specialized high-acre-value crops, including fruit, vegetable, tobacco, and sugar crops, measured in terms of land use, labor use, and value of product?

3. What innovations have taken place which give rise to emphasis on pasture crops?

4. Crops have traditionally been classed as intensive (or extensive) on the basis of units of labor requirement per acre. Why? Name some capital intensive crops. Why is there a shifting toward capital intensity on all crops (1940–1953)?

5. Crops have been classified by the U. S. Department of Agriculture, Production and Marketing Administration, into soil-improving and soil-depleting classes. What are the conditions which must be met if a crop is actually soil improving?

PROBLEM EXERCISE 9

Cropping Systems

Develop a cropping system for a selected farm (preferably the farm used in Problem Exercise 6 and Problem Exercise 7) based upon the land capability classes found on the farm. Write a description of the system setting forth both the strong points and its overall limitations in providing for use of other resources and by-products. What are its implications as to (1) type of feed, (2) livestock program, (3) labor utilization, (4) farm layout?

The purpose of this assignment is to provide training in developing plans for efficient use of the land resources of farms, plus contributions to maximizing returns on all resources. This training is given through the making of a plan for the use of the land on a specific farm (individual case farm). The assignment begins with a consideration of the land-use capability classes which were delineated in Problem Exercise 7 (the land-use map). The end objective is to have a good plan for the use of all the land on the home farm. It will include the making of decisions on the best use of each land class, considering the economizing principles given in Chapters 8 to 11. It will reflect these uses in terms of the cropping system made up of continuous cultivation, rotations, permanent pasture, woods, and/or other uses.

The student will need to have fortified himself with a knowledge of the biological characteristics of the plants used on farms in his area, a knowledge of the sequences of the types of crops usually grown (intertilled, small-grain, hay, pasture), a knowledge of formulating crop rotations, and a knowledge of the relative contributions of the various types of crops.

Procedure.

1. Think through the best use that can be made of each class of land. Decide if there is a sufficient relative amount of land in each class to justify separate handling. Note: There may be small patches of land of one class surrounded by land of another class and yet which are so small that they do not justify being handled as a separate unit.

2. Think through an arrangement of fields for the land-use units and for the farm as a whole which will permit making the best use of different classes of land and which will at the same time compromise irregularities in the boundaries of the land classes, small patches of land and other considerations, such as accessibility to the fields from the farmstead, length, width, and size of fields, etc.

3. Write a description of the way you think it would be most profitable to use each class of land.

4. Work out the specific rotations contemplated for each class (and units) of land on sheets of paper. Put the numbers of the fields on the left side of the sheets and the successive calendar years along the tops. Fill in the cross spaces. The vertical columns will show the contemplated use of the land for the farm as a whole for any single calendar year, and any horizontal column will show the contemplated use of each particular field for a series of years. The sequence of names of the crops will indicate the rotations (or other land use) in either direction, for example:

	1950	*1951*	*1952*	*1953*
Field 16	Corn	Rye	Hay	Pasture
12	Rye	Hay	Pasture	Corn
13	Hay	Pasture	Corn	Rye
9	Pasture	Corn	Rye	Hay

5. You are now ready to make Form I for the proposed reorganized land-management plan. This sheet is designed to show the crops program for one year only. Select a year sufficiently advanced to allow for a completion of your proposed crop system. This may require selecting some year as much as 3 to 10 years in advance. The vertical column headed *Crops* on Form I will correspond to the vertical columns on the sheets just completed. If there is land to be used by a crop in continuous cultivation, put the name of this crop on the first blank line. This will likely be on Class I land. List next the names of those crops on Class II and/or III land, etc. *Be sure to list the crops in the order in which they will be grown in the rotation.* For example, a 3-year rotation of corn-rye-clover will have the names listed in that order on Form I. If cover crops are to be used the name of the cover crop will be enclosed in parentheses and written in immediately under the name of the crop. For example, if you expect to have corn in continuous culture and to use a rye and vetch cover and/or green manure crop you will write in the same space, where the name of the corn crop is written, rye and vetch in parentheses as: Corn (rye and vetch). Complete columns 1, 2, 3, and 4 of Form I with data on the other types of land such as permanent pasture, farmstead, woods, etc., and total the acreage in the *Acres column.* This figure should correspond to the total acres of the farm.

6. Assign yields to various crops which may be reasonably expected under good land-management practices. Determine the total production. From the prices developed figure the gross production value for each crop and determine the totals for all crops on the farm. Express yields of pasture in terms of units of pasturage produced, and assign a value to each pasture unit equal to the value of a ton of hay. A unit of pasturage is that amount which will adequately feed an animal unit of livestock, such as a cow, throughout the pasture season which is usually 4 to 9 months. For those crops, or parts of crops, which are to be sold as such indicate the value of the sales in the sales column and total the figures in the sales column.

7. Write a description of the land-management plan including:

a. The county in which the farm is located, its distance from some town, the road or highway on which it is situated, the name by which the farm goes in the community, etc.

b. A description of the land of the farm including fertility, topography, past use, past treatment, conditions, etc.

c. A description of how you expect to use the land in each class, the land of the farm as a whole, and the reasons for your decisions.

Submit this complete description (item 7 above) together with a copy of Form I and such other materials (maybe a map, pictures, etc.) as are needed to fully explain your plan for handling the land on this farm.

Form I

In connection with the cropping system developed in this exercise, calculate the expected production of crops, the values, and the labor requirements for the crops selected.   Record your findings in a table as follows:

Proposed Production—Values and Sales

	Crop	Acres	Yield	Production	Value	Sales
Classes of Land						
	Totals		x x	x x		

CHAPTER 14

The Use of Livestock

What are the functions of livestock on generalized farms? What is meant by livestock farming? What are the differences in fixed resources on specialized dairy farms, hog farms, poultry farms, and beef cattle farms? Is there a difference between profitable livestock farming and profitable livestock enterprises?

Though harvested crops and pasturage are the primary products of farm production, livestock are the factories on feed-producing lands. They take the bulk of our crops, consisting of grains and forage, and convert them into food. Corn, grain sorghums, barley, oats, some wheat, and forage are processed by living animals into human food— T-bone steaks, leg of lamb, ham and bacon, golden butter, nutritious milk, breast of turkey, just to mention a few of the staple livestock products. Man can live on crops alone, but he cannot live well. Both kings of beasts and kings of men are meat eaters. Livestock are converters similar in one respect to steel mills or textile mills. They convert plants that the human stomach was not made to handle well into foods both easy to digest and delightful to man's taste. Without livestock there would be little need for some three-fourths of the nation's crops. Livestock gather grass from the western plains, glean the mountain sides and valleys, empty corn belt cribs, and grind the forage of New England meadows. They use to advantage millions of tons of factory products and by-products. For full measure they reconvert our table scraps.

Why Farmers Use Livestock

To the individual farmer livestock:

1. Change his feed into salable food.
2. Provide a way for him to sell some of his time.
3. Increase his opportunity for making profits.

4. Retain some of the fertility of the farm.

5. Express his personality.

On the great majority of farms the principal economic reason for keeping livestock is to market feed. Most farm-produced feeds are relatively bulky—the bulkier they are, the more costly they are to move and the poorer is the market price structure. With the general exception of protein concentrates, two prices exist for each feed on each farm. The first is the "barn door" or field price for the feed sold off the farm; the second is the price "laid down at the farm" for feed purchased. In the case of corn, the difference may be a few cents a bushel. In the case of hay, the cost of purchased hay is often twice that to be netted when hay is sold off the farm. In the case of green forage, the difference may run into several hundred percent. Although this problem is recognized, conceptually, by theorists, its empirical importance is often overlooked (1) by persons attempting to apply economic principles to farm management, (2) by persons criticizing traditional farm-management workers for their failure to use economic principles, and (3) by farm accountants. Actually, between the two price limits described above, a feedstuff is worth just what a farmer can get out of it; i.e., it takes on the nature of a fixed asset whose value is price determined. Thus, in using such a feedstuff, once produced, the main short-run economic problem is one of using up all the feed and equalizing margin value products among alternative livestock enterprises rather than of equating returns with market price and selling the remainder. And, if land capabilities impose limitations on the amount produced year after year, the procedure of following the land-use approach straight through to livestock enterprises has more validity than is quickly apparent to one thinking in terms of a single market price for each feedstuff. This limitation from a dollars and cents point of view usually means:

No feed—no livestock.

Much feed—much livestock.

A type of livestock suited to the type of feed produced.

Because of favorable location a few farmers have opportunity to do highly specialized livestock farming. These farmers often buy a major part of the feed from other farmers and sell their finished animals or animal products at premium prices. The large commercial poultry farms of the coast states serve as an excellent illustration.

Poultry use a high proportion of concentrates (a high specific value feed), convert inputs of feed into food at a high output ratio, and command premium prices for both meat and eggs on near-by markets. But for the general farmer the margin of profit (net revenue) received for converting the nation's feed crops into livestock and livestock products is very narrow. The competition is keen. Many farmers are willing to give or sell their labor at low rates, when working at livestock chores. Competition is thus so keen and feed-livestock price ratios so narrow that only those who are superior in ability or have superior marketing advantages (i.e., have high MVP's for feed in the production of livestock) can hope to pay the added costs of moving feed from farm to farm and gain a real profit. Hence, most of the great livestock farms are great crops farms, and livestock areas are first crop-producing areas. There is no great general livestock-producing region in the country that is not an important feed-producing region. It is thus axiomatic for both educators and farmers to advocate the production of abundant, cheap, and nutritious feed, especially forage, as a base upon which to develop profitable livestock programs.

In periods of low farm prices the value of livestock and livestock products produced on farms barely covers the value of the feeds used in producing them *when the feeds are priced at market prices*. In 1939, the value of all livestock and livestock products sold or traded in the United States amounted to about 3½ billion dollars, according to the 1940 Agricultural Census. The four important feed grains—corn, sorghum, oats, and barley—plus the hay produced and ignoring pasturage had a value of 2.7 billion dollars. BAE feed statistics show that about one-eighth of the total tonnage of feed fed is by-product concentrates. Adding an estimated value of 1.2 billion dollars for such feed, the total feed value equals 3.2 billion dollars. No value was placed on pasturage from some 800 to 900 million acres, providing perhaps one-third of the nutrients.

In periods of high farm prices, the feed-receipts ratio is more favorable. In 1945 farmers received some 12 billion dollars in value of livestock production against some 9 billion dollars in value of feeds, not including pasturage. The value of feed crops and prepared feeds in 1948 was estimated to be 11 billion dollars against an estimated value of livestock and products of 17 billion dollars. This was the highest year in feed-receipts ratio. Returns were $1.54 per dollar feed fed, not including the value of pasture.

Beef cattle fattening normally requires a purchase price-sale price margin for the farmer to break even on converting feed into finished cattle. That is, the price per pound of finished animal must exceed the price of the animal when put into the feed lot. The margin furnishes an added income equal to the original weight times the gain in price. Dairy cattle, using larger quantities of labor and capital, gross a return on feed of about $2 per $1 of feed value. Many farm-management surveys show gross returns of $1 to $1.50 per dollar of feed fed, depending upon the quality and type of livestock handled and practices of the farmers.

Let us further consider some of the relationships of livestock to the nation's agriculture, since these relationships help to determine what an individual farmer may profitably do with livestock on a specific farm.

The narrow margins of profit with which the nation's feed crops are converted into livestock and livestock products suggest the following rules of thumb in obtaining profits:

1. That the feed, especially roughages, be fed on the farms where produced, not only because there is no gain in digestible nutrients through transporting feeds but also because costs for baling, bagging, loading, storing, advertising, and commissions are costs in addition to transportation. Livestock require 3 to 8 pounds of feed to produce a pound of human food, and it is thus cheaper to ship the pound of food than the larger poundage of feed with lower specific values.

2. That purchased feeds be largely limited to those needed to supplement the feeds produced. Supplements that can be profitably purchased include factory products and by-products of high protein content, grains to supplement forage production, and in some cases forage —usually hay—to supplement home-produced forage. Many farmers use imported corn or other grains to supplement the hay and pasture produced on their own farms.

3. That "owner-management" is a limiting factor in most kinds of livestock production. The amount the owner can do is limited, and profits are usually not large enough on family-sized farms (or efficiencies to scale on larger farms) to hire the type of management and labor that supplies the delicate practices of the type provided by skilled owners. It has been said, "The eyes of the master fatten the cattle." "He that is a hireling, and not a shepherd, whose own the sheep are not, beholdeth the wolf coming and leaveth the sheep, and fleeth and the wolf snatcheth them, and scattereth them: he fleeth because he is a hireling and careth not for the sheep" (John 10: 12, 13).

4. That one of the economies in profitable livestock production is the use of livestock as supplementary enterprises to gain additional

income from the farm labor resources not otherwise as profitably employed. Dairy cows, for example, utilize between 75 and 150 hours of labor per year and use it during the hours of the day, days of the month, and months of the year when it would not always be advantageous to use it for other production purposes.

5. That many farmers have traditionally been willing to supply labor and some other resources for the feeding of livestock on their own farms for the benefit of the fertility (by-products) regained in the manure and the satisfaction of working with domesticated animals.

6. That a few head of livestock on most farms serve excellently for subsistence and scavenger purposes.

Livestock and Soil Fertility

It has been said that livestock farming is a soil-conserving or even soil-building type of farming, whereas crop farming is exploitive. These concepts have been carefully examined, first by Dr. Cyril G. Hopkins, of the University of Illinois, one of the foremost soil scientists, and later by others. It is doubtless true that fertility will be maintained longer on farms where the feed crops are fed and the manure resulting therefrom carefully used than on farms from which all the crops, both grain and forage, are sold. Livestock, however, do not create soil fertility. They return about two-thirds to three-fourths of the plant nutrients in feed, but only about one-third of the organic matter. With high-yielding crops and a livestock farming program, one should be able to produce about 2 tons of manure per acre of tillable crop land per year. If such crops were produced on fair to good soils and well fertilized and the resulting crops fed, and further, if the manure were carefully conserved and returned to the fields, organic matter would be maintained, provided that erosion was prevented. Nitrogen may be depleted, maintained, or increased, depending upon the proportion of legumes in the cropping system and the amount of grain sold and protein supplement feeds bought. Other plant foods—the minerals—can be maintained only through additions to offset removals.

Many Farmers Make Profits on Livestock Enterprises

Although it is true that typical or "average" farmers get just about the market value of the feed fed as returns, some do much better, a few even do twice as well as the average. When conditions are unusually favorable and the intensive types of livestock are used, the returns may run 3 to 4 dollars per dollar of feed.

Profits are returns above all costs, of which feed is only a part (usually, however, a major part). Superior livestock handlers make profits as well as gain great satisfaction and enjoyment.

Making Profits from Livestock

Profits are the top end of "high" receipts, or the remainder between normal receipts and "low" expense, or both. Profits are sometimes of the windfall variety, coming as the result of unanticipated changes. Upward change in demand accompanying wars, for example, shoots livestock prices skyward, and those having animals on hand profit handsomely because of it. This change occurred twice during World War II and its aftermath: first during 1940–1943 and, later, during 1946–1948, following removal of price controls. During the former period, livestock prices advanced 78 percent; during the latter another 50 percent.

It is not necessary, however, to have a "lucky break" to make profits. Profits can be and are made by superior handlers through careful buying, adjustment of feeding operations to price relationships, timely selling, and meticulous attention to good production practices. There are many ways to surpass the average. For example, in hog production each of the following will have considerable bearing on profits.

1. Selection of sow (a multiple of choices).
2. Time of breeding.
3. Number of pigs farrowed.
4. Number of pigs saved.
5. Condition of pigs when farrowed.
6. Weight when farrowed.
7. Weight at weaning.
8. Method of feeding and watering.
9. Cost of feed.
10. Balance of nutrients in relation to their relative prices.
11. Parasite and disease control.
12. Amount of labor used.
13. Weight at which sold.
14. Time of marketing.

Each of these could be subdivided into important production practices. Each has a bearing on profits. Each involves an action decision to be made on the basis of observation, accumulated information (experience), and analysis. The effect of each practice need not be large to be important, as

$$8 \text{ pigs} \times 225 \text{ pounds} \times 10 \text{ cents} = \$180.00$$

as compared with

$$7 \text{ pigs} \times 200 \text{ pounds} \times \$9.75 = \$136.50$$

which makes a material difference on the income side of production; on the cost side

$$120 \text{ bushels corn} \times \$1.00 + 40 \text{ hours @ } 75\cancel{c} = \$150.00$$

as compared with

$$130 \text{ bushels corn} \times \$1.05 + 50 \text{ hours @ } 75\cancel{c} = \$174.00$$

makes a material difference; thus, the profits might be $30 or minus $37.50.

Components of Livestock Costs

Costs are on the liability or negative side of livestock production. They are likely to be just as effective in determining profits as the incomes on the positive side. Cost reduction is productive of profits. Determination of the cost elements is the beginning of cost reduction. Scale of the livestock enterprise has a significant bearing on cost. Five cows cost more per cow to care for than 20 cows; 100 hens more per hen than 500; 3 sows more per sow than 15 sows. Optimum size will be reached at different numbers for different farms. For family farms the size of those livestock enterprises adapted to the feed and market situation should be pushed well toward full use of the limiting resource. For example, on feed-livestock farms having a comparative advantage for hog production, numbers produced should be pushed toward the upper limit that can be handled by the limiting resource. This will usually be the number the owner-manager can care for. It may be feed in one particular year, the supply of feeders in another. The farm business should be so organized that permanent improvements for the enterprise will be large enough to permit expanded use of variable inputs in favorable years, yet not so expensive and unadaptable that they cannot be left idle or readapted for other uses in unfavorable years. In most years efficient use will be made of both fixed and variable inputs. For example, water supplies, feeding floors, farrowing houses, feed storage should be ample (but not more than ample) to handle full numbers in good years without being completely idle in poor years.

Somewhat larger than average numbers of animals per family farm generally reduce costs of production because the average farm generally does not have enough animals to permit:

1. Good production practices to be employed.
2. Labor to be used efficiently.
3. Equipment to be used efficiently.

The usual cost of producing livestock and livestock products includes charges for:

1. Feed.
2. Labor.
3. Housing.
4. Replacements.
5. Fencing.
6. Use of machines and equipment.
7. Interest.
8. Water.
9. Veterinary, medicine, vaccines.
10. Marketing, commissions, transportation.
11. Taxes.
12. Insurance.
13. Salt, minerals.
14. Cost of collecting and analyzing information, i.e., managerial costs.

Other costs may be:

1. Association dues.
2. Advertising.
3. Registration fees.
4. Magazines.
5. Premium donations.
6. Showing.

Replacements and Depreciation

A cost of special significance in the production of livestock is replacement of animals, of maintenance, and of the investments.   Animals wear out or depreciate in usefulness and thus in value.   Livestock maintenance involves replacement.   Replacement costs are conditioned upon:

1. The value of the animal.
2. The length of natural life.
3. The ratio of feed prices to value of product.
4. The ratio of the animal's value as a producing animal to the value as a meat animal.

The skillful producer seeks to minimize these costs through efficient management.   Cows, chickens, sheep, and breeding beef cattle appreciate—increase—in value when young.   Appreciation goes on until the maximum production period is reached.   For illustration, let us use the dairy cow.   Grade cows increase in value until the second or third lactation period.   From this point, other things remaining constant—which they seldom do—a decline in value takes place.   After the first calving the value advances sharply, partly due to removing risk in calving and partly because the "heifer" has become a "cow."

From the first through the third lactation period the value is likely to increase, level off after the third, and turn down sharply thereafter.

The extent of the decline depends upon the ratio of value of the animal as a producer to the value of the same animal for slaughter. For example, a purebred cow worth $1,000 as a producer or $50 for slaughter will be retained as a producer longer than one worth $200 as a producer or $50 for slaughter. She may even be retained to an age of 12 to 14 years, or as long as there is a possibility that she may have another calf. The percentage rate of decline in value for such an animal is much slower than for ordinary grades, and the curve of values in relation to age is both lengthened and flattened.

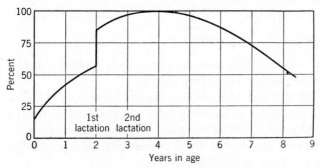

Fig. 14.1. Depreciation on cows.

Animals whose slaughter values are nearly equal to their production values are retained either longer or shorter periods, depending upon the price level. Farmers cull closely when slaughter values are relatively high and expected to drop and hold back when slaughter values are low.

Hogs do not depreciate in value to the extent other animals do, because of their early breeding age and rapid maturity rate. From the first pigging until the second to third pigging, sows increase in weight enough to offset the normal decline in price per pound.

$$250 \text{ pounds} \times 15\cent = \$37.50$$
$$375 \text{ pounds} \times 10\cent = \$37.50$$
$$425 \text{ pounds} \times 9\cent = \$38.25$$

Cost of producing litters of pigs are sometimes reduced through the two-litter-per-sow system. When sows are kept to produce but two litters they "dead head" during only one pregnancy period—the second. During the first pregnancy they are (1) increasing in value and (2) producing a litter of pigs. During the second they are producing pigs only. Thus, if kept for two litters they are "dead heading" but half time. If they are kept for three litters they must "dead head" for two-thirds of their litters; if for four, three-fourths of them.

The principal financial handicap to using the lighter breeds of chickens is the discrimination in price when they are sold for dressing. The hens also weigh less per bird. This is an outstanding disadvantage when using "all pullet" flocks. Starting with birds of equal value when placed in the laying house, we might have:

For Light Breeds		*For Medium Breeds*	
Value at beginning	$1.00		$1.25
Value in 8 months			
4 pounds at 20 cents	0.80	6 pounds at 23 cents	1.38
Loss or gain	−$0.20		+$0.13

Death losses in laying hens are higher than in other animals, averaging about 18 percent per laying season.

Sheep carry a high cost for replacement because of the low value of mutton in proportion to breeding value and the short productive period. Ewes usually lamb first as two-year-olds and have a productive life of about 4 years. Hence, the direct replacement cost is some 25 percent per year. The net is about as follows:

Starting with 100 ewes costing $16.00	$1,600.00
At end of 4 years 80 ewes valued $4.00	320.00
Net loss—4 years	$1,280.00
Loss per year	320.00
Loss per ewe per year	3.20

Skillful livestock producers diligently watch markets and outlook reports for chances or prospective chances to unload advantageously the animals to be replaced, and to secure or raise replacements at low cost. In fact, some farmers rarely take losses from any depreciation cause.

SELECTING THE KIND OF LIVESTOCK TO KEEP

Among the factors influencing the kind of livestock which should be selected for a farm are: (1) topography of land, (2) fertility of soil, (3) size of farm, (4) available labor, (5) relative prices for the different livestock products and feeds, (6) machinery, equipment, fences, and buildings, (7) diseases on or near farm, and (8) capacity and temperament of the operator. Great care and judgment should be exercised in making a selection because after the selection has been made changes are often expensive.

Topography of the land. Steep-land farms are best adapted to producing pasture and hay for grazing dairy cattle, beef cattle, and sheep. Hogs and beef cattle to be fattened in feed lots need large amounts of concentrates such as corn. These cannot be grown to advantage on steep land. The farmer who cannot use machinery on his farm because of topography of land should keep most of the land in hay and pasture, using a long crop rotation, and spend his efforts in increasing his pasture yields and caring for his livestock, with some intensive crop (on selected acreages) to use the remaining labor. Eastern pastures can be improved to the point where they will carry a unit of livestock on one to two acres. Such intensive sod crops give a better return for some land than is now being secured from feed-grain crops.

Alfalfa can be grown in many of the states. It may be used alone or as a base for mixed hay and for pasture. An acre of it provides an animal unit with roughage throughout 6 winter months. Thus, two acres of pasture and an acre of alfalfa cut for hay should provide roughage for an animal unit for a year. An extra advantage of alfalfa in some general farming areas is that it can be seeded with grasses, the land may be used for hay for 2 to 4 years, then for pasture a few years, and left at the end of a few years in splendid condition for intertilled crops.

Fertility of the Soil. Poor soils yield low marginal returns to labor in intertilled cropping. Many fields so cropped should be treated and put into pasture and grazed (see last sections, Chapter 10). This again would call for using cattle and/or sheep. In certain areas, fields of level wet land are generally used for corn production, to which they are ill adapted because of the difficulty of getting in corn in the spring and because of low productivity. In the south, these level fields are better adapted to hay and pasture with lespedeza or ladino clover and fescue as the base. The wet soil conditions in spring which interfere with getting in corn furnish good conditions for germinating seed. The dry hard conditions of the soil in mid-summer, again detrimental to corn, facilitate hay harvest.

Size of Farms. Small farms (about 70 acres or less) are not usually well adapted to handling sheep or fattening beef cattle. There are not enough fields in pasture to rotate the stock. Usually all stock, including horses or mules, have to run in one pasture. Sheep and fattening cattle do not do well under such circumstances. Hogs and sheep do not do well in the same field.

Not enough roughage is produced on most small farms to maintain a herd of beef cattle large enough to earn a comfortable living. After the workstock and milk cows (for home use) are fed, but little feed and pasture remain. If there is a small surplus, it is usually easier to add extra milk cows, the surplus products being sold, or to add a cow to be used in producing a baby beef. All the herd can then run together.

Beef cattle and sheep are considered extensive types of livestock. They need a high proportion of land to labor. Dairy cows and poultry are intensive and find a ready place on many farms, especially small farms. A few hogs may be produced on most farms raising corn, provided that conditions are suited for economical production.

Availability of Labor. The smaller the farm, the more labor is available per acre of land. The operator must have full employment (a high sustained rate of marginal returns) to secure a good income. His family is also in need of productive work.

On small farms a large percent of the time will be spent on crops and livestock requiring relatively large amounts of labor. A large amount of labor can be marketed through retailing milk and poultry products.

On farms where labor is scarce or where the operator is unable to work, extensive crops and extensive kinds of livestock may be kept. Some owners of large farms keep their farms entirely or almost entirely in pasture grazed with cattle bought as stockers or feeders to be sold in the late fall. This type of farming calls for a small proportion of labor.

Suitable hired labor for livestock is sometimes hard to get, especially near the large cities, and owner-management labor becomes a limiting factor in livestock production.

Markets Available. Before selecting the kind of livestock for a given farm, the relative prices for livestock and livestock products should be considered.

Beef, hogs, lambs, and live poultry can be shipped long distances and are priced in nationwide markets. Dairy farms succeed best when near enough to the large cities to market whole milk. Prices of milk for bottling are more localized than of milk to be manufactured into products entering national markets.

Many farmers take advantage of heavy automobile traffic by establishing roadside markets for farm products. Also, there may be a demand for fresh products sold direct to consumer, such as milk, butter, eggs and dressed poultry.

Machinery and Equipment, Fences, and Buildings. Machinery and equipment have a closer relation to raising crops than to livestock. It is becoming increasingly important, however, that they be considered in connection with livestock. The modern dairy usually necessitates the use of milking machines, modern barns, silos, silo fillers, litter carriers, manure spreaders, cooling and bottling equipment, trucks, and delivery equipment. Expenses for beef cattle and sheep equipment need not be so heavy. The farmer who produces beef on pasture has little need for expensive equipment.

Fences are required by livestock. We keep the animals out, rather than the crops in. Many farms are not adequately fenced, and some farmers make no attempt to keep livestock because of lack of fences. Good fences are needed for cattle and sheep, but especially good ones are needed for horses and hogs. Very intensive livestock production may call for much fencing, as many small lots may be needed. Hence, the fencing cost per acre and per year is high.

QUESTIONS AND PROBLEMS

1. Describe livestock farming.

2. If feeds are converted into animal products at low net returns, how can profits in specialized livestock-producing areas, such as the Los Angeles dairy area or the east coast poultry area, be explained?

3. If all outlays in national livestock production are calculated at current prices, livestock are normally produced at a monetary loss. What is wrong?

4. What are the time and place limitations on pasturage as a feed?

5. Calculate the annual depreciation on beef cows costing $600 at an age of 3 years, if the cows are valued for slaughter at $175, they are expected to have a production life of 4 remaining years, and there is a death rate of 5 percent per year. If a calf crop averaging 80 percent is expected, what is the fixed cost at birth per calf? (No cost for bull services.)

6. What are the objections to evaluating:

(a) All feed fed to livestock at market prices?

(b) Pasturage at total receipts from the livestock or livestock produced with it?

(c) Pasturage at rental rates?

(d) Value of pasturage by the substitution method?

CHAPTER 15

"Roughing Out" a Livestock Program for a Specific Farm

On the basis of the general usefulness of livestock on farms, economic principles and the implications of historical development of important geographic areas of livestock production, the typical farmer producing feed crops will market most of them through livestock in order to:

1. Use feed, i.e., to take advantage of savings in transportation and marketing costs.

2. Use some labor resources on livestock as supplementary or complementary enterprises.

3. Keep some of the fertility in the feeds on his farm; i.e., by-product complementarity.

The problem of developing the program is, therefore, one of finding a livestock program which provides the most profitable market for feed, labor, and other resources. As such, the problem posed is the one examined in the earlier chapters on economic principles. As in selecting crops, experience of farmers is valuable. The kinds of livestock and the proportions in which livestock are combined with crops have been adjusted in communities under competitive influences through trial and error and/or success. This process has gone on throughout the history of farming in most communities, and choices have changed from generation to generation as shifts have occurred in comparative advantage. This is a slow process. To follow experience of other farmers solely has the disadvantage of losing the gains that may accrue to those who make adjustments *in the earlier years of an innovation, or shift in comparative advantage.*

The joint use of budgeting and economic principles makes it possible to go from an appraisal of the fixed conditions in a situation to a crops and livestock program in a manner which saves years of trial and error.

That is, the learning process as described in Chapters 2 and 3 is shortened. The task of developing a livestock program is simplified by the availability of feeding standards (rough though they are), rough feed and labor unit requirements for each type and size of animal, and input-output data (i.e., production data in marginality form).

A Case Illustration

The technique to be used by students is illustrated by the following explanation of budgeting a tentative livestock program for the 335-acre farm for which a crops program was developed and presented in the preceding analysis of the farm in developing a cropping system.

The student should remember that the tasks of setting up the crop and livestock programs under a set of fixed conditions are mutually interrelated. These problems are attacked separately in this and the preceding chapter on developing a cropping system. The crop and livestock systems tentatively outlined in these chapters will be reconciled, integrated, and adjusted in the chapter on budgeting. This "putting together" process will employ marginal data, computations matching additional costs against additional returns, and economic principles.

Step I. Reviewing Table 13.2, we find we had an estimated production of feed as follows:

    105 units pasturage for the grazing season.
     84 tons hay (34 clover, 50 alfalfa mixed).
     46 acres corn stalk fields.
     42 tons barley straw.
  1,260 bushels barley.
  3,680 bushels corn.

Step II. Beginning with the pasture, we find we can keep approximately 105 animal units of livestock on pasture through the grazing season. The reason for beginning with pasture is that it is fixed as to place of utilization—on this farm—and largely as to time of utilization—spring into or through fall. It is worth what we can get out of it by using it between the following limits: (1) the cost of getting more pasturage, which is high once the seeding is done and (2) the sales price for it, which would probably be low due to harvesting costs or the cost of securing animals for the forage.

Step III. One hundred and five units of roughage-consuming livestock would utilize about 200 tons of dry roughage for 6 winter months or 100 tons of dry roughage and 210 tons of silage. We have 84 tons of hay—also some corn stalks and barley straw. Silage could be provided if later development of the farming program indicates advantage in so doing. Wheat, barley, hay, pasture forage, and corn are available for ensiling. Hence, we may conclude that there will be sufficient roughage for 100 units of livestock through both summer and winter. The roughage-concentrate balance is usually brought about by using beef production systems requiring more grain (in the extreme case, drylot feeding, see Chapter 18) or by utilizing the remaining quantities of grain with hogs or by selling the grain. Let us then reserve some of the pasture acreage for hogs, and for subsistence livestock, say, for trial at this point, 15 units, leaving 90 for cattle.

Step IV. We now continue our roughing-out process by selecting the type of roughage-consuming livestock. Beef cattle, dairy cattle, and sheep suggest themselves for this purpose. The choice between beef (including the different kinds of beef production; again see Chapter 18) and dairy cattle depends primarily on availability of labor, preferences, and marketing opportunities rather than on feeds, and is thus partially dependent on size of farm. On farms providing economic outlets in crops for less than the labor resources of the family, the choice would be dairy cattle when net earnings is the principal objective. Thus, either beef or dairy cattle may be used. The decision rests then on the managerial abilities of the owner of the farm and his desire for additional income. For purposes of this illustration we shall select beef cattle as the first approximation. Beef-cattle grazing is a usual practice on general farms in the area of this farm, labor is fairly well employed with the cropping system alone, the operator possesses beef production "know-how," and the necessary buildings are available.

Step V. We next need to select a type of beef production. The general types of production of all livestock are:

1. Subsistence.
2. General commercial.
3. Purebred.
4. Specialized quality product.
5. Self-expression.

For this farm and our purpose of illustration, let us choose general commercial because of its wide applicability. However, we must now go further and select a type of production within beef cattle (Chapter 18 contains a still more complete discussion of beef-production methods which the student may want to read at this point).

Some of the different types of beef production are:

1. Range production of stockers and feeders.
2. Stockers kept through the summer and sold grass fat in the fall.
3. Stockers grazed through one summer and fed concentrates through one winter.
4. Stockers carried through one winter and fattened on grass or grasses and grain the following summer.
5. Stockers grazed through a summer, fed through one winter, then finished on grain in summer.
6. Stockers roughed one winter, grazed one summer, and finished the second winter.
7. Feeders through one winter.
8. The cow-and-calf plan.
   (*a*) Calves sold as milk fat calves in the fall of each year.
   (*b*) Calves sold as stockers.
   (*c*) Spring calves finished the following winter on feed as baby beeves.
   (*d*) Calves carried through summer, one winter, and finished the next summer as long yearlings.
   (*e*) Purebred production with varying numbers of purebred animals, some sold as breeding stock and some for slaughter.

The choice for this farm having high-quality pasture and good hay, with some low-quality roughage and also corn and barley as concentrates, would lie among choices 3, 4, 5, and 7 as listed. The most accepted method of beef production for farms of this size and type in the eastern portion of the United States is to grow and finish cattle imported from the range states, though the cow-and-calf plans are increasing in number under the impetus of the various "green pastures" programs. Either of these plans would be applicable to this farm. Perhaps the quantity of grain suggests feeding, and the quantity of roughage suggests that grazing and feeding shipped-in stocker cattle would have a slight margin of comparative advantage.

We, therefore, tentatively elect beef-cattle feeding, using system 4, and hogs as livestock for this farm.

Step VI. The 90 units of pasturage would be used by 90 head of cattle purchased each fall or late summer (some 900 pounds each at springtime). They would be fed most of the hay (about 80 tons), some of the straw, whatever pasturage would be available in winter, and 3 to 4 pounds of corn and ground barley per head per day. In spring they would be placed on pasture, and finished on grass and limited grain in late summer or early fall, by using 10 to 15 bushels of corn per head, equal to 10 pounds per day for 60 days. They thus require about:

600 bushels of barley
1,420 bushels of corn (16 bu.
each)

The hay produced (except that for
a team and four cows)
90 units of pasturage

leaving:

2,260 bushels of corn
660 bushels of barley
15 units of pasturage

to be utilized by hogs or otherwise.

Step VII. Hogs are useful animals for marketing concentrates. They grow and fatten well when full-fed grain and supplement on pasture, but the relative quantity of pasturage utilized is small. They are a widely accepted type of animal throughout the country to market farm-produced grains.

A sow and litter of eight pigs to 225 pounds will use about 140 bushels of corn if they are efficiently fed with pasture and supplement. Tentatively assuming this to be the proper weight, the 2,920 bushels of grain (equivalent to 2,788 bushels of corn) remaining should then be well utilized through the production of about 20 litters of hogs which should be produced with perhaps 12 sows. The 15 units of pasturage should prove somewhat more than ample. Tolerance of 10 percent of the total quantities of each feed is low enough. This amount is probably within usual seasonal variation, though not within variation in desirable feed requirements caused by shifting price relationships.

The roughly budgeted feed and livestock programs may now be summarized as follows:

105 units pasture	{90 feeder cattle, 4 cows {12 sows, 160 porkers
84 tons hay	wintering the 90 beef cattle
46 acres corn stalks	browsing for the 90 beef cattle
42 tons barley straw	cattle feed and bedding
1,260 bushels barley	{600 to wintering cattle {660 to hogs
3,680 bushels corn	{1,420 to cattle {2,260 to hogs

The method of studying management as outlined in the text requires students to solve problems pertaining to specific individual farms. One of these problems is that of analyzing the opportunities of the specific farm being used for livestock production and of making decisions for use of livestock. A practice exercise (Number 10) has been set up for this problem and two blank forms have been provided. Tables 15.1 and 15.2 are reproductions of these forms and illustrate the way in which they are to be used with the data just developed.

Table 15.1. Livestock Table

Livestock Work Sheet—Form II   Farm of _____ 335-Acre Case Illustration _____

Name _____ Livestock Major _____   _____ Fayette _____ County

For year beginning _____ March 1, 1952 _____

Kind of Livestock	Number	Animal Units [1]	Inventory Value $ March 1	Number Sold	Value $	Number Bought	Cost $
Horses and mules (work)	2	2	200				
Horses (productive)							
Beef cattle	90	90	19,000	89	26,433	90	15,120
Dairy cows—subsistence	4	4	(800)	Property of crop pers			
Dairy heifers							
Dairy calves							
Hogs—sows	12	6	1,500 [2]	12	768		
Hogs—other	160	32		148	3,673 3,330		
Sheep—ewes and ram							
Sheep—lambs							
Poultry—chicken hens							
Poultry—chicks							
Total		134			34,204		15,120

[1] 1 cow (1,000 lb.) = 1 unit; 1 heifer = 0.5 units; 5 hogs (1,000 lb.) = 1 unit; 5 ewes and lambs = 1 unit; and 100 chicken hens = 1 unit.
[2] Sows and spring pigs valued together.

Table 15.2. Livestock Which Can Be Kept on the Feed in the Reorganized Farm Plan

Feed Use Livestock Work Sheet—Form III

Name _____ Livestock Major   County _____ Fayette   Farm of _____ 335-Acre Case Illustration

For year beginning _____ March 1, 1952

	No.	Corn, bu.	Barley, bu.	Barley Straw	Mixed Hay, tons	Legume Hay, tons	Corn Silage, tons	Stover, acres	Pasture Units	Bedding, tons wheat S.	Mill Feed	C.S.M. L.S.M., cwt.	Tankage, cwt.
Feed provided in cropping system		3,680	1,260	42	50	34			105	23			
Feed Needed for	No.												
Horses	2				2				2				
Beef steers	90	1,420	600	42	50	30		23	90	20			
Sows	12	300	280						12	2			
Porkers	160	1,960	380						12				
Dairy cows	4	100				8				2			
Total amounts	xx	3,780	1,260	42	52	38			104	24			
Balance 1		−100	0	0	−2	−4		0	+1	−1			

1 If feed provided in the cropping system exceeds the quantity needed, indicate by putting a plus (+) sign before the number of units in the space labeled "Balance." If the feed needed exceeds the amount provided in the cropping system, indicate this by putting a minus sign (−) before the number.

QUESTIONS AND PROBLEMS

1. Explain the relationships existing between kinds of crops and kinds of livestock in your home neighborhood.

2. Increased livestock numbers have long been recommended to farmers of the old cotton states. Under the farm economy which prevailed until 1940, what were the limitations of these recommendations?

3. Defense plants employing thousands of workers are being constructed. What new opportunities are afforded to farmers in near-by areas in livestock production? Where will the additional feed come from?

4. If the Missouri River watershed is developed as proposed, what changes may be expected in livestock production along its upper waters?

5. What effect is mechanical refrigeration having upon dairying in the South?

6. Two opposing trends are apparently developing in crop and livestock production practices. One trend is toward intensive pasture production with relatively little machinery and buildings. What are the encouraging factors?

7. Rank hogs, poultry, beef cattle, dairy cattle, and sheep on the basis of national geographic distribution: (*a*) on the basis of commercial production, (*b*) on the basis of subsistence production, i.e., which ones are most widely distributed, least widely, etc.

8. From your studies in animal industry and economics, and your farming experiences, what evidence can you present that farmers are using variable inputs on livestock enterprises to the "right" or the "left" of the point where $MFC = MVP$?

PROBLEM EXERCISE 11

Rations and Feed Requirements

Calculate daily rations for the kinds of livestock to be kept on the individual case farm for winter and summer. Accompany with explanations.

PROBLEM EXERCISE 12

Depreciation

Make a table for showing depreciation of livestock to be kept on the individual case farm. Make the table with the headings as follows:

Replacement Estimates for Livestock in Reorganized Farm Plan

Kind of Livestock	Number to Be Kept	Replacement Rate	Number Needed for Replacement	Number Expected to Die	Number of Animals to Be Sold

Write a summary of the livestock depreciation and replacement problems of your individual farm.

PROBLEM EXERCISE 13
Livestock Plans for the Individual Case Farm

Develop a plan for handling livestock on your individual case farm. Use prices agreed upon in the class exercise (adjusted for quality of livestock and location of farm). Follow the procedure illustrated in Chapter 12, with the 335-acre case farm.

1. Write a description of the farm from the viewpoint of handling livestock, describing topography, water, buildings, other improvements, markets, and feed.

2. Write a narrative of the management practices for each class of livestock.

3. Submit daily rations for each class of livestock to be used.

4. Submit copies of Forms II and III with the description, narrative, and rations.

5. Keep rough draft copies of work for future needs.

CHAPTER 16

Input-Output Relationships
in Pork Production

The last chapter ended with a first approximation to a livestock program to be reconciled with a similar first approximation to a cropping system in the final budgeting process. Some of the following kinds of questions were not asked and none were specifically answered in devising the tentative livestock program. Would dairy or beef production be more profitable? Was the type of beef production selected the most profitable? Was the selected weight (225 pounds) for selling hogs the most profitable at existing price relationships? If dairy were selected, what level of feeding would be justified at existing price levels? This incomplete list of questions serves:

    1. To emphasize the tentative nature of the crop and livestock programs roughed out thus far.

    2. To bring out the need for additional information and reasoning processes for answering such questions.

This chapter will present some of the existing information and data for pork production which are useful in answering such questions. Subsequent chapters will present similar material for dairy and beef. Information and data, available to students from animal husbandry courses in livestock production, will prove helpful and both basic and fundamental.

This chapter is the first to integrate the theoretical concepts presented in the preceding chapters with actual data pertaining to a specific enterprise. Data on the pork enterprise have been accumulating since before the turn of the century. In 1898, W. A. Henderson published data on feeds and feeding in connection with the pork enterprise. These data were based, in part, upon earlier studies. Through the years since then, various people including Ashby, Carroll, Case, Ross, Wilcox, and Hornung of the University of Illinois, and Hopkins and

Jennings of Iowa, as well as people from other experiment stations, have made their contributions. Over this half century of work, the data and information secured were gradually formulated in terms of the input-output relationships or production functions of the type studied in the preceding chapters. This chapter will present such input-output data as exist for pork production. And, after presenting such data, this chapter will also examine certain production relationships not yet accurately measured by our animal husbandrymen but which are, nevertheless, very important in the management of the pork enterprise. Thus, in addition to training students to answer certain specific questions concerning the management of the pork enterprise, this chapter will give the student a frame of reference for use in organizing his thinking concerning pork production; it will train him to ask the "right" questions from an economic standpoint. This dual objective can best be accomplished if the problems of the pork enterprise are considered with respect to the planning spans or lengths of run in which they occur.

The first length of run to be considered will be a short run dealing with the "feeding out" of a particular drove of hogs. Following this, attention will be devoted to longer lengths of run in which the number of hogs involved can be varied. Following this, still longer lengths of run will be examined in which breeds of hogs, production methods, and major items of equipment can be changed.

The Short Run Involving the Feeding Out of a Particular Herd

When feeding out a particular herd or drove of hogs, the basic question to be asked and answered, assuming good production methods, is: How heavy should the hogs be fed? Three publications are available for answering this question. As noted at the beginning of this chapter, these three publications are based upon a great deal of early work. This work led up to experiments at the state agricultural experiment stations in Iowa, Illinois, Missouri, and Ohio. The three publications are (1) *U.S.D.A. Technical Bulletin* 894 entitled "Feed Consumption and Marketing Weight of Hogs," by L. J. Atkinson and John W. Klein; (2) *U.S.D.A. Technical Bulletin* 917, entitled "Feed Consumption and the Production of Pork and Lard," by the same authors; and (3) an article published in the January, 1949, issue of the *Agricultural Situation* and entitled "How Heavy Should I Feed My Hogs?"

The experimental data upon which these publications are based indicate that healthy, lard-type hogs gain, under the feeding conditions maintained in the experiment, in the manner indicated in Figure 16.1.

In Figure 16.1, days from birth are plotted on the horizontal axis and live weight is plotted on the vertical axis. Two curves are plotted: first, a growth curve, or total physical product curve, and, second, the daily gain curve, or marginal physical product-per-day curve.

The basic question—*How heavy should I feed my hogs?*—is answered by comparing the value of extra gain with the cost of securing

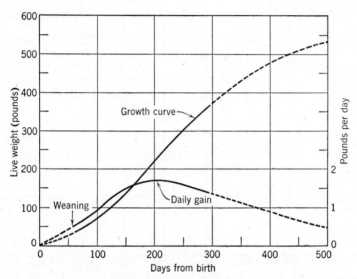

FIG. 16.1. Growth curve and rate of daily gain of hogs. (Based on 813 hogs in 12 experiments.) Solid portions of curves represent the range of the experimental observations; broken portions represent extensions of curves to periods prior to and following the period of observation. The greatest daily gain was 1.7 pounds in the 200–210 pound range, but gains were only 10 percent less at 300 pounds. The hogs reached 225 pounds in about 205 days from birth.

that gain. The data presented in Figure 16.1 are converted into a more useful form for answering this question by plotting a portion of the total growth curve against the total feed consumed instead of days. The resultant figure is presented in Figure 16.2. From the total growth curve plotted in Figure 16.2, it is possible to compute the amount of gain from each additional hundred pounds of feed fed.

A complication enters into the computation at this point. As hogs get heavier the percentage of fat in their carcasses increases and as a result their value per pound falls. Thus, in calculating the additional value resulting from the feeding of another dollar's worth of feed to a hog, more than the value of the additional weight must be considered.

At heavier weights, the original carcass becomes less valuable because it becomes fatter. Thus, when considering whether or not to put additional gain on a hog, we first estimate what a hog is worth before more gain is put on. This is found by multiplying his present weight by his present worth per pound. A 225-pound hog at $25.00 per 100 pounds is worth $56.25. Suppose that, after taking this hog up

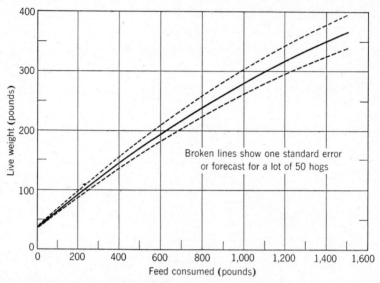

Fig. 16.2. Feed consumption and gain of hogs after being weaned. (Average of 12 experiments involving 813 hogs.) The average relationship between feed consumption of hogs after being weaned and their live weight is somewhat curvilinear; that is, additional feed produces a somewhat smaller live-weight gain as weight increases.

to 275 pounds, he is worth only $23.75 per 100 pounds, or $65.31 in all. Then the increase in value for adding the 50 pounds of gain is $9.06. The input-output relationship derived in the bulletins referred to above indicates that it takes 4.6 bushels of corn to put 50 pounds of weight on a 225-pound hog. If corn is worth $1.50 a bushel, the net gain, disregarding certain accompanying costs such as interest and additional labor, is $9.06 minus $6.90 (for 4.6 bushels of corn), or $2.16. These computations are quite involved and difficult to make. Hence, the researchers doing this work computed a table which is very useful in deciding how heavy to feed hogs. This table is reproduced as Table 16.1 of this chapter.

Table 16.1 gives the necessary selling price for hogs, that is, the break-even price after putting on 50 pounds extra weight when corn and hogs are selling at different prices. In other words, this table indicates how much must be received for hogs after putting on 50 pounds more gain in order to break even at the existing price for corn and the present price of hogs at their present weight. For instance, assume, in using Table 16.1, that a 225-pound hog is worth $25.00 per hundredweight and that corn is now worth $1.50 per bushel. Look in the column under $25.00. Go down that column to the section dealing with hogs weighing 225 pounds now. Within that section come down to the row of figures opposite the present price of corn which, in this example, is $1.50 per bushel. At this point $23.59 is found: this is the price which must be received for a healthy lard-type hog worth $25.00 a hundredweight now in order to break even when putting on an additional 50 pounds of weight with corn at $1.50 per bushel.

It should be pointed out that thus far information has not been presented on what a 275-pound hog should be expected to sell for by the time he gets to 275 pounds. Table 16.1 just states that if the hog sells for less than $23.59 money would probably be lost. In a later chapter, specific attention will be given to the problem of forecasting or estimating future prices.

It should also be stressed that Table 16.1 applies to healthy, unstunted, lard-type hogs of the breeds common in the corn belt. Retarded, diseased, or worm-infested hogs which are definitely stunted should be expected to require more feed to put on an extra 50 pounds than assumed in this table. On the other hand, healthy, well-grown but thin, older hogs should be expected to put on 50 pounds of gain with less feed than assumed in this table. When faced with such problems, a hog producer must adjust the data presented in Table 16.1 on the basis of his experience and his knowledge of the particular situation which he faces.

In the chapter dealing with production concepts involving one input, it was stressed that most production concepts consider output as dependent on certain variable inputs with other inputs fixed, while a third category of inputs is neither studied nor fixed. Table 16.1 assumes as the fixed input one healthy lard-type hog. Among the inputs or variables which are neither fixed nor held constant are the effects of weather, differences in production procedures, differences in rations, etc. These uncontrolled differences introduce elements of error into the estimates of the input-output relationships (note the standard error of forecast estimates in Figure 16.2). Table 16.1 assumes that these

Table 16.1. Necessary Selling Price for Hogs One Month from Now to Permit the Feeder to Break Even in Putting on 50 Pounds Additional Weight on Hogs of Different Weights with Different Prices for Corn and Hogs Now [1]

Price of Corn per Bushel Now, dollars	Price of Hogs in Dollars per Hundred Pounds, Now										
	5.00	7.50	10.00	12.50	15.00	17.50	20.00	22.50	25.00	27.50	30.00
On Hogs Weighing 200 Pounds, Now											
0.50	5.12	7.12	9.12	11.12	13.12	15.12	17.12	19.12	21.12	23.12	25.12
0.75	5.68	7.68	9.68	11.68	13.68	15.68	17.68	19.68	21.68	23.68	25.68
1.00	6.25	8.25	10.25	12.25	14.25	16.25	18.25	20.25	22.25	24.25	26.25
1.25	6.81	8.81	10.81	12.81	14.81	16.81	18.81	20.81	22.81	24.81	26.81
1.50	7.38	9.38	11.38	13.38	15.38	17.38	19.38	21.38	23.38	25.38	27.38
1.75	7.94	9.94	11.94	13.94	15.94	17.94	19.94	21.94	23.94	25.94	27.94
2.00	8.50	10.50	12.50	14.50	16.50	18.50	20.50	22.50	24.50	26.50	28.50
2.25	9.06	11.06	13.06	15.06	17.06	19.06	21.06	23.06	25.06	27.06	29.06
2.50	9.62	11.62	13.62	15.62	17.62	19.62	21.62	23.62	25.62	27.62	29.62
2.75	10.18	12.18	14.18	16.18	18.18	20.18	22.18	24.18	26.18	28.18	30.18
3.00	10.75	12.75	14.75	16.75	18.75	20.75	22.75	24.75	26.75	28.75	30.75
On Hogs Weighing 225 Pounds, Now											
0.50	5.14	7.18	9.23	11.27	13.32	15.36	17.41	19.45	21.50	23.55	25.59
0.75	5.66	7.70	9.75	11.79	13.84	15.88	17.93	19.97	22.02	24.07	26.11
1.00	6.18	8.23	10.27	12.32	14.36	16.41	18.45	20.50	22.55	24.59	26.64
1.25	6.71	8.75	10.80	12.84	14.89	16.93	18.98	21.02	23.07	25.12	27.16
1.50	7.23	9.27	11.32	13.36	15.41	17.45	19.50	21.54	23.59	25.64	27.68
1.75	7.75	9.79	11.84	13.88	15.93	17.97	20.02	22.07	24.11	26.16	28.20
2.00	8.27	10.32	12.36	14.41	16.45	18.50	20.55	22.59	24.64	26.68	28.73
2.25	8.80	10.84	12.89	14.93	16.98	19.02	21.07	23.11	25.16	27.21	29.25
2.50	9.32	11.36	13.41	15.45	17.50	19.55	21.59	23.64	25.68	27.73	29.77
2.75	9.84	11.88	13.93	15.97	18.02	20.07	22.11	24.16	26.20	28.25	30.29
3.00	10.36	12.41	14.45	16.50	18.55	20.59	22.64	24.68	26.73	28.77	30.82
On Hogs Weighing 250 Pounds, Now											
0.50	5.17	7.25	9.33	11.42	13.50	15.58	17.67	19.75	21.83	23.92	26.00
0.75	5.67	7.75	9.83	11.92	14.00	16.08	18.17	20.25	22.33	24.42	26.50
1.00	6.17	8.25	10.33	12.42	14.50	16.58	18.67	20.75	22.83	24.92	27.00
1.25	6.67	8.75	10.83	12.92	15.00	17.08	19.17	21.25	23.33	25.42	27.50
1.50	7.17	9.25	11.33	13.42	15.50	17.58	19.67	21.75	23.83	25.92	28.00
1.75	7.67	9.75	11.83	13.92	16.00	18.08	20.17	22.25	24.33	26.42	28.50
2.00	8.17	10.25	12.33	14.42	16.50	18.58	20.67	22.75	24.83	26.92	29.00
2.25	8.67	10.75	12.83	14.92	17.00	19.08	21.17	23.25	25.33	27.42	29.50
2.50	9.17	11.25	13.33	15.42	17.50	19.58	21.67	23.75	25.83	27.92	30.00
2.75	9.67	11.75	13.83	15.92	18.00	20.08	22.17	24.25	26.33	28.42	30.50
3.00	10.17	12.25	14.33	16.42	18.50	20.58	22.67	24.75	26.83	28.92	31.00
On Hogs Weighing 275 Pounds, Now											
0.50	5.17	7.29	9.40	11.52	13.63	15.75	17.86	19.98	22.10	24.21	26.33
0.75	5.64	7.76	9.87	11.99	14.10	16.22	18.33	20.45	22.57	24.68	26.80
1.00	6.11	8.23	10.34	12.46	14.57	16.69	18.80	20.92	23.04	25.15	27.27
1.25	6.58	8.70	10.81	12.93	15.04	17.16	19.28	21.39	23.51	25.62	27.74
1.50	7.06	9.17	11.29	13.40	15.52	17.63	19.75	21.86	23.98	26.09	28.21
1.75	7.53	9.64	11.76	13.87	15.99	18.10	20.22	22.33	24.45	26.56	28.68
2.00	8.00	10.11	12.23	14.34	16.46	18.57	20.69	22.81	24.92	27.03	29.15
2.25	8.47	10.58	12.70	14.81	16.93	19.04	21.16	23.28	25.39	27.50	29.62
2.50	8.94	11.05	13.17	15.28	17.40	19.52	21.63	23.75	25.86	27.98	30.09
2.75	9.41	11.53	13.64	15.75	17.87	19.99	22.10	24.22	26.33	28.45	30.56
3.00	9.88	12.00	14.11	16.23	18.34	20.46	22.57	24.69	26.80	28.92	31.04

[1] By "break even" is meant to get back the cost of feed at present prices for the extra month plus 25 percent for other costs such as labor, use of equipment, and risk.

errors "average out." Some of these errors result in greater than average productive efficiency; others result in less than average productive efficiency. At this point, in the development of this book, we proceed on the assumption that the average will be attained. In this chapter, average returns are not discounted because of the risk of error.

Table 16.1 establishes the weight at which hogs should be sold under various price conditions. It does not indicate how much feed is required to take hogs to a given weight or to change their weight a given amount from any specific level. Such data are needed in making plans for the hog enterprise and in budgeting and are furnished in Table 16.2.

Table 16.2. Relationship of Feed Consumed by Hogs after Weaning, Measured Both in Feed Units and in Pounds of Feed, to Live Weight

Live Weight, lb.	Feed Consumed after Weaning		Rate of Gain in Live Weight	
	Feed Units	Pounds	Per 100 Additional Feed Units,* lb.	Per 100 Additional Pounds of Feed, lb.
35	0	0	. . . .	. . . .
50	64.7	50.7	23.2	29.3
75	172.8	137.5	23.0	28.2
100	281.8	227.8	22.8	27.2
125	392.1	321.7	22.4	26.1
150	504.5	419.6	22.0	25.0
175	619.5	521.7	21.4	23.9
200	737.7	628.5	20.8	22.9
225	859.8	740.6	20.2	21.8
250	986.3	858.1	19.4	20.7
275	1,118.3	982.0	18.5	19.6
300	1,256.3	1,112.8	17.7	18.6

* A feed unit is equivalent to 1 pound of corn.

The column labeled "feed units" gives the number of feed units required after weaning to take hogs to various weights. A feed unit is equal to 1 pound of shelled corn; 1 pound of soybean oil meal is equal to 1¾ feed units; 1 pound of tankage is equal to 2½ feed units; and 1 pound of dry skim-milk is equal to 2 feed units. According to Table 16.2, it takes 258.5 feed units to increase a hog's weight from 225 to 275 pounds. This number of feed units is the equivalent of 4.6 bushels of corn, the quantity used earlier in this chapter in figuring out the profitability of adding 50 pounds of weight to a 225-pound hog.

Thus far the discussion has been confined to feeding problems encountered in the short planning spans in which the number of hogs is fixed. When longer planning spans are considered, many additional variables and inputs must be handled.

One- and Two-Year Planning Spans

In somewhat longer planning spans, the number of hogs to be fed out becomes of prime importance. Size of herd can be varied by two methods: (1) the buying of additional feeder pigs and (2) the raising of additional feeder pigs. By and large, successful farmers follow one but not both of these practices in maintaining and in changing the size of their feeder droves. The farmer who raises his own feeder pigs is reluctant to bring purchased feeders on to his farm, as they may carry diseases. The farmer who buys his feeder pigs is reluctant to raise pigs because the pigs raised are likely to be made ill by the purchased hogs.

In the longer planning spans, a question which should be asked is, What proportion of lean and lard should the herd be expected to produce? In periods of war emergency, the demand for fat is high and it is profitable to carry the lard-type hog to heavy weights. In peacetime periods, when the hog producer is dependent upon the domestic consumer, the demand for lard falls off and it is less profitable to feed lard-type hogs to heavy weights. Thus, in planning hog enterprises to utilize the corn produced on the farm, a farmer should ask himself how many hogs it will take at the weight he desires to feed them to use up his corn.

Packing houses force hogs to be marketed at lighter weights in peacetime periods by placing a heavier discount on the heavier hogs. They do this because the heavier hogs contain a higher proportion of fat. The same studies presented earlier in this chapter also examine the relationship between the percentage of lard in a hog carcass and the live weight of the animal. Figure 16.3 shows how the additional product per 100 additional feed units changes as hogs are taken from around 160 pounds to 280 pounds.

Table 16.1 can be used to determine the weight of hogs which should be produced under any given set of discounts for heavier hogs. The process for doing this is the same as that explained before. After determining the weight of hog which should be produced, a farmer can determine from Table 16.2 the feed required to take each hog to the proper weight. This, in turn, determines the number of hogs required to consume the grain which will probably be on hand. As a result of

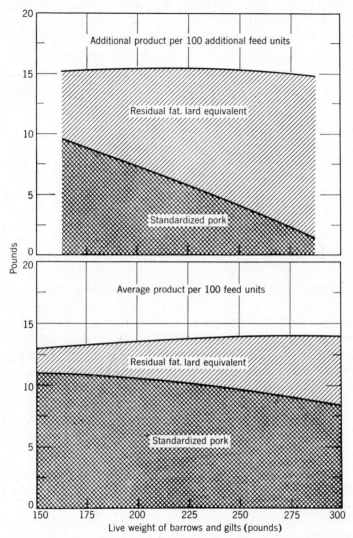

Fig. 16.3. Comparison of average and of additional output of standardized pork and residual fat per 100 feed units from hogs for various weights.

following this procedure, a farmer will produce a higher proportion of lean in the periods in which the demand for lean is high relative to the demand for fat. And, in war periods, when the demand for fat is high relative to the demand for lean, a farmer will be producing a high proportion of fat. In both cases the farmer will be producing that proportion of fat and lean most profitable for him. The farmer who sees the changes coming and adjusts to them is better off than the farmer who is forced to change by the forces of competition; "loss" is a more compelling competitive force than profits.

Longer Lengths of Run

In longer lengths of run, farmers can change the proportion of fat and lean which they are producing by changing breeds of animals. The bacon type of hog, of course, produces a higher proportion of lean. A recent development which makes it possible for farmers to adjust to changes in the demand for fat and lean is the development of the so-called hybrid hog. By using a bacon-type "hybrid" boar with lard-type sows and gilts, it is possible to increase greatly the proportion of lean produced by the herd. Similarly, by switching back to a lard-type hog, in periods of national emergency, it is possible to secure the efficiency of the lard-type hog in producing fat. The hybrid animal gives a much greater degree of flexibility than was previously obtainable when the breeding programs could be changed only as a result of 10 or 20 years of careful selection of breeding animals. Other long-run production problems involve such questions as type of housing, water systems, the advisability of having a pork enterprise on the farm, etc.

A perennial long-run management problem involves advisability of producing hogs with forage in contrast to concentrates. The literature contains several articles advocating the extensive use of forage in the production of pork. Some articles indicate that a great deal of pork can be produced per acre of forage by using forage as a supplement. The results of the forage experiments reported indicate that (1) forage economically provides supplemental proteins and vitamins to a full-feed grain ration, (2) it is easier to keep hogs free of parasites on rotated pastures, (3) ground alfalfa hay is a valuable feed for gilts and sows before farrowing, (4) the feeder pigs are efficiently produced with their mother's milk and grain feeding while on pasture, (5) attempts to limit grain while attempting to carry hogs to heavier weights in order to force them to eat additional forage are often uneconomical because of seasonal price declines encountered.

One of the better pieces of research done on feeding forage to hogs was done at the Pennsylvania Experiment Station.[1] This research yielded data on the effect of pasture on both corn and protein supplement requirements in pork production. These data, if changed in form by computational procedures, yield an approximate picture of the iso-product maps for protein supplement and corn in the production of live-weight pork when feeders are (1) grazed on alfalfa, (2) grazed on red clover, (3) grazed on rape, and (4) fed in dry lot. The data on alfalfa and dry-lot feeding have been plotted in Figure 16.4.

Figure 16.4 is made up of two separate iso-product maps—one for alfalfa and one for dry lot. In both cases, the hogs were on full feed. The protein fed was from both animal and plant sources and is expressed in terms of soybean oil meal equivalent (40.6 percent protein). If soybean oil meal equivalent were worth three times as much per pound as corn, the iso-cost lines superimposed on Figures 16.4a and 16.4b would result. The two lines determined by the points of tangency between the iso-cost and iso-product lines indicate the most profitable proportions in which to expand the use of corn and protein at these relative prices. These lines are the scale lines or expansion lines referred to in the chapters on multiple-production relationships.

The scale line for feeding hogs on alfalfa indicates that, from 50 to 175 pounds, hogs should be fed about 7 pounds of SOM equivalent for each 100 pounds of corn fed if 3 pounds of corn are worth 1 pound of SOM equivalent. The scale line for feeding hogs in dry lot indicates that, from 40 to 200 pounds, hogs should be fed about 15 pounds of SOM equivalent for each 100 pounds of corn fed when 3 pounds of corn are worth 1 pound of SOM equivalent. With SOM equivalent relatively more expensive, smaller proportions of it would be profitable. With SOM equivalent relatively less expensive, as it generally is, a higher level of protein feeding would be profitable.

Obviously, alfalfa substituted for a considerable amount of protein supplement and corn in producing pork in this experiment. On the scale line, 140 pounds of corn and 25 pounds of SOM equivalent carried a 38-pound pig to 88 pounds in a dry lot. By contrast, 100 pounds of corn and 15 pounds of SOM took a 54-pound pig to 104 pounds on alfalfa pasture. On the basis of these amounts, the alfalfa grazed in producing 100 pounds of pork would be worth somewhat less than 80 pounds of corn and 20 pounds of SOM equivalent. In terms of corn alone, at the assumed price relationship, the equivalent of 140 pounds of corn were saved by grazing hogs on alfalfa.

[1] Reported in *Pennsylvania Bulletin* 407.

If the curves in Figure 16.4 are regarded differently (incorrectly), it can be noted that 50 pounds of SOM equivalent and 270 pounds of corn produced about 125 pounds of pork on alfalfa (179 − 54 = 125).

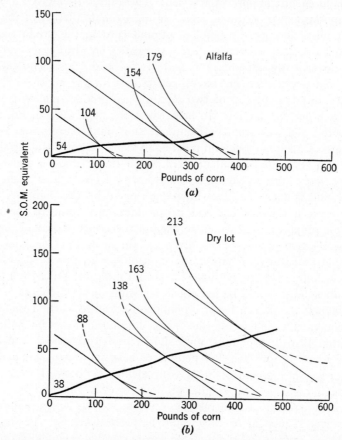

FIG. 16.4. Iso-product maps for pork production per animal from corn and soybean oil meal equivalent. (Based in part on linear interpolations which partially upset law of diminishing returns.)

Fifty pounds of SOM equivalent and nearly 310 pounds of corn produced about 125 pounds of pork in dry lot (163 − 38 = 125). Only one of these last two sets of figures was taken from the scale line. On the basis of these figures, the alfalfa grazed in producing 100 pounds of pork is worth almost 40 pounds of corn.

If the curves in Figure 16.4 are regarded still differently (and still incorrectly), it can be noted, on the basis of extrapolated iso-product lines, that 2.5 pounds of SOM equivalent and 140 pounds of corn would have produced about 50 pounds of pork from a single 54-pound pig on alfalfa pasture. Similarly, 2.5 pounds of SOM equivalent and about 240 pounds of corn would be required to produce 50 pounds of pork in dry lot from a 38-pound pig. On the basis of these figures, the alfalfa grazed in producing 100 pounds of pork is worth about 200 pounds of corn. Let's see—10 pigs per acre, 6 times per year to produce 3,000 pounds of pork, 200 pounds of corn saved in adding each 100 pounds of gain ($10 \times 6 \times 0.5 \times 200$ pounds = 6,000 pounds) or 107 bushels of corn saved per year. The proportions of protein fed in this case were too small especially in the dry lot to be economical in producing hogs at the assumed prices. The marginal physical productivity of additional protein from any source was so high that the alfalfa made a large contribution to production and corn was used very inefficiently in the dry lot.

Of the three sets of computations above, the first is the only one which makes economic sense. The first set of computations is based upon data taken from very near the scale line. The other two sets of data were secured by feeding uneconomic proportions of protein.

In the first case, the SOM equivalent and corn saved per 100 pounds of pork produced was equal in value at the assumed price relationships to about 140 pounds of corn. If 10 pigs were kept per acre and if this process were repeated six times per year to produce 3,000 pounds of pork, alfalfa would save 4,200 pounds of corn (worth about 1,400 pounds of SOM equivalent); either statement represents an approximate measure of the value of alfalfa forage as a substitute for both corn and protein supplement at the assumed price relationships. On this correct basis, an acre of alfalfa replaces about 75 bushels of corn.

In the second case, where excess SOM equivalent was feed, the equivalent of but 21 bushels of corn was saved per acre, figuring 60 hogs, each gaining 50 pounds (40 pounds saved per cwt $\times$ 30 cwt of hogs is 1,200 pounds or 21 bushels).

It should be stressed that the above iso-product lines are subject to some error—they were derived by linear interpolations (which partially obscure diminishing returns along the scale line) and extrapolations (see Figure 16.4). The interpolated and extrapolated data and figures based thereon are used here for two reasons: (1) they illustrate, in a semifactual way, the importance of understanding substitutability and price effects in evaluating inputs, (2) they serve to put the student on his guard against statements derived by less reliable computational procedures concerning the values of substitute inputs, especially forage and roughage. Animal husbandrymen and economists have much joint work to do before accurate practical recommendations can be made concerning the substitutability of forage for grain and protein in pork production.

QUESTIONS AND PROBLEMS

1. If corn is worth $1.75 per bushel now and a 250-pound hog is worth $20 a hundred, how much will he have to bring to make it worth while to fatten him to 300 pounds?

2. If a hog weighs 200 pounds now and is worth $20 a hundred, with corn at $1.75 per bushel, how much will have to be received for him when he weighs 250 pounds if it is to be profitable to feed him to that weight?

3. How much feed does it take to increase the weight of a hog from 200 to 250 pounds, from 275 to 300 pounds, and from 225 to 275 pounds?

4. Discuss how protein requirements depend upon the relationship between protein supplements and corn prices.

5. Discuss how protein requirements with a given ratio between protein supplement and corn prices depend upon the kind of pasture furnished to feeder pigs.

CHAPTER 17

Input-Output Relationships in Dairy Production

Introductory Statement

This is the second chapter which applies the marginal principles of economics to specific farming problems. This chapter concentrates upon the relationship between feed inputs and milk outputs, in the short run. In the later portions of the chapter, longer runs involving changing herd sizes and changing barn sizes are also considered.

Many different lengths of run are important in dairy production as well as in other lines of production. This chapter will analyze the dairy enterprise with respect to three lengths of run or planning spans: (1) short-run planning spans in which the dairy herd, equipment, barn, etc., are fixed, (2) intermediate lengths of run in which size and quality of the dairy herd are variable and in which barns, pasture areas, and cropping programs are fixed, and (3) long-run planning spans in which barns, pasture areas, and cropping programs are variable and in which management only is fixed.

Short-Run Planning Span in Which the Dairy Herd, Equipment, Barn, etc., Are Fixed

In recent years, a considerable amount of research has been devoted to determining the input-output relationship for milk production in the lengths of run or planning spans in which feed is the major variable factor of production. At the instigation of John D. Black of Harvard University, a Bankhead-Jones special research fund was provided for examining and doing research on input-output relationships in milk production. The research is based on a vast amount of earlier work in the fields of agricultural economics and dairy husbandry. Ten different state agricultural experiment stations cooperated in producing the required physical input-output data. This work was summarized under the leadership of three agricultural economists, Einar Jensen,

John W. Klein, and Emil Rauchenstein, and two dairy husbandrymen, T. E. Woodward and Ray H. Smith. These five men represented a unique combination of economic and technical talent rarely assembled in agricultural research. The summarized results of the research are published in *U.S.D.A. Technical Bulletin* 815, entitled "Input-Output Relationships in Milk Production." This bulletin, as its serial title indicates, is a rather technical bulletin. Then, an article entitled "More Grain for Your Dairy Cows" was published by John W. Klein and Ralph D. Jennings in *The Agricultural Situation* for February, 1949. The research reported in these two bulletins provides the basic information included in this section.

In terms of the earlier chapter entitled "The Need for Economizing Principles," the production function investigated by Jensen, et al., was the following: milk output per cow as it depends, under certain fixed conditions, upon (1) inputs of a balanced concentrate ration and (2) inputs of good-quality roughages. The fixed conditions are essentially: (1) that the cow involved be capable of yielding between 6 and 12 thousand pounds of milk per year and (2) that the technical conditions for production be about the average of those encountered on the typical experiment station farm (by and large these conditions are not far from those typical of the average on farms operated by members of Dairy Herd Improvement Associations). In the actual experiments, a considerable amount of variation occurred both in the quality of cow used and in technical conditions. The average quality of cow probably was not too different from those on many farms operated by members of the D.H.I.A.

In the experiments, cattle were fed at different percentages of the standard feeding ration. Some of the cattle were fed more; others less than the standard ration. The resulting production of milk definitely showed that the law of diminishing marginal returns applies as intake of digestible nutrients per cow is increased.

The cows were first fed their concentrate ration and then permitted to eat all the good-quality hay that they desired. Thus, in all cases the cattle were filled. Increases in digestible nutrient intake were brought about by increasing the concentrate ration. A hypothetical product contour map indicates how the cattle were fed concentrates and roughages.

In Figure 17.1, grain is plotted on the vertical axis and roughage is plotted on the horizontal axis. Because so little is known about this product contour map, the axes are not scaled. The figure is presented in order to give the student a conceptual idea of the nature of the experimental feeding program. A line, such as the line AB in the diagram, exists which can be called the "maintenance line." At least the quantities of roughage and concentrates represented by the different points along this line are necessary to maintain the dairy animal. The line BC can be dubbed the "stomach limit line." This line represents the limit of the cow's capacity to consume hay and concentrates . . .

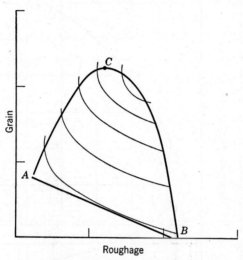

Fig. 17.1. Product contour map showing milk production as it hypothetically depends on grain and roughage input.

she simply will not eat more than the quantities represented by this line. The line CA can be dubbed "the concentrate limit line." Beyond this line consumption of more concentrates would make the cow ill; she would eat more concentrates than this line permits but they would make her ill. The experimenters expanded the intake of digestible nutrients along the horizontal or roughage axis until the cows were eating all the roughage they could eat. Increases in digestible nutrient consumption beyond this point were secured by expanding consumption of concentrates, thus reducing consumption of hay.

Because of the particular way in which digestible nutrient consumption was expanded, the question of locating the scale line between roughage and grain, in accordance with relative prices, was circumvented. All expansions or contractions of feed input occurred along the roughage axis or along the stomach limit line with the exception of a smaller subexperiment which simultaneously investigated limited hay and limited grain feeding. The procedure of free feeding hay was, and is, in accordance with feeding practices recommended by dairy husbandrymen. Dairy husbandrymen evidently concluded that hay is

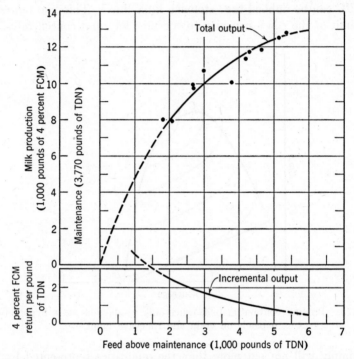

FIG. 17.2.   Response in milk production to increased feeding. Differences in production of balanced groups of cows fed at different levels for 3 years at experiment station B.

generally so cheap relative to concentrates and relative to the ratio between the productivity of concentrates and hay that it always pays to feed as much hay as a cow will consume at any level of grain intake.[1]

The input-output functions were presented in *U.S.D.A. Technical Bulletin* 815. These two functions are presented as Figures 17.2 and

[1] The recommendation presupposes that:

$$\frac{MPP_{\text{hay(milk)}}}{MPP_{\text{conc.(milk)}}} > \frac{P_{\text{hay}}}{P_{\text{conc.}}}$$

17.3. One of these functions was calculated from data secured from cows giving between 7,500 and 12,250 pounds of milk per year under experimental conditions. The other was calculated from data secured from cows giving between 8,000 and 13,000 pounds of milk per year.

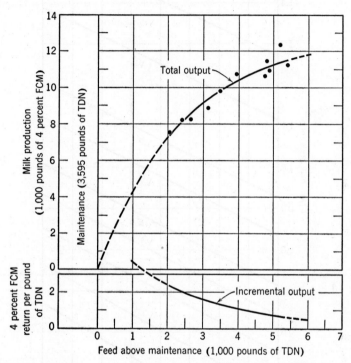

Fig. 17.3. Response in milk production to increased feeding. Differences in production of balanced groups of cows fed at different levels for 3 years at experiment station A.

The experimenters combined the data plotted in Figures 17.2 and 17.3 with other data to arrive at an overall input-output relationship for milk production (see Figure 17.6). Once the experimenters knew the general nature of the input-output relationship for producing milk, they were in a position to ask themselves the following question. For the type of cow used in the experiment and under the management conditions which prevailed on the experimental farms, *how should the feeding of hay and concentrates be varied as the price of milk and the price of hay and the price of concentrates change?* In the *Technical*

Bulletin this question was answered with Figure 17.4. Figure 17.4 has the grain-milk price ratio on the vertical axis and the hay-milk price

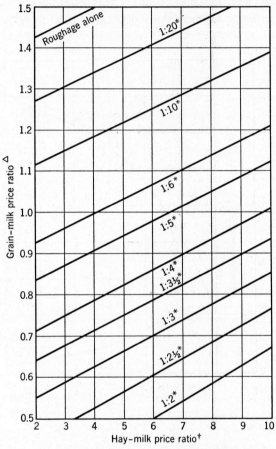

*Cows fed 1 pound of grain to every 2 pounds of milk during the lactation period are said to be fed at the level of 1:2: etc.

△ Price of 100 pounds of grain divided by price of 100 pounds of 4 percent fat-corrected milk.

†Price of 1 ton of hay or hay equivalent divided by price of 100 pounds of 4 percent fat-corrected milk.

Fig. 17.4. Chart showing the most profitable level of grain feeding, when cows have free access to good roughage.

ratio on the horizontal axis. Footnotes on the figure indicate how these ratios are computed. A series of parallel lines cross the diagram in a diagonal direction. Each of these lines is labeled with a ratio. For instance, the bottom line is labeled with the ratio 1:2. This ratio indicates that a cow should be fed 1 pound of grain to every 2 pounds of milk produced under specified price conditions. The next to the top line is labeled with a ratio of 1:20; the top line is labeled "roughage alone." In order to answer the question posed in this section, one first computes the grain-milk price ratio, then the hay-milk price ratio, both at the farm. He then locates (with respect to the appropriate axis) that point on the diagram at which the lines representing the two ratios cross. The following example will make this procedure clear: Suppose that the price of grain is $3.00 per hundredweight and that the price of milk is also $3.00 per hundredweight. The grain-milk price ratio is thus 1. Now suppose that hay is selling for $12 a ton. The hay-milk price ratio then becomes 4. The horizontal line representing a grain-milk price ratio of 1 intersects the vertical line representing a hay-milk price ratio of 4 near the diagonal line labeled 1:6. Thus, we conclude that when (1) milk is $3.00 a hundredweight, (2) grain concentrate is $3.00 a hundredweight, and (3) hay is $12.00 a ton it pays to feed cows of the quality studied in this experiment and under the conditions of this experiment at a ratio of 1 pound of grain for each 6 pounds of milk produced throughout the lactation period. Control of the ratio at which grain is fed controls TDN consumption. According to the study, feeding at this ratio will equalize the value of the marginal product of a digestible nutrient with its cost. As demonstrated earlier, this condition maximizes profits from feeding.

The study also showed, as indicated by Figure 17.5, that a heavy level of feeding in the early stages of the lactation period results in both (1) a higher peak in milk production and (2) sustained production over a longer period.

As indicated earlier, *U.S.D.A. Technical Bulletin* 815 was supplemented in 1949 by an article entitled, "More Grain for Your Dairy Cows." This article, which was published in *The Agricultural Situation,* 1949, also applies in the short-run planning span in which herd, barn and major items of equipment are fixed. *Bulletin* 815 is difficult to understand. The later article is more easily understood and in addition presents information (1) on how rates of feeding should be varied for different quality cows and for cows producing milk of different fat content and (2) on how limited hay feeding affects the most profitable ratio of feeding concentrates. Because this article is so well written and understandable, it is reproduced in its entirety on the following pages.[1]

[1] Reproduced from *The Agricultural Situation,* Bureau of Agricultural Economics, U. S. Department of Agriculture, Volume 33, Number 2, February, 1949.

Whether it will pay to feed more grain to dairy cows is a question each dairy farmer must figure out for himself. But the results of feeding experiments that the Department of Agriculture made in cooperation with 10 State Agricultural Experiment Stations will help him in his calculations.

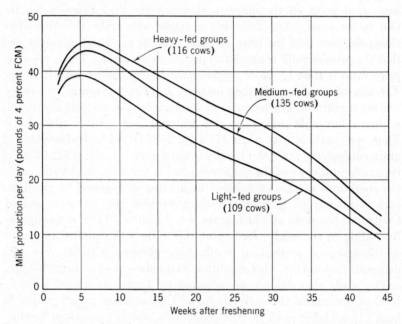

FIG. 17.5. Average lactation curves showing peak of production and persistency for cows divided into three groups according to level of feeding—360 unbroken lactation records at nine stations conducting Series I and II experiments.

Whether it will pay to feed more grain to dairy cows depends on the prices of grain, hay, and milk. While it is generally recommended that farmers feed plenty of good hay and other roughage, heavier feeding of grain to cows is likely to be profitable on many dairy farms the next year or so because there is a continued strong demand for milk; larger supplies of feed grains are available, and feed prices are low in relation to milk prices.

As more grain is fed, in general, less and less milk is produced per pound of grain. Even so, if grain is cheap compared with milk it may pay to feed grain heavily. This article may help you to decide just how heavy it will pay to feed.

Two Feeding Experiments. The quality and quantity of roughage available for feeding is very important in determining the amount of grain to be fed. Cows will consume more good-quality roughage than roughage of poor quality and will get more nutritive value out of each pound. Also, when farmers have a lot of roughage available per cow and little opportunity for using it for other purposes they prefer to feed more per cow than when the amount of roughage is limited and its price is high.

Methods of feeding roughage and the amount fed per cow vary considerably. In the following, the results of only two feeding experiments are presented. In the first, cows were fed all the good-quality roughages that they would eat. In the second, good-quality roughage was limited to 18.5 pounds of hay or its equivalent per 1,000 pounds liveweight daily. The most profitable rate of grain feeding is considerably different in the two situations. A dairyman should decide whether either situation fits his conditions before using the information in this article.

All the Hay They Want. *Cows with free access to good roughage.* Generally, if cows are allowed to have as much good hay or other roughage as they want and then the grain ration is increased, they eat more grain but eat less hay and other roughage. The figures show that for each additional *100 pounds of grain fed 60 to 75 pounds* less hay is consumed.

Total milk production is increased, but as you feed more grain you get less and less milk per additional pound of grain. This is partly due to the fact that this grain replaces some roughage but it is also true that with heavier feeding cows make less efficient use of the nutrients in their feed.

For instance, cows fed 1 pound of grain for each 6 pounds of milk will produce 97 pounds more milk for each additional 100 pounds of grain. Cows fed heavier than 1 to 6 the year around will produce less milk per 100 pounds of additional grain as shown below.

Level of Feeding Grain	Pounds Milk from 100 Pounds More Grain
1:6	97
1:4	77
1:3	59
1:2½	45
1:2	31

This information could be used to figure out whether it will be profitable for a dairyman to feed additional grain to his cows. Let us assume that he has a herd of medium-sized cows testing 4 percent butterfat and that he is feeding his herd the year around about 1 pound of grain to 3 pounds of milk; and that the price of milk is $4.25 per hundred pounds. Grain is $3 per hundred pounds and hay is $25 per ton.

Figuring Returns. He would first calculate the value of the additional milk by multiplying the pounds of additional milk (59 pounds in this case) by the current farm price for milk. He would figure on 68 pounds of hay or about one-thirtieth of a ton saved for each additional 100 pounds of grain fed. His calculation follows:

Value of 59 pounds additional milk at $4.25 per hundred pounds	$2.51
Value of hay saved (68 lb. at $25 per ton)	0.83
Total credits	$3.34
Cost of 100 pounds grain fed	3.00
Return per $1 of additional grain fed ($3.34 divided by $3.00)	1.11

So in this instance, it would pay to feed more grain. Any return higher than $1 per $1 of grain fed is usually profitable, because any extra labor or other costs are too small to count.

How much more grain would it pay to feed? The general rule is that increasing grain feeding will pay up to the point where the cost of the last increase in the grain ration just equals the value of the additional milk produced. Figuring this "break-even point" in grain feeding for cows of different size and butterfat test is easy by using Table 17.1. Most profitable levels of feeding shown in this table were figured by the method just described.

How to Use Table 17.1. In using the table, first find the pounds of milk it takes to pay for 100 pounds of grain. If grain is $3.00 a hundred pounds and milk is $4.25 a hundred or 4¼ cents a pound, it takes 71 pounds of milk to pay for 100 pounds of grain. Go down the first column of Table 17.1 until you come to 70, then across to the column that fits your conditions. For example, if hay is worth $25 a ton (6 times the price of milk per hundred pounds) and your cow is medium sized, testing about 4 percent butterfat, then column 6 is the one to use. In that column you find 2.7 opposite 70 in the first column. Therefore, the most profitable rate of feeding is 1 pound of grain to about 2.7 pounds of milk. But, if hay is cheap and abundant, 1 pound of grain to 3.1 pounds of milk would be the answer (column 3). If the cow is large, testing 3½ percent butterfat, the most profitable rate of feeding would be 1 to 2.8 (column 5), or 1 to 3.2 (column 2), depending on the price of hay.

Table 17.1. Most Profitable Rate of Grain Feeding [1]

Feeding 1 Pound of Grain to the Pounds of Milk Given Below

Pounds of Milk Equal in Value to 100 Pounds of Grain or Mixed Feed	Hay Price per Ton 3 to 4 Times Milk Price per 100 Pounds			Hay Price per Ton 5 to 7 Times Milk Price per 100 Pounds		
	Large Cows Testing 3½% Fat	Medium Cows Testing 4% Fat	Small Cows Testing 5% Fat	Large Cows Testing 3½% Fat	Medium Cows Testing 4% Fat	Small Cows Testing 5% Fat
(1)	(2)	(3)	(4)	(5)	(6)	(7)
120	7.7	8.2	8.5	6.3	6.5	6.6
110	6.1	6.2	6.3	5.2	5.2	5.2
100	5.0	5.0	5.0	4.4	4.3	4.2
90	4.2	4.1	4.1	3.7	3.6	3.4
80	3.7	3.5	3.4	3.3	3.1	2.8
70	3.2	3.1	2.8	2.8	2.7	2.4
60	2.8	2.6	2.4	2.4	2.3	2.1
50	2.4	2.3	2.1	2.1	2.0	2
40	2.0	2	2	2	2	2

[1] For cows of different size and butterfat test getting all the good hay or its equivalent in other roughage they will eat with different relative prices of grain and hay to milk.
[2] All they will eat without injury.

Limited Roughage. *Cows fed limited quantities of good roughage.* But what happens if you do not have enough roughage to give the cows all that they will eat, as is the case on many farms? Suppose you give them about 18.5 pounds of good hay a day per 1,000 pounds liveweight (20 pounds of average hay), or the equivalent in other roughage. (Figure that 3 pounds of silage are equal to 1 pound of hay.)

If you feed additional grain, your cows will eat about the same amount of hay or other roughage as before; you will not save in hay, and no saving will appear in the calculation. But you will get more milk from 100 pounds of additional grain than if the cows had all the hay they would eat because the cows are not getting as much feed in total and also because they do not reduce their hay consumption when the grain ration is increased.

Using Table 17.2. From Table 17.2 you can determine the additional milk that you can expect from each 100 pounds of additional grain fed. If you are feeding your herd (assuming medium-sized cows) at the 1 to 2.5 level and add 100 pounds of grain, you may expect 85 pounds of additional milk (first column, Table 17.2). This compares with only 45 pounds when cows have all the roughage they can eat.

What is the most profitable level of feeding cows where the feeding of roughage is limited? This also is shown in Table 17.2. Assume that milk sells for $4.25 a hundred, or 4¼ cents a pound, and grain is worth $3 a hundred pounds. Then 100 pounds of grain will equal in value 71 pounds of milk (3 ÷ 0.0425 = 71). Running down the first column in Table 17.2 to 70 (the nearest figure to 71) and reading across, you will find these different rates of grain feeding given. If your cows are medium sized, testing 4 percent butterfat, for example, your most profitable level of feeding would be 1 pound of grain to 2.3 pounds of milk.

Table 17.2. Most Profitable Level of Grain Feeding [1]

Pounds of Milk Equal in Value to 100 Pounds of Grain or Mixed Feed [2]	Feeding 1 Pound of Grain to the Pounds of Milk Given Below		
	For Large Cows Testing 3½% Fat, lb.	For Medium Cows Testing 4% Fat, lb.	For Small Cows Testing 5% Fat, lb.
175	4.1	4.0	3.9
160	3.7	3.5	3.4
145	3.4	3.2	3.1
130	3.2	3.0	2.8
115	3.0	2.8	2.6
100	2.9	2.7	2.4
85	2.7	2.5	2.2
70	2.4	2.3	2.1
55	2.1	2.0	[3]

[1] For cows of different size and butterfat test where roughage is limited to 18.5 pounds of good hay or its equivalent per 1,000 pound cow daily with different relative price of grain to milk.

[2] The figures in this column are also the pounds of additional milk obtained from feeding 100 pounds additional grain at the specified rates of feeding.

[3] All they will eat without injury.

Higher Level Unprofitable. Now let us see if feeding your medium-sized cows at the 1 to 2 level would be less profitable, assuming the same prices. You obtain only 55 pounds of additional milk from 100 pounds of additional grain when feeding at the 1 to 2 level. (See footnote, Table 17.2.)

Value of 55 pounds of additional milk at $4.25	$2.34
Cost of 100 pounds of additional grain at $3	3.00
Hay saved (none)	....
Loss on each 100 pounds additional gain	$0.66

In this case, it is not as profitable to feed cows 1 to 2 as 1 to 2.3 because money was lost on the last few pounds of grain fed.

In the experiments that provided the figures used in this article the cows were barn fed throughout the lactation period, but the figures will apply to pasture feeding as well. The results shown for good cows that have access to unlimited roughage (Table 17.1) probably would apply when feeding grain to cows on pasture if the pastures are good to excellent. The results shown in Table 17.2 probably would apply if the pasture is only fair.

On Poor Pastures. If the pasture is poor, then 100 pounds of additional grain probably would increase milk production more than is shown in Table 17.2. Farmers usually cut down their rate of feeding grain to dairy cows during the summer when the cows are on pasture. It probably would pay to feed grain heavily right through the pasture season.

Once the appropriate ratio of grain to milk production is ascertained from either Figure 17.4, Table 17.1, or Table 17.2 (whichever is appropriate), the question of how much grain and other feeds will have to be fed per year has to be answered. This question needs to be answered for purposes of making long-run plans and budgets. Table 17.3 presents feed-requirement data for various levels of milk production. The data plotted in Figure 17.6 are from Table 17.3.

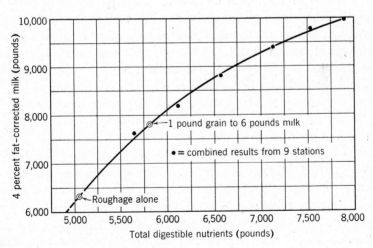

Fig. 17.6. Chart based on the smoothed data of experiment Series I and II combined, and roughage alone of Series II. Nonpasture stations (Table 27), after adjustment of Series II data for difference in basic producing ability of the cows.

Table 17.3. Smoothed Data from 6 Feeding Levels at 9 Stations and 2 Feeding Levels at 2 Stations, Prepared for the Purpose of Estimating the Most Profitable Rate at Which to Feed Grain

Level of Feeding from Lowest to Highest	Live Weight, lb.	Roughage Expressed as Hay Equivalent per 100 Lb. Live Weight, lb.	Total Hay Equivalent Fed in a Year, lb.	Grain Fed in a Year, lb.	Grain Fed during Lactation Period, lb.	Adjusted Total Digestible Nutrients, lb.	Estimated Quantities of Milk These Feeds Would Produce, lb.	Milk Produced per Pound of Grain Fed during Lactation, lb.
1	1,080	2.9	11,338	0	0	5,102	6,438	....
2	1,090	2.8	11,048	450	420	5,376	7,020	16.7
3	1,100	2.7	10,751	900	840	5,642	7,517	8.9
4	1,110	2.6	10,447	1,350	1,260	5,901	7,947	6.3
5	1,120	2.5	10,136	1,800	1,680	6,154	8,317	5.0
6	1,130	2.4	9,817	2,250	2,100	6,400	8,639	4.1
7	1,140	2.3	9,492	2,700	2,520	6,638	8,915	3.5
8	1,150	2.2	9,159	3,150	2,940	6,868	9,156	3.1
9	1,160	2.1	8,818	3,600	3,360	7,091	9,366	2.8
10	1,170	2.0	8,471	4,050	3,780	7,307	9,550	2.5
11	1,180	1.9	8,116	4,500	4,200	7,514	9,708	2.3
12	1,190	1.8	7,754	4,950	4,620	7,713	9,847	2.1
13	1,200	1.7	7,385	5,400	5,040	7,905	9,971	2.0

The column in Table 17.3 entitled "Grain Fed during Lactation Period" and the column entitled "Estimated Quantities of Milk These Feeds Would Produce" can be used to determine the total quantities of grain which would be fed per year when cows of the quality represented by the data are fed at any given ratio of grain to milk production. For instance, if Table 17.1 indicated for a given set of price relationships that a cow should be fed at the rate of 1 pound of grain to 3 pounds of milk and if the cows concerned were capable of yielding between 6,500 and 10,000 pounds of milk (depending upon rate of feeding), then Table 17.3 could be used to determine the probable amount of hay and grain required per year. Table 17.3 indicates that somewhat over 3,000 pounds of grain fed to such a cow would produce between 9,100 and 9,300 pounds of milk. This is feeding grain at approximately 1:3, the ratio which current prices indicate is correct to feed. Along with the grain requirement, Table 17.3 indicates that the cow would eat somewhat over 8,800 pounds of hay equivalent per year. *These two figures*, one for grain and one for hay, *are the basic figures required for budgeting and planning.*

Table 17.3 is for large cows capable of producing 6,400 pounds of milk per year with no grain and almost 10,000 pounds of 4 percent fat-

corrected milk per year when fed grain at a ratio of 1 pound to 2
pounds of milk. A very high percentage of the cows milked in this
country are of lower quality, and a considerable number of the cows
milked in this country are of higher quality. If farmers having higher
and lower quality cows than represented by the data in Table 17.3

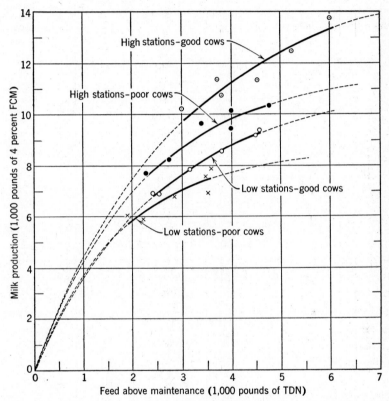

FIG. 17.7. Input-output curves of cows of different inherent productivity at the
nine experiment stations.

are to be able to plan total feed requirements per year, they must have
information for cows of various qualities comparable to that presented
in Table 17.3. Figure 17.7 presents total productivity curves for cows
of four different qualities.

The data used in constructing Figures 17.7 are presented in Table
17.4. These data are useful in ascertaining total feed requirements for
dairy animals of qualities similar to those from which the data were

Table 17.4.   Influence of Differences in Inherent Productivity of Cows upon Response in Output to Increased Feed Inputs; Yearly Averages per Cow—Combined Data from 9 Stations

Level of Feeding	Records, No.	Average Live Weight, lb.	Basic Producing Ability, 4 Percent Fat-Corrected Milk, lb.	4 Percent Fat-Corrected Milk Produced, lb.	Hay, lb.	Silage, Corn (or Sorghum), lb.	Silage, Alfalfa, lb.	Mangels, lb.	Pasture 1 Day—15 Pounds Total Digestible Nutrients, days	Grain 75 Percent Total Digestible Nutrients, lb.	Ratio of Grain to 4 Percent Fat-Corrected Milk during Lactation	Roughage Expressed as Hay Equivalent per Day for Each 100 Pounds Live Weight	Total Digestible Nutrients Consumed in a Year
Low Stations, Poor Cows													
1	14	936	6,549	6,035	3,870	8,225	43	...	2.0	1,641	1:3.80	2.02	4,742
2	23	944	6,524	5,938	4,470	9,554	...	...	2.8	1,423	1:4.50	2.27	5,040
3	19	996	6,562	6,795	3,871	10,652	43	...	4.7	2,242	1:3.25	2.15	5,656
4	17	995	6,431	7,602	3,908	10,151	...	...	2.2	3,354	1:2.37	2.06	6,309
5	16	998	6,572	7,893	3,696	9,035	86	...	8.6	3,662	1:2.30	1.97	6,395
6	14	1,080	6,444	6,894	4,054	6,154	259	...	5.2	3,944	1:1.82	1.68	6,326
Low Stations, Good Cows													
1	13	1,099	8,833	6,864	5,005	9,614	...	...	3.7	1,775	1:3.94	2.09	5,578
2	11	1,078	8,831	6,855	5,004	10,406	...	...	9.5	1,538	1:4.70	2.29	5,736
3	14	1,054	8,948	7,887	4,748	10,736	146	...	5.1	2,562	1:3.19	2.26	6,332
4	17	1,089	8,966	8,544	4,810	11,848	...	...	2.2	3,219	1:2.76	2.26	6,971
5	9	1,244	8,956	9,354	4,810	10,945	...	...	2.1	4,250	1:2.29	1.97	7,739
6	31	1,134	8,864	9,201	4,106	7,950	31	...	6.8	5,257	1:1.79	1.77	7,667
High Stations, Poor Cows													
1	17	1,142	8,793	7,618	3,474	11,710	1,488	356	24.5	1,687	1:4.68	2.09	5,697
2	20	1,147	8,913	8,207	3,087	11,064	943	111	47.5	2,343	1:3.64	2.08	6,182
3	10	1,207	8,738	9,624	3,270	12,599	848	217	30.2	3,115	1:3.16	2.00	6,817
4	17	1,239	8,851	10,118	3,470	11,654	751	152	32.6	3,972	1:2.61	1.95	7,448
5	14	1,180	8,907	9,434	3,424	10,561	674	236	34.9	4,111	1:2.35	1.96	7,365
6	27	1,267	8,823	10,347	3,188	9,578	747	75	41.6	5,448	1:1.94	1.73	8,142
High Stations, Good Cows													
1	17	1,201	11,518	10,195	3,432	13,277	584	192	60.5	2,207	1:4.71	2.23	6,624
2	14	1,191	11,482	11,322	3,634	12,576	612	275	32.5	3,407	1:3.37	2.13	7,266
3	20	1,198	11,445	10,768	3,482	11,630	930	316	50.2	3,418	1:3.21	2.16	7,351
4	17	1,271	11,554	11,311	3,527	12,273	980	233	44.7	4,320	1:2.66	2.05	7,448
5	12	1,302	11,489	12,506	3,464	12,472	604	147	48.2	5,225	1:2.46	2.00	8,750
6	18	1,352	11,389	13,736	3,710	11,140	227	...	32.2	7,068	1:1.96	1.71	9,592

secured. In addition, Table 17.5 is presented to indicate grain and hay requirements for light cows of poor quality. Table 17.5 was derived from data presented in *Bulletin* 815 as well as from data gathered from a variety of other sources. Tables 17.4 and 17.5 give the student when making budgets an idea of how the data presented in Table 17.3 and the data plotted in Figure 17.6 can be adjusted to feeding situations involving cows of different qualities. It should be emphasized that Tables 17.1 and 17.2 and Figure 17.4 do not apply to low-quality cows of the type considered in Table 17.5 or to cows of exceptionally high quality. In general, it probably does not pay to feed low-quality dairy cows at as high a ratio of grain to milk as it pays to feed high-quality dairy cows. The procedure for using Table 17.4 will be illustrated in connection with the budgeting problem in Chapter 21.

Table 17.5. **Annual Feed Inputs and Milk Production of Dairy Cows Fed at Different Levels, 305-Day Lactation Period, Predominately Jersey Cows (Holsteins, Guernseys, and Mixed Breeds Are Present), Largely Spring Freshening (Estimated 75%), Average Hay and Pasture for the Area (Probably Poor Hay and Pasture in Relation to the Best in Kentucky and Northern States), 800-Pound Cows, 4% F.C.M., South Central Kentucky** [1]

Producing Ability of the Cows, Milk	Level of Feeding		Pasture TDN (180 days equivalent), lb.	Hay [2]		Grain [3]		Milk Production, lb.
	% TDN from Roughage, lb.	Total TDN Consumed, lb.		TDN, lb.	WT., lb.	TDN, lb.	WT., lb.	
Low	100%	3,578	1,764	1,814	4,146	0	0	3,650
4,950 lb. milk at 1:4 milk	90%	3,831	1,700	1,748	3,995	383	532	4,350
grain ratio during lac-	80%	4,113	1,622	1,668	3,812	823	1,143	4,822
tation	70%	4,414	1,524	1,566	3,581	1,324	1,838	5,160
	60%	4,745	1,404	1,443	3,298	1,898	2,636	5,358
198 lb. fat	55%	4,916	1,334	1,370	3,132	2,212	3,072	5,422

[1] James A. Wells, "A Technique for Synthesizing Cost of Production Data with Special Reference to Dairy Enterprises in Green and Taylor Counties of Kentucky," Unpublished Master's Thesis, Department of Farm Economics, University of Kentucky, p. 38, May, 1951.

[2] Weight of hay includes hay wasted and refused. Weight of TDN is only the amount consumed. Hay is approximately 49% TDN average from the following kinds: 15% alfalfa, 41% clover and timothy, and 44% lespedeza.

[3] Grain mixture = 1,100 lb. corn-and-cob meal, 450 lb. wheat bran, and 450 lb. cottonseed meal, approximately 18% protein, and 72% TDN.

A principal shortcoming of the input-output data presented herein results from the way pasturage was handled in the experiments. Most of the data were secured under barn feeding conditions. Further, most of the data were secured under the assumption that TDN's from hay are cheaper than TDN's from grain and that, therefore, a cow should always be fed all the hay possible for any given level of TDN intake.[1] It is distinctly possible that the production relationships used in this chapter are changed when dairy cows are fed high-quality pasturage and high-quality dry roughage. Currently, a large number of farm-management research workers are concerned with utilization of the forage produced under soil-conserving programs. They feel that additional research should be done on the input-output relationships involved in feeding high-quality pasturage and high-quality roughage to dairy animals. The authors hope that such research will be undertaken and that it will be possible, at a later date, to extend this section of this chapter to include, in a more complete form, the economics of feeding high-quality pasturage and dry roughage to dairy animals of different qualities.

Intermediate Length of Run in Which Size and Quality of the Dairy Herd Are Variable as Well as Amount of Feed and Minor Items of Equipment: Buildings, Major Items of Equipment, Pasture, Land and Management Fixed

Fewer data and less information are available to aid in handling the problem peculiar to the intermediate planning span.

Elementary logic indicates that when size of herd is expanded beyond the limits of the barn, efficiency in the use of labor falls off; that productivity per cow is probably reduced as the result of crowding and improper control of feeding, etc. Thus far, little research has been done to indicate the seriousness of these inefficiencies under practical farm conditions. Apparently, these inefficiencies are important because capacities of barns are rarely exceeded by more than 20 to 40 percent, according to observations made by the authors.

The question of capacity of cows appears to be one of the most important problems for this planning span. Figure 17.7 shows total production of 4 percent FCM per cow for animals of different qualities. The four qualities of cows are such that when fed concentrates at a ratio of 1 to 3 the highest-quality cows produce around 11,000 pounds, the next lower quality about 9,700 pounds, and the next lower quality about 8,200 pounds, and the lowest quality about 7,000 pounds.

Inspection of Figure 17.7 indicates great differences in the efficiency of the four animals in utilizing digestible nutrients. These differences are even more pronounced when the curves are appraised in marginal terms. It is obvious that as quality of cow increases marginal returns

[1] John C. Redman, op. cit.

increase and are more sustained; this condition can result in higher profits per cow only for a given set of feed and milk prices. The data plotted in Figure 17.7 are not conclusive, but they should indicate to the student that quality of dairy animals is a tremendously important factor determining productive efficiency. The quality of animal which it is desirable to keep, of course, depends upon the cost of such animals. One can rather safely conclude, however, that in producing dairy animals it is much more profitable to produce the high-quality than the low-quality animal. This is especially true since artificial insemination has eliminated much of the overhead cost of owning expensive sires. If their price is too high to make it profitable to milk the higher-quality cows thus produced, it will obviously be more profitable to sell their calves than to sell the calves of lower-quality animals. Feed and labor costs per calf change only slightly with quality of animal.

Long-Run Planning Span in Which Barns, Pasture Area and Cropping Programs Are Variable: Management Fixed

This is almost the ultimate long run as far as dairy production and a single farmer are concerned. It is only seldom in the lifetime of a farm manager that he has an opportunity to engage in such long-range planning. Such events occur only when major changes in cropping systems are in the offing, when dairy barns are undergoing major overhauls, or when new dairy barns are being built.

In recent years, two problems have occupied a prominent place in the long-run thinking of dairymen. The first of these problems is that of dairy barn arrangement. The second of these problems is that of forage and roughage production.

Dairy Barn Arrangement. In connection with the problem of dairy barn arrangement, a considerable amount of research has been done on the pen type-milking parlor arrangement for milking cows. When this arrangement is used, cows are brought to the milking machines in a small room especially equipped for milking and feeding concentrates to the animals. After being milked and fed their concentrate ration, the animals are turned loose in a rest shed, where they eat hay, have access to water, and await the next milking, except, of course, in the summer when they are turned out to graze. Considerable research work has also been done on improving the arrangement of standard stanchion-type barns. Both of these types of research indicate that very great improvements can be made in the productivity of labor in the dairy enterprise through proper barn arrangement. In old established dairy areas, few farmers have had an opportunity to replan buildings to take advantage of this research. In newer areas just now increasing dairy production seriously, many farmers are currently operating in planning situations which permit them to utilize this research.

Most experiment stations have done work on the problem of dairy barn arrangement. *Bulletin* 845 of Cornell University, entitled "Labor and Dairy Barn Chores," *Minnesota Farm Business Notes*, dated September 30, 1949, entitled "Does Loose Housing Save Labor?" and *Circular Bulletin* 195, Michigan State College, entitled "The Pen Barn and Milking Rooms in Michigan," are sufficient examples. *Work Simplification News Letter*, dated July, 1948, published by Purdue University, contains an article entitled "The Comparative Analysis of Stanchion and Milking Parlor Barns." *Wisconsin Bulletin* 470 is entitled "Dairy Housing in the North Central States." This list is by no means complete.

Work done at the University of Kentucky prior to March, 1950, is partially summarized in a *Farm Economic Information Circular*, dated March 17, 1950.[1] This circular is indicative of the type of research done on this problem and is reproduced here for the benefit of the student. (Pages 262–267 are quoted.)

Labor in dairying ranks second only to feed as an item of production costs. All dairymen are interested in easier and quicker ways of doing dairy chores and thereby reducing costs. Proper work methods, equipment, and building arrangement reduce travel and save labor in doing dairy chores. Proper location and arrangement of buildings lower overhead costs of shelter as well as save time and walking in dairying.

Dairymen using carefully planned work methods and effective building arrangements do dairy chores (feed, bed, milk, clean stables, wash utensils, and care for the milk) with 50 to 70 man-hours per cow annually. By the ordinary methods 120 to 150 man-hours are usually being used.

Motion-and-time studies of ··· dairy farms point the way to efficient use of labor and convenient building arrangements in doing dairy chores.

Before undertaking the building of any type of dairy barn or milk room, contact should be made with the county sanitarian or the milk inspector to have a thorough understanding of the requirements that must be met.

[1] Written and prepared by George B. Byers on the basis of his time-and-motion economy studies.

STANCHION-TYPE BARN

Dairy chores in the conventional stanchion-type barn may be reduced to less than 70 man-hours per cow annually by convenient building arrangement and efficient work routine.

Table 17.6. Annual Man Labor and Travel per Cow in Stanchion Barn, and in Four-Cow-Abreast Walk-Through Milking Room and Rest Shed

(Machine Milking)

	Stanchion Barn		Four-Cow Walk-Through Milking Room	
	Usual	Improved	Usual	Improved
Man labor, hours per cow annually				
Turn-in, fasten, turn-out cows	15.7	6.7	5.2	5.2
Wash, assemble, and move utensil and water	18.2	7.9	10.8	4.4.
Wash udders, milk, strip, and empty milk	71.3	34.4	37.4	31.2
Feed hay and bed	12.0	6.1	4.2	3.5
Feed grain	4.8	1.8	2.1	1.0
Clean barn and milk room	19.6	9.1	1.9	1.9
Total man-hours per cow annually	141.6	66.0	61.6	47.2
Travel, total miles walked per cow annually .	52	19	28	14

Close study of dairy-chore operations reveals detailed changes that reduce man-hours and travel in caring for dairy herds.

Time and distance walked in turning-in, fastening, and turning-out of the cows may be greatly reduced by well-hung, conveniently located doors and gates and the use of a rod or rope control that permits fastening or loosening of each line of cows from one position near the entrance or exit door. Further time and walking are saved by having a rod or rope control to open the exit door from the position at which the stanchion control is located.

In the washroom convenient location of drying racks for cans, pails and milkers, wash tubs, and water supply reduces walking and time to a minimum for washing, assembling the dairy utensils, preparing water for sterilizing the utensils and for washing the udders. Location of milk and washroom near the milking area further reduces time and travel in moving milkers and wash water to and from the milking area.

Washing udders, milking, and stripping time in the stanchion-type barn represent over half of the time required on all the dairy chores. Facing the cows out and following "Peterson's rapid milking procedures" make possible a reduction from over 70 man-hours per cow to less than 35 man-hours per cow annually for these three operations alone. Dr. W. E. Peterson's four steps in rapid milking procedures are essential in this time reduction. Careful watching and machine stripping just as the milk flow is finishing prevent tissue injury and avoid hand stripping; thus time is saved and injury to the cow's udder is prevented.

Time and travel in feeding grain and silage may be reduced to a minimum by having feed carts or carriers and using circular travel. By having protein supplements and grains mixed in one feed ration, by having a cart holding sufficient grain mixture for all cows for one feeding period, and by having an alleyway at each end of the two lines of cows, the feeding operation may start and finish by circular travel at approximately the same place. Walking "empty-handed" is avoided. With the silage chute near the grain storage area a minimum amount of time is required to start feeding silage. With a silage cart that just fits in the silo chute, silage may be pitched directly from silo to cart. Then, in a round trip with the silage cart the cows can be fed silage with a minimum amount of work. Several hay chutes conveniently located over feed alleys save time and walking in feeding hay.

Enough shovels, brooms, and small tools, conveniently located behind the cows, and a gutter cleaner or litter carrier speed up cleaning the barn. Facing cows out reduces time required to clean and lime the milking area. Liming may be done more easily and quickly by having lime in a porous bag which is dragged and shaken around the area.

Following the above work routine reduces the usual travel from over 50 miles per cow to less than 20 miles per cow per year.

Four-Cow Walk-Through Milking Room

Many · · · dairymen are saving additional labor and walking by using the four-cow-abreast *walk-through* milking room. In this type of milking arrangement the cows are fed grain and milked in a four-cow walk-through milking area; they are fed roughage and silage and are bedded and slept in another part of the barn, which is sometimes called the "loafing" or "loose housing" area.

With the usual arrangements in the four-cow walk-through area an average of 62 man-hours and 28 miles of travel per cow annually were used. Careful study by timing the operation with a stop watch and measuring the travel in work areas with a steel tape have shown that dairy chores can be done with less than 50 man-hours per cow and less than 15 miles of walking per cow annually. A detailed and accurate study of dairy chores on two farms with walk-through milking rooms, rest sheds, and milk rooms has shown that the dairy chores are done with less than 50 man-hours per cow and less than 15 miles of walking per cow per year for a 9-cow dairy herd and a 22-cow dairy herd. (See Table 17.6.) Other dairymen, with four-cow walk-through milking rooms, are doing dairy chores with similar requirements of labor and walking.

Turning-in, fastening, and turning-out the cows in the walk-through area require less time than in the conventional stanchion barn since the cow is turned out immediately after the milker is removed from her and placed on an adjacent cow. No walking is required to turn the cows out, as a pull cord controls the exit door from each "stall" area. The cows are turned in two at a time, requiring a minimum of walking.

Moving utensils and water to and from the milk room is reduced by having doors located midway of the four-cow walk-through milking area to the rear of the cows. Thus a minimum of walking is required in getting milker units from the wash room to the milking area. A bucket of disinfectant for the teatcups at each milking unit saves time and walking within the milking area. Further savings in time and walking are brought about by having a bucket of water to wash the udder at each area where a milking unit is used.

Locating the milk room convenient to the walk-through milking area and following the rapid milking procedures reduce time and walking to a minimum in washing udders, milking, machine stripping, and emptying milk. Owing to convenient location these operations in the walk-through milking rooms are done in less time and travel than was possible in conventional stanchion barns.

Time and travel in feeding hay and bedding cows are reduced to a minimum by having hay racks that are filled directly from the hay loft. Some dairymen are reducing this time further by feeding sufficient hay at one feeding to satisfy the cows for a 24-hour period.

Grain feeding time and travel are reduced to a minimum by having overhead feed bins built to carry the grain by gravity to an opening between the feed boxes of each two cows at the area where the milk unit is operated. It should be recognized that a convenient method should be used to put the feed above the walk-through milking room.

After each cow is milked, stripped, and the milker placed on the next cow, the dairyman pulls a rope opening the door containing the grain-feed box, allowing the cow to *walk out forward* into the rest area. As the cow is walking out, the control in the gravity feed chute is opened allowing the desired quantity of grain to drop into a bucket marked off in pounds. This grain is then placed in the feed box as the door containing the feed box closes. Little or no walking is required to turn the cow out and feed grain. Where grain cannot be conveniently located in a grain bin above the cows, a storage area to the rear of the cows is usually best. As the rope is pulled to open the door in front of each cow just milked, permitting her to pass into the rest area, the dairyman steps back and gets the desired amount of grain in a scoop or bucket and feeds the next cow.

In the four-cow walk-through milking room procedures above, each cow is allowed about 10 to 15 minutes in which to eat the grain. Careful studies have shown this to be a sufficient amount of time for eating if cows are fed according to their production.

Time and travel in *cleaning* the four-cow walk-through milking area were reduced further from a possible low of 10 man-hours per cow annually for the stanchion barn to less than 2 man-hours per cow annually for the dairy barn with a walk-through milking area and rest shed. The saving in time and walking is made possible by having to clean out only the area of four walk-through "stalls." The fact that each cow is in the area only 10 or 15 minutes and no litter is used in this area reduces the amount of manure to be cleaned out.

Construction costs also are lower by having to provide stall area, feed box doors, and tight walls for only a four-cow area instead of for the entire herd. Cost of the loose housing area will vary with size of herd, and with use made of present barn. Studies show a significant saving in building costs when a loose housing arrangement is compared to a stanchion barn arrangement for the same size herd. Since the walk-through milking area may be used for varying numbers of cows, greater flexibility is provided by the walk-through milking area and rest shed type of dairy barn than by the stanchion dairy barn. Further flexibility may be obtained by the walk-through milking area and rest shed in that the rest shed area may be used as readily for sheep and beef cattle as for the dairy cows.

With cows sleeping on the manure pack in a rest shed more bedding *must* be used to keep the cows clean. Approximately 2 to 3 times as much bedding is required for the rest shed as for the conventional stanchion-type barn. Study has shown that the additional bedding conserves more of the liquid manure and results in larger amounts of plant food nutrients being returned to the soil, offsetting all or a large part of the cost of the extra bedding. Also the manure is allowed to accumulate in the rest shed, which provides shelter and prevents the loss from leaching of the plant food nutrients that occurs when the manure is thrown in a pile in the lot. Furthermore, the manure may remain in the barn without loss until the crop that will make the greatest use of the manure is ready or until a convenient time for hauling and spreading.

The "boss" cow problem is increased with the use of the rest shed. In this study, however, only a small percentage of the dairymen thought of this as a serious problem. Where the problem did arise "boss" cows were placed in an area to themselves or were sold from the herd. Farmer opinion is that all cows should be dehorned if they are to be housed in a rest shed or loose housing arrangement.

Forage Production. Forage production in connection with the dairy enterprise is a long-run question of importance and interest, but one on which more opinions than facts exist. Most of the facts available are of a case-study nature. Workers at experiment stations and in state agricultural extension services know of farmers who have vastly improved the productivity of dairy farms through pasture fertilization and the use of improved pasture measures. Overall financial records on such farms indicate that tremendous increases in profitability have occurred. These results, however, are generally confounded with changes in size of business, increasing price levels, additional managerial inputs, changes in quality of dairy animals (already indicated to be highly important in dairy efficiency), etc. The indications are that the average farmer is not even remotely close to the profitable margins in increasing the yield and quality of forage and hay for use in the dairy enterprise. However, these long-run questions, currently asked almost continuously by the best dairy farmers, are not yet adequately answered by our experiment stations.

Cost Schedules for the Three Different Lengths of Runs Considered in This Chapter Are "Wheels within Wheels"

For a given short run in which the size and quality of a given herd are not variable, average total and marginal cost schedules composed mostly of feed and labor costs exist. The average total cost schedule when plotted is tangent to another average cost schedule. This other average cost schedule is the average cost schedule for the length of run in which size and quality of the herd is variable.[1]   It has a corresponding marginal cost curve. In turn, this average total cost schedule is tangent to a third average total cost schedule. The third average cost schedule is for the long-run period in which buildings, forage programs, etc., are variable but in which management is fixed. It also has a corresponding marginal cost curve. Sketches of such average and marginal cost curves are presented in Figure 17.8.[2]

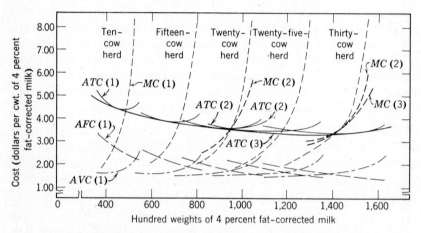

(1) Lengths of run in which only feeding level is variable, herd size and barn fixed.
(2) Lengths of run in which herd size is variable and barn size is fixed.
(3) Lengths of run in which barn size, as well as herd size and feeding level, is variable.

Source: Synthesized from secondary data.

FIG. 17.8. Overall structure of milk production costs for south central Kentucky.
(Based on data in Table 17.5 and prepared by James A. Wells.)

It is important for the student to realize that the average cost schedule $ATC(2)$ for the intermediate length of run plotted in Figure 17.8 is not the only cost schedule for that length of run which is tangent to the long-run average cost curve in which buildings are variable. For instance, there is an intermediate length of run, average total cost schedule for every conceivable size of barn which might be fixed by long-run decisions. Similarly, within every one of the intermediate, average total cost curves are a large number of short-run average total cost curves. In fact, there is one such average cost curve for every conceivable size of herd which might be handled under the fixed conditions

[1] Quality of cow could also be variable in this length of run.
[2] James A. Wells, op. cit.

determined by longer-run decisions. The picture, of course, is infinitely complex. Cost of production and management are also infinitely complex. This is why it is so difficult for researchers to do cost of production research applicable in a large number of practical situations. This is why there is such a tremendous diversity among dairy setups. This is why farm management students must necessarily be taught principles rather than precise practices.

Figure 17.8 permits the student to see how varying feed inputs changes MC, ATC, AFC, and AVC in milk production with herd size fixed. At the left of that diagram is a set of such costs curves ($ATC(1)$, etc.) for a ten-cow herd. From this set of curves it can be noted that, for the poor-quality cows involved, MC's vary from less than $2.00 a hundred to over $8.00 as feeding levels are changed. AVC's over about the same feeding range run from about $1.50 to $2.50, while AFC's fall from over $3.00 to almost $2.00. ATC's range from over $5.00 down to a low of about $4.40.

For a thirty-cow herd the cost curves are much different—in general they curve upward much less abruptly. MC's vary over about the same vertical range as for the ten-cow herd. The same is true for AVC's. AFC's, however, are much lower than for the ten-cow herd and, as a consequence of this, the ATC's are lower, ranging down from around $3.60 to around $3.40.

The "envelope curve" going around all the smaller ATC curves is $ATC(3)$ for lengths of runs in which barn size, as well as herd size and feeding level, is variable.

The data have considerable significance as they show the economies attainable by changing herd sizes, i.e., ATC's are lowered almost 25 percent and AFC's are cut almost in half by going from a ten- to a twenty-five-cow herd.

These data are of basic importance in considering size of herd, barn construction, and herd-financing problems.

The Ultimate Long Run

None of the three lengths of runs discussed above treated management as a variable factor. In practice management occasionally becomes variable. For instance management may be shifted from other enterprises to the dairy enterprise, or vice versa. Another way of increasing management is to produce more management. Management was functionally defined in the beginning of this book as observation, analysis, decision making, action, and acceptance of responsibility with respect to the problems of running a business. Management devoted to the dairy enterprise can be increased or produced by training, on the part of the manager, (1) to be a close observer of dairy production and marketing problems, (2) to be a keen analyst of dairy problems which includes learning to ask himself the right questions concerning the business, (3) to be an adept decision maker, (4) to be efficient in putting decisions into practice, and (5) to be able to see and bear responsibility for actions taken.

QUESTIONS AND PROBLEMS

1. Are the milk iso-product contours vertical at the "concentrate limit" line?

2. Does a relationship exist between the slope of an iso-product line at its intersection with the stomach limit line and the usual ratio of the price of roughage to the price of grain? What is this relationship?

3. From Figure 17.4 indicate the rate at which grain should be fed to a cow capable of giving between 6,000 and 7,000 pounds of milk when fed 1 pound of grain to each 4 pounds of milk in each of the following price situations:

(a) When 100 pounds of grain is equal in value to 90 pounds of milk and when a ton of hay is equal in value to 400 pounds of milk.

(b) When 100 pounds of grain costs $5.60, 100 pounds of milk sells for $4.00, and a ton of hay costs $26.00.

(c) When 100 pounds of grain is worth $2.40, 100 pounds of milk is worth $4.00, and a ton of hay is worth $34.00.

4. For budgeting purposes, what are some reasonable feed-requirements data to use when feeding 1 pound of grain to 5 pounds of milk to a cow capable of giving 8,600 pounds of milk when fed at a ratio of 1 to 4.1?

5. When the price of hay is 6 times the price of milk and 70 pounds of milk are equal in value to 100 pounds of grain, at what rate should the grain be fed to large cows producing milk testing 3½ percent butterfat? To small cows producing milk testing 5 percent butterfat?

6. When feeding 800-pound cows capable of producing about 5,000 pounds of 4 percent milk when fed at a ratio of 1 to 4, what pasture-, hay-, and grain-input data would be usable in Kentucky?

7. Discuss the effects of adopting a walk-through barn on dairy cost structures in the length of run long enough to permit herd sizes, but not barn sizes, to be variable.

8. Discuss the effect upon dairy cost structures of shifting from a herd of dairy cows capable of producing 5,000 pounds per year of milk when fed grain at a ratio of 1 to 4, to a herd capable of producing 9,000 pounds of milk per year when fed grain at a ratio of 1 to 4.

CHAPTER 18

Input-Output Relationships in Beef Production

Introductory Statement

This chapter on the application of economic principles in beef production concentrates primarily on ways of using such principles in *thinking* about beef production problems. It does not concentrate upon specific adjustments in feed inputs. As a result of price changes and the wide variety of ways in which beef can be produced, hence, there is a lack of adequate data on these different ways of producing beef. Questions of how beef should be produced are relatively more numerous than questions of how pork should be produced; this chapter concentrates on the use of economic principles in thinking about the way in which beef should be produced on particular farms. The kind of roughage available, the proportion in which a farm advantageously produces grain relative to roughage, and the availability or non-availability of feed floors, cribs, and granaries, all influence the appropriate type and way in which beef should be produced on particular farms.

Perhaps no other farm product is produced in as many different ways as beef. A group of farm-management research workers from the north central states has set up an incomplete list of 13 different ways of operating the beef-fattening enterprise. These 13 ways, of course, could be combined with a number of ways of producing the feeder animals themselves. The list follows:

Beef Production Systems

I. Fall purchase of 400-pound calves.

    A. System 1.

        1. Full feeding, dry lot.

            a. Begin October 15 at 400 lb.

            b. End at 1,000 lb.

B. System 2.
  1. Begin October 15 at 400 lb.
  2. Winter on roughages.
  3. Full grain feeding on pasture.
  4. End at 1,000 lb.

C. System 3.
  1. Begin October 15 at 400 lb.
  2. Winter on roughages.
  3. Pasture with no grain during first half of grazing season.
  4. Grain during last half of pasture period.
  5. Finish in dry lot at 1,000 lb.

D. System 4.
  1. Begin October 15 at 400 lb.
  2. Winter on roughages.
  3. Pasture with no grain during grazing season.
  4. Fatten in dry lot for 90–100 days.
  5. End at 1,000 lb.

E. System 5.
  1. All-roughage system.
  2. Begin October 15 at 400 lb.
  3. Winter on pasture and dry roughages.
  4. Pasture with no grain during grazing seasons and sell.

II. Purchase of 650-lb. (medium to low grade) feeders.

A. System 1.
  1. Begin in April or May at 650 lb.
  2. Full grain feeding on pasture.

B. System 2.
  1. Begin April or May at 650 lb.
  2. Pasture with no grain during grazing season.
  3. Fatten in dry lot.

C. System 3.
  1. Begin October 15 at 650 lb.
  2. Winter on roughages.
  3. Pasture with no grain during grazing season.
  4. Fatten in dry lot.

III. Purchase of 650-lb. (high-good to choice) feeders.

A. System 1.
  1. Begin April or May at 650 lb.
  2. Full grain feeding on pasture.

B. System 2.
  1. Begin April or May at 650 lb.
  2. Pasture with no grain during grazing season.
  3. Fatten in dry lot.

    C. System 3.
        1. Begin October 15 at 650 lb.
        2. Winter on roughages.
        3. Pasture with no grain during grazing season.
        4. Fatten in dry lot.

IV. Purchase of two-year-olds.

    A. System 1.
        1. Begin October or November at 800 lb.
        2. Fatten in dry lot.
        3. Finish to:
           a. Medium to low-good.
           b. High-good to choice.

    B. System 2.
        1. Begin April or May at 800 lb.
        2. Fatten with grain on pasture.
        3. Finish to:
           a. Medium to low-good.
           b. High-good to choice.

Requirements Data for Different Systems

As this book was being written, the members of the North Central States Farm Management Research Committee, representing 14 midwestern states, were compiling requirements data for each of the above systems. These data will probably be available at several of the midwestern experiment stations by the time this book is published.

The nature of the beef production process is complicated by the change in the quality of the carcass which occurs with gain in weight. This problem was present to a lesser degree in the discussion of pork production.

Because of the great number of ways in which beef animals can be grown and fattened, it has been difficult for research workers to estimate useful input-output relationships or production functions for beef production. Probably the most systematic approach made thus far is reported by Aaron G. Nelson in *U.S.D.A. Technical Bulletin* 900, entitled "Relation of Feed Consumed to Food Products Produced by Fattening Cattle." Unlike the research work reported for hogs and dairy cattle, the research work for beef animals has not determined, for different feed prices and different beef prices, how much beef animals should be fed and at what weight they should be sold. Despite the incomplete analysis of input-output data presented in *Bulletin* 900 the authors feel that the data help students understand the capacity of different types of beef animals to utilize feed in the production of

(1) pounds of beef and (2) quality of beef as determined by dressing weight and the fat/lean content of the carcass.

Technical Bulletin 900 reports results of feeding three different groups of beef animals. The first group consisted of steer calves, weighing 400 pounds and grading choice feeders when started on a fattening ration. These calves were increased in weight (1) about 400 pounds to grade good and (2) about 600 pounds to grade choice as slaughter animals. The second group of steers weighed about 640 pounds and graded choice as feeders when put on feed. After gaining 270 pounds, these animals graded good. After gaining an additional 170 pounds, they graded choice. The third group was made up of two-year-old feeder steers weighing about 835 pounds and grading choice as feeders when put on feed. After gaining 200 pounds, these animals graded good for slaughter purposes and after gaining an additional 150 pounds graded choice for slaughter purposes.

These animals were fed a standard corn-belt ration in dry lot. Thus, the first group of animals was produced under System 1 listed above for feeding calves. The second group of cattle, the yearling steers, was fed in dry lot under a system not listed above. The third group of cattle, the two-year-olds, was fed under System 1 above for feeding two-year-olds in dry lot.

Figure 18.1 presents live weight of the three different groups of feeders as it increased with digestible nutrients consumed. In terms of the principles presented in earlier chapters, the three curves in Figure 18.1 can be regarded as total physical productivity curves in the production of beef under the three systems being studied.

Figure 18.1 is a source of TDN requirements data for use in budgeting these three dry-lot beef-cattle feeding systems. Once TDN requirements are known for taking a steer from 800 to, say, 1,100 pounds they can be broken down into feed requirements data for similar dry-lot beef-cattle feeding systems.

Figure 18.2 presents average gain per 100 pounds of digestible nutrients consumed and additional or marginal gain for each 100 pounds of digestible nutrients fed under the three systems.

The curves in these diagrams are really average physical productivity curves and marginal physical productivity curves for feed fed in the production of beef under the three systems. The student can easily observe that the marginal physical productivity curves for the steer calves are higher and more sustained than those for the yearling steers. Though the marginal physical productivity curve for two-year-old steers is approximately the same height as the curve for

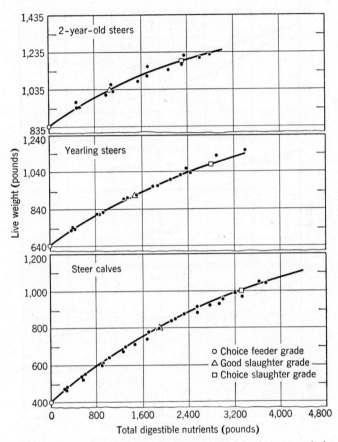

Fig. 18.1. Relation of live weight to total quantity of feed consumed throughout the fattening period.

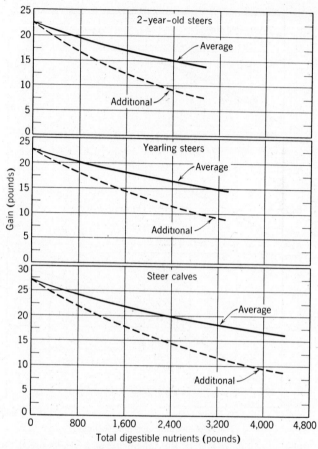

FIG. 18.2.   Gain in live weight per 100 pounds of total digestible nutrients consumed throughout the fattening period.

yearling steers, it is not as sustained. The student should note that these figures are in terms of live weight.

When data for gain in edible body weight are compared with data for gain in live weight, a considerably different picture results. Figure

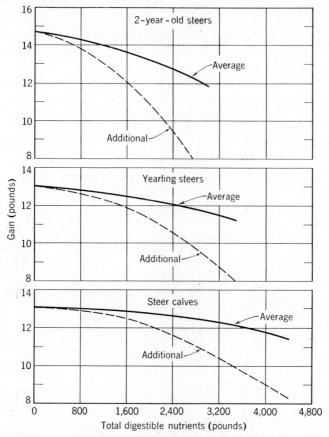

Fig. 18.3. Gain in edible body per 100 pounds of total digestible nutrients consumed throughout the fattening period.

18.3 presents data on the average gain in edible body weight produced per 100 pounds of digestible nutrients fed and additional gain per 100 pounds of total digestible nutrients fed to the animals in each of the three feeding systems. The curves in Figure 18.3 are really marginal physical productivity curves and average physical productivity curves in the production of edible body. These curves indicate that both marginal and physical productivity of two-year-old steers reach a higher level than those reached for yearling steers and that, in turn, the levels for the yearling steers are as high as those for the steer calves. On the other hand, rates of return for feeding steer calves are sustained over a much wider range than are returns for feeding yearling steers. Similarly, both average and marginal returns for feeding yearling steers are sustained for a much greater range than for the two-year-old steers. Figure 18.3, thus, indicates one reason why quality increases with feeding so much more rapidly for the older and more mature animals.

The nature of the gain is broken down even further in Figure 18.4, which shows average fat and additional fat as well as average lean

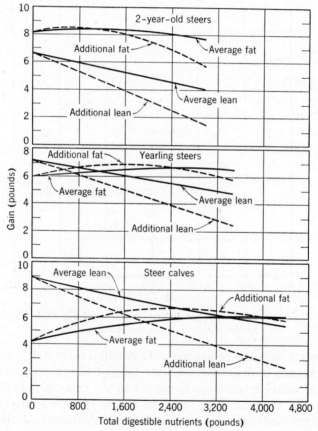

FIG. 18.4.   Gain in edible lean and fat per 100 pounds of total digestible nutrients consumed throughout the fattening period.

and additional lean per 100 pounds of digestible nutrients fed under each of the three feeding systems. As the student can see by inspecting Figure 18.4, gains in lean are higher and more sustained for the younger animals. Gains of fat, on the other hand, are lower for the younger animals than for the older animals, though very sustained in the case of the younger animals. The higher gain in dressing percentages, noted from Figure 18.3, and the quickness in reaching a maximum rate of fattening for the larger and more mature animals, noted in Figure 18.4, explain why the more mature, heavier animals finish into higher grades so much more quickly than the lighter younger animals.

It is regrettable that no one has, thus far, set up tables to equate the marginal factor cost of feed with the values of the marginal physical product produced by feed for different price relationships and for the different systems of feeding. One of the main reasons for delay in setting up such tables probably lies in the instability of the differences in grade prices for beef animals. Further, as a main object of beef fattening is to improve quality, both quality and price per pound change as the animals are fattening. Still further, beef animals are forage consumers, and forage (often a fixed asset) is hard to price or evaluate. These considerations, combined with the instability of grade-price differentials, cause the value of the physical productivity of feed fed in the production of beef and the marginal factor cost of feed to be an uncertain, unstable, everchanging thing not easily handled in tables for equating marginal factor cost and value of marginal products.

Grain-Forage Substitution in the Production of Beef

Though beef animals do well on high-quality forage, there is perhaps a wider range over which grain and forage can be substituted in beef production than for other farm animals. Substitution of forage or roughage for grain occurs mainly in connection with decisions as to the system to employ in feeding the animals, as only a moderate amount of substitution is possible within any feeding system. Decisions as to how much forage and roughage are to be fed relative to grain are reached in the length of run or planning span in which (1) feed supplies are being planned, (2) the method of producing beef is being decided upon, and (3) the weight of animals to be purchased is being determined.

Iso-product maps relating grain consumption to forage and roughage consumption can be drawn which will indicate how farmers, in practice, substitute grain for concentrates, and vice versa, in producing beef animals.

The four hypothetical diagrams in Figure 18.5 contain 13 diagonal lines some of which are curved and some of which overlap in part.

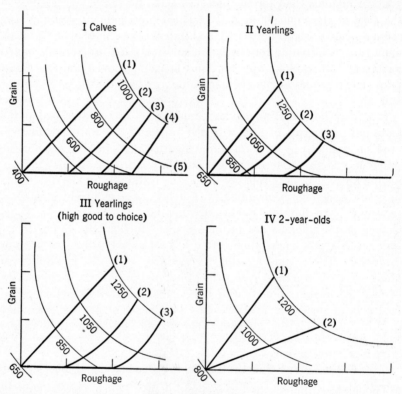

FIG. 18.5. Hypothetical iso-product curves for beef production; 13 different systems of beef production.

These lines correspond to each of the systems of producing beef outlined in the beginning of this chapter. They present a wide range of variation in the use of roughage relative to grain, i.e., System 5, in Diagram I, is based on a 100 percent roughage ration, whereas System 1, in the calves diagram of Figure 18.5, utilizes more grain, relative to roughage, than any of the other calf feeding systems. The calf feeding systems are the most versatile. Calves can be carried on roughages for varying periods and then placed on full grain feeding. The same is true, but to a lesser extent, of yearlings. Two-year-olds need rather heavy grain feeding throughout the fattening period.

In this intermediate length of run, the selection of feeding systems and forage grain production plans involves questions which it is advantageous to answer jointly. From the above discussion, it is evident that a beef fattening system can be selected to utilize grain and roughage in about any proportion in which it is advantageous to produce them on a given farm. Such systems, however, cannot be put into operation at a moment's notice (or even a year's notice). Thus, development, say, of an expanded forage production program should be paralleled by development of the beef producing system if the forage is to be utilized with beef. Breeding herds may have to be developed, hay and grain storage may have to be planned, feed floors may be required, shelters may have to be built, financing arrangements may have to be established, etc.

If the farm involved is capable of producing a high proportion of grain, one of the systems utilizing a high proportion of grain can probably be selected advantageously. It may also be advisable to combine the beef fattening and hog fattening enterprises in order to utilize more grain and in order to take advantage of by-product complementarity. The hogs, by scavenging undigested and spilled grain from the beef enterprise, increase the efficiency of the feeding operation. As the size of the hog enterprise is increased the proportion of grain used in relation to roughage increases for the two enterprises considered jointly.

Recently, the need to conserve soil has stimulated grass-land farming. Farms producing proportionally more grass have tended away from pork production toward beef production and away from grain-fed toward grass-fed beef production. Apparently, the first of these trends coincides with a trend in demand away from the fatter pork cuts toward beef. Whether the trend in production toward grass-fed beef is accompanied by an increasing trend in the consumer demand schedule for such meat is not yet clearly evident. The technology of grass production is advancing rapidly, and as a result the real cost of producing roughages is being reduced. Decreasing fertility, on the other hand, is increasing the cost of grain production, a development continually being offset by improvements in machinery and in varieties of grains. These changes in the cost of producing forage relative to grain vary among farming regions. As the cost of grain production increases or decreases relative to forage production producers will find it profitable to substitute the two inputs for each other within the limits set by consumer demand (as reflected in prices) for the two kinds of beef.

Conceptually, the optimum adjustments are those described in Chapters 9 and 10. Beef contrasts with dairy production in that forage-grain substitution occurs in the longer planning spans instead of in the short run.

Longer Planning Spans for Beef Production

In still longer planning spans, beef producers are basically concerned with the provision and construction of buildings, fixed equipment, and forage or roughage. This section will concentrate on buildings and equipment, as it is assumed that a system of beef production can be secured for advantageously handling the combination of grain and roughage produced on any farm—this is not to say that the beef system which fits forage output will provide full employment for the labor of the operator and working members of his family. Most of the current literature on building beef barns and feeding sheds stresses (1) minimum requirements for the climate in which the farm is located, (2) simplicity and durability, as sources of low-cost construction and maintenance, and (3) what is still more important, arrangement of feed storage and feeding areas so as to minimize the labor required for handling feeds, roughages, bedding, and manures.

The third point listed above requires additional emphasis. Currently, very few beef feeding enterprises are so organized, physically, as to utilize labor effectively. Mechanization in the usual sense has not been applied in beef fattening—yet major savings of labor can be made in beef fattening by:

1. Arranging feed storage adjacent to the feeding area in such a way as to eliminate handling of feed.
2. Arranging sheds and feed floors so that they can be cleaned with power scoops.
3. Arranging an automatic water supply.
4. Providing handy loading and unloading facilities.

None of these arrangements need to be costly, but they must be planned. Opportunities to rearrange feed storage, feeding sheds, etc., occur infrequently. These opportunities occur in connection with long-run planning operations. If full advantage is not taken of such opportunities, the beef enterprise remains an inefficient user of labor. In some of the heavy beef-feeding areas, renters carry out a large amount of beef feeding and rarely have an opportunity to do long-run planning concerning the type of arrangements noted above. The landlords, on the other hand, are not motivated to make such plans. This situation explains, in part, at least, the continued existence of beef feeding enterprises which use labor inefficiently.

QUESTIONS AND PROBLEMS

1. Which of the 13 beef production systems outlined in this chapter would be appropriate for a level North Illinois farm capable of producing corn on one-half of its acreage year after year?

2. Which of the 13 systems would be appropriate on a Missouri farm capable of producing pasture for at least 8 months of the year, and capable of producing corn on 10 percent of its land?

3. List as many systems of beef production, in addition to the 13 listed in this chapter, as you can think of. How many of these have special characteristics which adjust them to specific farms and feeding situations?

4. Discuss the influence of initial weight of steer on (a) the rate of liveweight gain per hundredweight of TDN, (b) the rate of gain per hundredweight of TDN in edible body, (c) the rate of gain per hundredweight in edible lean vs. the rate of gain per hundredweight in fat, (d) changes in quality of animal.

5. Discuss the relations among initial weight of animal, feeding system used, and the production of (a) pounds of edible beef and (b) quality. Relate your discussion to the question of grassland vs. grain farming.

6. Describe the beef fattening process as a process of equating $MVP_{(feed)}$ with the price of feed.

7. Work out a set of plans for "mechanizing" the feeding of 240 steers per year.

8. How would you estimate the number of TDN required to take an 800-pound steer to 1,200 pounds in dry lot?

CHAPTER 19

Labor and Working Capital

This chapter first considers labor and equipment separately and in rather general overall terms. It then presents, on a separate basis, tentative labor and machinery programs for the 335-acre case study farm and, finally, discusses the integration of such programs with the rest of the farm.

Labor may be considered as one major category of productive assets. Land, together with the man-made things on the land, such as ditches, irrigation, buildings, soil amendments, etc., constitute one important category of inputs often referred to as fixed capital. The other main category consists of working capital, such as labor-saving machines, seed, feed, fertilizer, cattle, growing crops, cash, and supplies. On the basis of this classification, some of the items usually classed as capital by classical economists have been grouped with the land factor. Many of the capital items, such as tiling, water systems, ground limestone, and phosphate, quickly become parts of the land (real estate) itself and are so considered by farmers.

Given 100 or 1,000 acres of land plus the land improvements thereon and a set of prices, there is an economically optimum amount of labor and operating capital which should be associated with it. The same principle holds true if one starts with 1 acre of land, 1 day of labor, or 1 bag of seed. The law of diminishing returns decrees that the returns from increasing quantities of one input or category of inputs must eventually diminish, if the other inputs are held constant, and also that the returns from additional units of the other inputs must likewise eventually diminish, if the first is held constant. In simple marginal terms, labor, capital, and land are combined in the correct proportions when (1) additional investments and expenditures in any of the categories yield equal returns and (2) when no further investments or expenditures on either will return a profit above cost or personal reservation price.

A man is an inefficient producer by himself until he is equipped with a considerable quantity of capital investment. If the capital investment is small in relation to what competitors are using, he will be forced toward subsistence production and multiple-enterprise subsistence farming. Perhaps a hundred different items and services will be attempted for the use of himself and his family. The scale of production of the different items (farm enterprises) will be small and will usually be consumed on the farm rather than sold, as the farmer will probably have but a cow, a team, a few chickens, a garden, and a few acres of grain on a few acres of unproductive land. In this chapter, we are concerned with working capital and labor.

When a unit of a farm product is sold it meets the competition of all other similar units being sold. A hog produced in Maine is priced on the basis of hogs produced in Iowa, Illinois, and California. Even fluid milk is in competition with milk in other areas, except as restricted by regulations and shipping. Competition is both direct (from farm to farm on a single product) and indirect (from farm to farm on other products through the working of comparative advantage). The same is true of other farm products because of the worldwide system of markets. If one produces a hog, or the corn with which to feed a hog, he must accept a return for services in proportion to the quantity (and quality) produced rather than what is put into getting that production. If one nets but a bushel of corn for a day's labor in the Appalachian Mountains while another nets 25 bushels for the same amount of time in Iowa, the real wages are a bushel a day to the Appalachian farmer, 25 bushels to the Iowa farmer. In order to compete advantageously, a farmer must have enough capital associated with him to enable him to produce as efficiently as other farmers producing similar products. The average commercial farmer in the United States uses approximately $30,000 of fixed and working capital (1950). There are about 3 million farm businesses in the United States which produce some 90 percent of the marketed farm products. Each of these businesses employ an average of about 2.5 workers and have an investment per worker of some $12,000 at 1950 values.

Labor as a Variable Input

Measures of Labor Productivity. Men are interested in the returns to labor as related to the amount of labor services expended. In current language they "want things to be worth their while"; in terms of the businessman they "want it to pay"; in the language of the professional economist they want returns to the last unit of services expended to be equal to its cost or their reservation price, i.e., $MVP = MFC$.

When is $MVP = MFC$? How much is MFC? or MVP? How many days of labor are to be used to equate the two? We do not know the exact answer because:

1. We have not, except for one or two instances, carried out the necessary computations.[1]
2. We do not know the future price of the products.
3. Family labor is often a fixed asset whose value is price determined.

Several methods of analysis are available, however, which, when analyzed by trained, experienced minds, provide rough estimates.

How many things may a farm worker be expected to get done in a year? We could ask farmers, for example, the number of acres of cotton or of wheat that one man might reasonably be expected to produce per year. Out of the background of their observations and their experiences they should be qualified to make fair estimates. The chances are that, within a given locality, the estimates would vary over a narrow range. There might be one or two extremely high and a few extremely low. The chances are, further, that the bulk of the answers would be "bunched" rather closely. By this method one could get a rough idea of what one man could be reasonably expected to get done in growing one crop. If we carried the inquiry to several crops to be grown simultaneously, there would be greater variation in the estimates because of the interrelationships, but estimates could be obtained.

The Productive Man Work Unit. Because of the need for refining farmers' estimates and the more urgent need for a way to add time requirements for several crops and several kinds of livestock, studies have been made to determine the number of days of work used by farmers on the farm enterprises, by areas, over the nation. Many labor (time requirements) records have been kept and many surveys conducted. Illinois, New York, Minnesota, and Iowa were early leaders in the field of enterprise cost accounting and labor analysis. Most

---

[1] Earl Heady's work at Iowa and work currently being developed by Lou Drake, Michigan State College, provide estimates of the marginal value productivity of labor. Similar work now being done at the University of Kentucky was presented in Chapter 10.

other states have done considerable work, and the office of farm management in the Bureau of Agricultural Economics, U. S. Department of
Agriculture, has made extensive computations within types of farming areas.   In each study 20 to several hundred farms were used.
In these studies it was found that "A" used 6 days or 60 hours to grow
and harvest an acre of corn, "B" used 43 hours, "C" 19, "D" 28, "E"
32, etc.   From the number of records compiled an average of the
amount of time required by all the farmers was determined.   This
average has come to be known as a *productive man work unit*.   In
technical terms, a PMWU is the average over a large number of
farms of the physical product of all inputs per day of labor used.
The fact that the PMWU concept is not simple, though it appears to
be, is often responsible for its misuse.   PMWU's have been determined
also for other crops and for the principal types of livestock.   In recent
years, further refinements have been made for different classes of land
and for different modes of production, such as the use of tractor machines as compared with horse-drawn machines.   The records, in many
cases, have also been broken down (or compiled) by months and by
jobs.   The results of these research projects give us an estimate of the
amount of labor services needed to produce a unit of an enterprise
under historical price relationships and in conjunction with other
inputs.

If farmers, on the average, use a given number of days (or hours)
to grow an acre of a crop or to care for a unit of a livestock enterprise
and if farmer "Slothful" uses the average amounts of other assets and
considerably more labor in producing the same quantity and quality
of the same enterprise, may we not say that he is less efficient (i.e.,
received less average total output per unit of labor) than the average,
mythical though the average be?   By the same reasoning, if farmer
"Scotch" accomplished the same production with the average amounts
of other assets and with somewhat less than the "average" amount of
labor, may we not say that he is more efficient?

We may also add things done on the farm (enterprises × quantities)
and find yearly accomplishments, which can be compared with those
of neighbors, as calculated in Table 19.1.

The foregoing measures of productive man work units accomplished
show that "Slothful" used 4,091 hours (409.1 days) to do what the
average typical farmers accomplish in 3,245 hours (324.5 days or
PMWU's).   On the other hand, "Scotch" got the same acreages of

Table 19.1.   A Comparison of Hours of Labor Used and Work Accomplishments by Two Illustration Farmers with Typical Requirements

Enterprises	Work Accomplished	Average Requirements in Hours [1]		Requirements of	
		Per Unit	Total	Slothful	Scotch
Wheat	106. A.	3.7	392.2	476	318
Corn	41. A.	12.6	516.6	820	410
Other small grains	114. A.	4.0	456.0	570	342
Hay	34. A.	1.3	44.2	102	60
Cattle	25.6	25.0	640.0	840	500
Milk cows	6.	130.0	780.0	960	720
Hogs	15.4	7.0	107.8	125	75
Poultry	103.	1.7	175.1	103	103
Work stock	1.9	70.0	133.0	95	90
Total used			3,244.9	4,091	2,618

[1] BAE calculation.

crops produced and head of livestock kept with an input (or outlay) of 2,618 hours, equal to 261.8 ten-hour days. With these we can construct a labor efficiency, or perhaps proficiency, index as follows:

For "Slothful"

$$\frac{\text{Average needed } 3,245}{\text{Actual used } 4,091} \times 100 = 79$$

This device is useful for individual farms. If the answer is larger than 100 the farmer may tentatively rate himself as efficient in the use of labor as compared with his competitors; if below, inefficient. The higher *probably* the better; the lower *probably* the worse. The measure has many limitations but it also has some usefulness. The limitations grow principally out of the difficulty of finding an individual farm having the *same other assets as the average*. Obviously, if an individual farm has more tractors than the average, it may accomplish more PMWU's and at the same time have lower average and marginal physical productivity for both labor and capital. Another limitation on the PMWU concept grows out of the fact that it is a total (at best, as used, an average) not a marginal concept. Thus, it is possible for a farmer receiving negative marginal returns for his labor to accomplish more PMWU's than a farmer who successfully equates the *MVP* of labor with its cost or reservation price. It is obvious that the productivity of labor depends upon the amount of machinery and equipment used in conjunction with it, and vice versa. Thus, the two are considered jointly in this chapter.

Farmers who accomplish 250 or more PMWU's (2500 PMWH's) per year are usually rated as securing good output from labor inputs. An occasional performance runs up to or above 400. Obviously, what is good, too little, or too much depends on equalization of marginal returns with marginal factor costs for all inputs contributing to the PMWU's.

To find the PMWU's accomplished per worker per farm two quantities are needed:

1. The amount of accomplishment on the farm.
2. The number of workers.

The number of workers are reduced to a *man-equivalent index*. A man equivalent is one worker used for 12 full months. Family labor is added to that of others. Thus, if there were used on a farm:

The operator for 12 months,
operator's son for 3 months,
hired labor for 2 months,
miscellaneous family for 3 months,

making a total of 20 months, there were 1.66 man equivalents used (20 ÷ 12). The total number of PMWU's can then be divided by the man equivalent to get the average output of all inputs per man or the PMWU's accomplished per worker for the farm. "PMWU's per man employed," as a concept, is really the productivity of all inputs, including labor, per unit of labor employed and is, hence, a relatively poor, though widely used, measure of labor productivity.

Crop Acres Index. Number of crop acres which have been produced per man is another measure of labor effectiveness which serves some purpose in areas where crop rotations consist of individual crops more or less proportionate in acreage from farm to farm, or in single-crop areas such as those where wheat is the main product. However, where both intensive and extensive crops are being considered, this measurement is of little value. It can readily be seen that acres of intensive crops cannot be considered on the same basis for work accomplishment as acres of extensive ones. The productive labor units accomplishment per man is, therefore, a somewhat better measurement of efficiency in the use of labor. Both are subject to the limitations noted earlier, i.e., they measure the productivity of inputs other than labor and they are total (at best average) instead of marginal concepts.

The Productive Man Work Unit Further Analyzed. Productive work as defined is not all the work that must be done on a farm. For this measure, work is counted as productive only when producing items to be sold directly or indirectly. Work often not counted in determining productive units includes such work as hauling manure, building fences, cutting weeds, and caring for workstock. Such work must be done in addition to the productive units.

A productive man work unit—PMWU—is a way of establishing a rough "normal" relationship between total output and labor requirements and serves its best purpose when so used. It is a tricky and dangerous analytical measure. For example, Jones plows an acre a day, whereas Brown plows 10 acres. Jones has accomplished but $\frac{1}{10}$ as much production or productive units as Brown; or Brown has accomplished 10 times as much as Jones. Again, Jones milks and cares for a cow in 30 minutes a day or 183 hours per year, the equivalent of 18.3 ten-hour days. Brown milks and cares for a cow in 67 hours per year, equivalent to 6.7 days. Both have accomplished the same amount of productive work units. By adding Jones' accomplishments on all the farm enterprises he used, one gets his accomplishment per year in terms of the average of his area competitors, as illustrated previously.

Brown plows 10 times as many acres per day as Jones, partly because he had equipped himself with more dollars in the form of machines. Actually *Brown* and *the machines* did the plowing. If Brown has sufficient plowing to use the machines, as well as himself, efficiently, he sells his time more advantageously as a result of having the machines. However, if Brown has an insufficient total of acres to plow, Jones may have been more efficient than Brown in the use of total time (cost of the machines plus cost of labor to do the plowing). Similarly Brown might have accomplished more work than Jones because his labor was supported by other investments, such as investments in forage and livestock.

Measures of the marginal value productivity of labor are needed for analytical purposes. Workers at the Iowa Experiment Station have made some progress in estimating the total and marginal value productivity of categories of inputs. At Michigan State College similar work is being done with data from farm record books. Such work leads to tables such as Table 19.2 for Marshall County, Kentucky, upland farms.

Table 19.2. Forage and Livestock Marginal Returns per Month of Labor Employed for Different Investments and Different Amounts of Labor, Marshall County, Kentucky, Upland Farms

Forage and Livestock Investment	Months of Labor Used				
	3	6	9	12	15
	Marginal Return to Labor in Dollars				
$3,016	148	80	58	45	37
6,032	202	111	78	61	50
9,048	248	136	96	75	62

This table illustrates nicely how the earning power of labor depends on what it has to work with and on how much labor is used.

Combinations for Selling Labor at High Rates

Our next task is examining methods and practices which would result in a high output from the inputs of labor used, whether it be family labor, hired labor, or both. A full-time farm operator probably should not be satisfied with the labor output of his business until he has passed 250 PMWU's per man equivalent per year with satisfactory earnings at the margin. Usually this may be accomplished by:

1. Having a business sufficiently large to permit combination of labor with land and capital equipment in nearly the usual proportions found on profitable commercial farms. For example, on dairy farms, the handling of about 20 dairy cows, together with the production of farm-grown feeds for them, per man is probably a minimum.

2. On harvest-crop farms, having a sufficient acreage of adapted crops to use at least the major portion of the time of all family laborers when the laborers are equipped on a basis equal to their competitors.

3. Using a type of livestock which gives intensity in relation to acreage. Dairy cows and/or poultry on "small" farms, as they use more labor per acre operated than beef cattle.

4. Having enough supplementary enterprises to provide productive work throughout the year unless the business is big enough from the main enterprises so that year-round employment is not important to the operator, or unless off-farm work is readily available at sufficiently high rates. An example of the former is the typical corn-belt farm producing corn as the principal crop with soybeans, small grains, beef cattle, and hogs as supplementary enterprises. Examples of the latter are the larger wheat, sugar beet, potato, or tobacco farms and cattle ranches.

5. Planning the work program (on seasonal and day bases) to help distribute (and use) labor resources. Some jobs can be shifted a few days through devices such as use of different varieties, time of planting, and production practices.

6. Employing implements and labor-saving machines.

7. Providing time-saving arrangement, location, and shape of fields, farmstead, and buildings.

8. Using labor-economizing work methods, technically called work simplification—an opportunity to produce some 50 percent more per hour than the average competitor on hand-labor operations.

Let us examine some of these more fully.

Size—a Factor. Size of business is important in farming. This is true because it is easier to combine units of men, units of machinery, and units of capital into an effective organization on the larger farms. When a farm business has become large enough so that full units of men, machines, acreages, etc., may be added and subtracted, the problem of effective organization becomes simpler. Since men can be subdivided only with difficulty (hour or daily employment which costs more than monthly and yearly employment) and since men must use machinery for effective competition with other men, one man plus a unit of each machine needed becomes an effective planning unit. One man, for example, plus a tractor, a tractor plow, units of other tillage tools, a mower, rake, baler, combine, corn picker, and trailer wagon, constitutes a production "outfit" for corn-belt cropping. It is more difficult to use a half unit of one input or a third of another.

Land (space for using machines and other resources) must be considered in determining what machine to use even under given price conditions. To use machines efficiently is just as important as to use labor efficiently. Since some of the time of one man on a farm must be used on jobs not requiring machines, the machines must be idle much of the time on one-man farms or on small-acreage farms.

It is not known exactly what the optimum size of business is from the standpoint of efficient use of all factors. It is certainly much larger than most farms provide. Perhaps it is somewhat larger than even most larger farms provide. So few farms are operated entirely for profit that the exact "most profitable size" from a dollar and cents standpoint has not been determined. Many farmers reduce intensity of operations when they acquire large acreages. Efficient size has increased rapidly with changing technologies. Size has not kept up with technology and prices; however, some farm businesses have gone into the million dollar class. The most profitable size would be large enough to use all units of the factors of production at optimum rates, i.e., $(MFC = MVP)$. Again, farming is not entirely a dollar and cents proposition, or a matter of profits, because the business is closely associated with the life of the family. Many farm businesses, though, are too small to provide the operators average wages or even to give them serious consideration as business enterprises.

Crops, Livestock, and Enterprise Combinations. Many one-crop farmers fail to make satisfactory incomes because crops call for operations which are largely seasonal. That is, they do not have opportunity to use all the labor services that they can produce during the year. The growing of two or three crops helps the use of labor and, therefore, may increase the amount of income earned. When the production of livestock can be added to the production of crops, a further means of using labor may be secured. An operating farmer on a small farm does well to consider the production of adapted, labor intensive crops such as tomatoes, cotton, tobacco, beans, and truck and labor intensive types of livestock, such as dairy cattle and poultry, because these types of enterprises provide an opportunity for the larger use of family labor. Another means by which the small operator can increase income is by work off the farm. Still another is the making of things used on the farm and in the home.

The appropriate size or kind of tool is important in saving labor. The hand corn planter, the one-row planter, the two-row planter, and the tractor planter are successive sizes of corn-planting implements. With them one man can plant about three, five, twenty, and sixty acres per day, respectively. The same choice holds for many kinds of machines. Perhaps farmers in some sections do not use as large machinery as they should.

Another consideration which will increase efficiency in the use of labor and machinery is arrangement of fields and buildings. A few farmers have probably failed because the poor arrangement of fields, or bad layout of the farm, imposed too much distance to be covered in unproductive ways. Long, narrow, and L-shaped farms are bad from the standpoint of good use of labor. It is desirable to have the fields so arranged, and the farm and the fields so shaped, that labor will be centered on the operation. On some farms, 20 percent of the day is required to make a round trip from farmstead to the opposite end of the farm. Such farms are more adapted to beef cattle and sheep than to dairy cattle, as dairy farming necessitates larger amounts of hauling feed to the farmstead dairy barn and hauling manure from the barn. The cows have to be brought to the farmstead twice a day, which requires considerable low-productive time, whereas beef cattle need not be driven back and forth so often.

The same principle holds true for the location and arrangement of buildings as for fields and farmstead, since arrangement is a factor affecting the amount of time needed to do work and, therefore, labor and machinery efficiency. Farm buildings have been located and arranged on most farms either through personal desire or for some other uneconomic reason. For example, cribs were traditionally located 20 to 75 feet from feed barns on account of rats and fire, though only a sick rat would stop because of a few feet of distance. Feed rooms and bins should be located in or adjoining feed barns and at a point determined on the basis of saving time. A crib 75 feet from the barn necessitates walking 25 miles a year if five trips a day are made. Besides, the contents have to be carried by hand over the same distance.

Labor Problems on Large Farms. As the farm business increases in size administration of labor becomes increasingly important. Good administration of men comes as a result of experience. Training, however, will enable one to shorten the years of experience needed. Hired workers, and croppers who also help as day laborers, are transitory. Many croppers stay in one place but 1 or 2 years. This is often undesirable for both cropper and operator. It requires about 1 year for the operator and the cropper or hired men to get acquainted with the weak points of each other. It also takes time for hired men to learn to use well the owner's teams, tools, fields, and buildings. In time, one learns to avoid ditches, stumps, and other pitfalls. The workers also learn the points of weakness in machinery and teams. Again, they learn how to safeguard the health of livestock. The owner in one season learns something of the particular weaknesses of hired men and thus may be on guard the second year. Good men should be carefully selected and, then, by granting them better wages and living conditions than the average receive, should be encouraged to stay. Whether to rent land to such men or to employ hired labor, either by the month or day, must be settled by each operator. A deciding factor is the amount of supervision, management, and labor the operator wishes and can afford to give. Some must be given with either method. If close supervision can be economically provided by the operator, the system of using hired labor will usually return larger income, since the operator provides the risk-bearing, supervisory, and managerial services needed. On the other hand, if the operator must be far removed from the scene of operations, a good tenant may prove the more profitable.

Labor relations are significant when one to several men are employed. Housing, methods of paying, bonuses, training, schooling for both adults and their children, internal family affairs, gardens, truck patches, poultry, cows, and dogs become problems for management to handle. Transportation of workers, credit assumptions, and prepayments are additional parts of the problem. Tenant houses or labor camps, insurance, workingmen's compensation, and trade unions are other challenging labor problems in the management of the larger farm businesses.

Machinery and Equipment [1]

The use of machinery is, of course, an important way to increase output per worker. For thousands of years the principal tools of farming were the crooked sticks, used as plows and hoes, and the reaphook. The Biblical story of Ruth gleaning in the fields of Boaz is illustrative of the methods used. Returns per day were very low. Ruth gleaned an epah (about 1 peck) of barley, an unusual day's accomplishment, because Boaz instructed the reaper to drop straws intentionally.

[1] Farm equipment consists of machinery, implements, and tools. Machinery, strictly speaking, consists of mechanical devices of the more complicated variety and is usually thought of as having moving parts such as gears or pulleys. Implements are pieces of equipment of a more simple design; plows, harrows, buck rakes and milk buckets are examples. Tools are the smaller things such as hoes, single trees, forks, and shovels. However, the distinctions in the various categories are not closely drawn, and the name "equipment" is generally used for all classes.

"Plowing" was done by hand. It is estimated that a man could "plow" an acre in a month with a crooked stick. With the modern spading fork he can do the same amount of "plowing" in 8 days, with a team and 12-inch plow in 1 day, with the three-plow tractor in 1 hour. Little change was made until about 100 years ago. Many of our grandfathers used the tools of Boaz. During the 1830's the mechanical reaper and the steel plow heralded a revolution. By 1860 horses and horse-drawn implements were beginning to replace oxen and homemade tools. The steel plow, the disk harrow, the corn planter, the grain drill, and the twine binder came in rapid succession. Farming during the last half of the last century was carried on with horses and horse-drawn implements. Then steam tractors, threshing machines, and multiple-hitch combines came to the western prairies. Large acreages, dry weather at harvest time, and a scarce labor supply encouraged the adoption of machines. Shortly after the turn of the century the gas engine was mounted on frames and chained to cleated wheels. Improvements came faster. High prices for farm products during World War I provided money to farmers to buy mechanical power and impetus to expand efficiency per man. Machines expanded capacity to handle acres. During the 1930's three ideas in the use of machines developed. One of these was speed and economy accomplished through putting rubber tires on farm machines. Rubber paved the way for lifting farm operations above the walking gait of man and horse. It was one of the great adaptations of all time, outranking the invention of the horse hoe, and surpassing the replacement of the ox. The second of these post-war innovations in agriculture was the fitting of the implements to the power units. The first tractors pulled plows, harrows, mowers, and planters. The modern tractor carries them. Operation is more efficient as the operator can see the operation better and less power is required. The third innovation is the mounting of power units on the machines. The self-propelled combine and the self-propelled cotton pickers are the latest developments. Production per man increased about 140 percent from the Civil War to World War II, and has made a further increase of about 50 percent since 1940. The time for planting and harvesting an acre of corn has dropped from 5 days in 1915 to 5 hours at present, for planting and harvesting an acre of wheat from 2 days to 2 hours, for harvesting a ton of hay from 1 day to 1 hour.

In addition to saving time by the use of machines, we have learned also to improve quality of product. Quality in hay is a notable example. Fifty years ago hay was dry, harsh, stemmy, unpalatable, and unproductive. Today it can be made leafy, green, nutritious—high in protein and vitamins—palatable and productive.

Equipment Selection. The problem of selecting equipment for a particular farm may be examined with reference to the quantity of equipment for the farm as a whole, and to purchase of the individual pieces. In viewing the problem from the whole-farm angle, an owner-operator cannot have a majority of his total capital investment in equipment; however, a tenant-operator on a cash-grain farm has practically all of it so invested. One short on operating capital may be forced to forego otherwise desirable machinery purchases. To farm, land and land improvements are needed, as well as farm equipment. One may need to put money into productive livestock, and is likely to need funds for soil improvement. As noted many times, the problem is one of allocating capital so as to get equal marginal returns from the last dollar spent on each part of the whole farm business. The solution calls for examination of the cost, the use, and the probable returns of each piece of equipment.

The following questions throw light upon the general desirability of particular purchases:

1. Is the farm or farming business adapted to its use, considering size, topography, scope of enterprises, land obstructions, and soil conditions?

2. Does the system of farming necessitate use of this machine?

3. Would the necessary investment earn more if invested otherwise, as in soil-improving materials, seed, or livestock?

4. Will the last dollar spent in getting more of the item be covered by additional earning power?

5. Is it good collateral for a loan at a reasonable interest rate? Is risk excessive on money if borrowed?

6. Will this particular piece increase the quality of the product, or timeliness of the operation?

7. Is it more economical to rent a machine or have the job done by a contract operator?

8. Is it more economical to do the work by hand or make other adjustments on the acreage involved?

9. Are there good opportunities to do custom work with it?

10. Should a new or used machine be selected?

11. What size and model suits the needs best?

12. Is a competent operator available?

13. Is joint ownership desirable?

14. What are the relative prices of labor and machinery?

Components of Machinery Costs. The ownership and operation of machines are costly and thus desirable only when the machines can be made to return all costs and something in addition, either through saving other costs, removing drudgery, increasing timeliness, or improving quality of product. Let us then determine what the components of costs are. Costs are made up of overhead, or fixed costs, and operation, or variable costs. Overhead costs are usually the principal items. They include interest and time depreciation. They may be estimated as follows for a field chopper expected to last for 12 years:

Original cost	$2,000
Interest ($1,000 for 12 years at 5%)	600
Other overhead costs (housing, taxes, insurance)	192
Total to be regained in 12 years	$2,792
Amount of overhead or fixed costs per yr.	233

The overhead cost of the use of the field chopper on the basis of the above assumptions—original cost of $2,000, an expected life of 12 years, and interest at 5 percent, other overhead at 8 percent—is $233 per year. It should be noted that interest is charged on but half the investment rather than on the full investment, because one-twelfth of the purchase price is being charged off each year through time depreciation. Thus, at the end of the first year one has left in the machine but eleven-twelfths of the original cost, and at the end of eleven years one-twelfth. Therefore, one has the full $2,000 invested for only half the life of the chopper, or has an equivalent of about half the investment for the full life.

An examination of depreciation reveals that it is caused by two factors—time and use. Time depreciation, generally referred to as *obsolescence*, takes place regardless of the amount of use. For illustration, a tractor purchased 20 years ago but never used would be worth little more than junk value today because of changes in models and types. Use depreciation is, of course, largely in proportion to the number of days used. One of the factors causing high costs in use of farm machines is that they are usually used but a few days each year. The total days of use in the life of the above illustrated field chopper might be about 60 days on the typical farm using field choppers. Since the number of days used per year is necessarily low for most field machines, it may be assumed, for purposes of analysis in connection with buying machines, that time depreciation or obsolescence will account for the depreciation due to use.

Let us now examine operating costs, consisting of power to operate the machines: grease, fuel, oil, and repairs. Wages of the operator are an additional cost. With the exception of wages and repairs, these are easily estimated. Repairs are heavier for the true machines—those

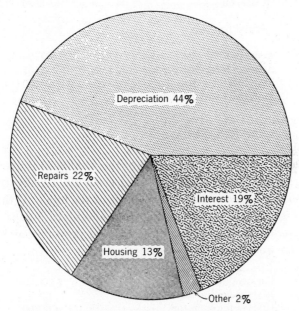

Fig. 19.1. Relative importance of machinery costs.

with bearings and moving parts, cutting machines such as mowers. Repairs are lower for the simplified pieces of equipment, such as plows and milk cans. Various studies indicate that farmers estimate repairs at one-third to one-half of depreciation costs, an average of about 3 percent of the cost of the machine new. Repair costs are low when machines are relatively new, and high when relatively old. The above figures on cost of repairs do not usually include costs for making the purchases or for the labor used in making the repair.

A Cornell University study made by Hertel and Williamson in New York state gives the relative importance of the different machinery costs shown in Figure 19.1.[1]

[1] J. P. Hertel and Paul Williamson, "Costs of Farm Power and Equipment," *Bulletin* 751, Cornell University Agricultural Experiment Station.

Let us now complete our examination of the cost of the use of the field chopper under estimated conditions for a specific farm.

Overhead cost per year (fixed costs)	$233.00
5 days for tractor	30.00
5 days for operator	30.00
Repairs at 3% of original cost	60.00
Grease, oil	3.00
Total per year	$356.00
Average total cost per day (5 days)	$71.20
Average total cost per ton (150 tons)	2.37
Marginal [1] cost per day	24.60
Marginal [2] cost per ton	0.82

[1] Average marginal for 5 days.
[2] Average marginal for 150 tons.

Our examination reveals that $233 of the total $356 is overhead. It has been stated that overhead or fixed costs are usually the largest items of cost, in this case about two-thirds of the total. If the chopper could be used by two farmers, using it an additional 5 days, overhead costs or average fixed costs would be reduced proportionately and the cost per ton would be:

For overhead	$233.00
10 days for tractor	60.00
10 days for operator	60.00
Repairs	120.00
Grease, oil, etc.	6.00
Total per year	$479.00
Average total cost per day	$47.90
Average total cost per ton (300 tons)	1.60
Marginal cost per day	24.60
Marginal cost per ton	0.82

The above computations show constant marginal costs when the rate of use is varied between 5 and 10 days per year. This is probably fairly realistic. However, were the rate of use to be stepped up even further, stepped up use depreciation, repairs, inefficiencies in scheduling, etc., would cause marginal costs to increase.

Days of use per year are most important. When two-plow tractors were used but 22 days per year the average total cost was $8.78 per day.[1] When used 167 days, the corresponding cost was $3.20.

The student should now figure the cost of the use of a selected machine or other piece of equipment for his individual case farm. Record the figures in the form such as presented below:

Name of machine _____
Overhead
   Original cost $_____
   Estimated life (____ years) $_____
   Interest at ____% on ½ original cost
     for ____ years $_____
   Other overhead (housing, taxes, insur-
     ance) $_____
   Total to be regained in ____ years $_____
   Amount per year $_____
Operating
   Power (for year) $_____
   Operator (for year) $_____
   Repairs (for year) $_____
   Grease, oil, etc. (for year) $_____
   Total operating $_____
Total overhead and operating for one
   year $_____
Average total cost per day $_____
Average total cost per unit used $_____
Marginal cost per day $_____
Marginal cost per unit $_____

Depreciation Examined Further. In the foregoing analysis the straight-line method of figuring time depreciation has been used. This method is easiest, and, for one owning or expecting to own a machine throughout its useful life, is fairly satisfactory. There are other methods in use, however. When one is expecting to buy or sell a used machine, a more realistic method is to calculate depreciation on the basis of farm sale values. Sale values indicate that farmers depreciate machinery more heavily in the first years of use than in later years. This method has been described as the diminishing balance method. The Cornell study previously referred to reveals that the price of a machine for any year is about 85 to 90 percent of the price of the previous year.

[1] George B. Byers, "Costs in Owning and Operating Farm Implements and Machinery in Kentucky," *Bulletin* 484, Kentucky Agricultural Experiment Station.

For example, for a machine costing $1,000 when new and depreciated at 15 percent of the value for the previous year we have:

New Value	1st yr.	2nd yr.	3rd yr.	4th yr.	5th yr.	6th yr.
$1,000	$850	$722	$614	$522	$443	$377

	7th yr.	8th yr.	9th yr.	10th yr.	11th yr.	12th yr.
	$320	$272	$231	$197	$167	$142

This method is also somewhat more realistic when applied to machines almost worn out. Such machines are valued by farmers at junk value and depreciate but little more regardless of further use.

A good rule-of-thumb measure of the total annual cost for using a piece of machinery is to take 15 percent of the original cost (when new) for the more complicated machines and 10 percent for the less complicated ones. For illustration, a machine such as a pick-up baler costing $1,500 when new may be expected to have a total yearly cost of about $225. Will the machine return $225 a year?

Fundamental Principles. The fundamental economic principle with respect to the profitable use of machines is the same as that with respect to other production factors. One must equate the marginal cost of using a machine with its marginal value product. Marginal returns include labor saved, value of marginal physical product, timeliness, and increased quality of product.

If the value of the labor saved over its lifetime plus the value of increased quality and quantity of product is equal or exceeds the cost of using the machine, it is profitable to use it. For example, if it costs $160 per year for each of 10 years to buy and use a machine, the total cost, ignoring interest, is $1,600. If labor is worth $3.00 per day, this expense will require a saving of 533 days of labor to save the total cost in terms of labor alone. Let us suppose that it will save 100 days of work for each of the 10 years (with no savings in other inputs) and that no change occurs in value or quantity of product. This is a total of 1,000 days and a resulting net gain of 467 days (1,000 − 533) of labor or $1,401 in costs. If the machine could save but 40 days a year, there would be a resulting net loss of 133 days of work. High labor costs are encouraging use of machines in farming as in other industries. A machine is frequently justified on other grounds, such as timeliness, increased production, or improvement in the quality of product. In any event, the returns from the machine must exceed the costs, and, at the margin of use, costs must equal returns if machines are being used at an optimum degree.

Used Machines May Reduce Costs on Small Farms. Some farm operators show good judgment in keeping machine costs low by selecting secondhand or used machines. A farmer having small need for a machine may justify its use, avoid risks of borrowing on a low equity basis, and save by choosing a used one. The choice depends on scale of enterprise and available assets. Farmers having a large amount of work for a machine, together with large work crews and other machines, may best have new machines of the latest models. Those farmers at the other extreme, having low equities, perhaps small amounts of work for the machine, together with mechanical ability and surplus time of their own, may often use cheaper machines or older models to advantage. The risk is lower for smaller operations, and there is usually more time to cover a given job. Delays to the small-farm operator are often not as expensive as the added cost of newer machines. The cheaper price reduces the initial cost, the interest, and the risk of borrowing. All machines are "used" machines, many are secondhand. Hertel and Williamson in *Cornell University Bulletin* 751 present an excellent statement on the use of secondhand machines in reducing costs. They say:

. . . Farmers purchase used equipment not only because they lack capital but also because they have found that they can reduce the operating cost of equipment by buying it secondhand. This study showed that the average cost of operating tools purchased secondhand was usually less than for tools purchased new although secondhand tools were used less than those purchased new. The average cost of operating tractor plows purchased new was 56 cents per acre, as compared with 36 cents for those purchased secondhand; the similar costs for mowers were 29 cents and 21 cents; for dump rakes, 10 cents and 7 cents; for grain drills, 30 cents and 22 cents; for grain binder, 70 cents and 49 cents.

One of the most common arguments against the use of secondhand tools is that they are unreliable. This argument would be more logical if all the secondhand tools that were available were those that other farmers were selling because they no longer worked satisfactorily. On the contrary, most secondhand tools are purchased at farm auctions where they are sold, not because they are unsatisfactory, but because the operator has died or is quitting the farm. The farmer who buys his equipment new and wears it out is using the equivalent of secondhand equipment most of the time. Secondhand tools offered for sale may be in any condition. Some may be almost new, others very old; some may be in good repair, while others may need repairs that can be made at a reasonable cost; and still others are beyond repair. Good judgment is required to buy secondhand tools that will be serviceable without paying too much for them. . . .[1]

[1] Hertel and Williamson, op. cit.

Tractor and Tractor Machinery

The choice of using tractors and tractor machinery is no longer debated by most farmers. There are now over three million tractors on American farms. This is an average of approximately one for each commercial farm. Tractor machinery, too, is replacing horse-drawn machinery rapidly. One-plow tractor costs averaged $3.94 per day on 46 Kentucky farms when used 67 days per year; 2-plow tractor costs averaged $4.33 per day for 78 days' use on 70 farms (1942). The total annual costs were $264.32 for the 1-plow tractors and $337.56 for the 2-plow units.

Systems of Farming and Equipment. As stated, the purpose of using machinery, implements, and tools is that labor or other inputs may be saved, timeliness increased, or the value of production increased. The system of farming to be followed largely determines the need for the kinds of equipment on farms, though available machinery also determines to some extent the land-use plan. Intensive crop and livestock farming necessitates a large use of power machines and of planters, cultivators, harvesters, silage cutters, haying machinery, feed grinders, manure spreaders, specialized equipment such as milk coolers, etc. Extensive farming with a large proportion of the land kept in pasture necessitates but a small amount of equipment. The intensive type calls for more hauling of feeds and manure than does the extensive type. Enterprises, too, influence the need for machinery. Tobacco needs little expensive machinery. Corn and wheat call for a heavy investment in machinery for economical production. Dairy cattle call for more equipment than do beef cattle or sheep.

Topography of land is another determining factor in the use of machines. Level or gently rolling land is best suited for most farm implements and machinery. Level land is likely to be found on large crop farms. Large farms have large fields conducive to the best use of machines. Hilly land is less adapted to the use of equipment, particularly power machines. The crop land on such farms is usually found in small irregular, disconnected patches, all of which make profitable use of machines difficult.

Contracting Machinery Work. One method of reducing machinery costs per unit of work is through doing jobs on contract. Savings are made by some through hiring the work done and by others through doing work for neighbors. Farmers can usually hire machine jobs at 10 to 20 percent above the usual average total cost of the job through ownership. If the scale of the operation is small, the average total cost per unit of work is likely to be much more than 20 percent above the usual average total cost. For still smaller operations, it may run 200 to 300 percent above contract rates.

Many farmers and farmers' sons buy expensive machines with the expectation of justifying ownership partly through contract operations. Also, a growing number of farm management services and machinery operators are providing machinery services to communities of farmers as a part of their business. It is likely that such practices will expand until enough contractual services are side lines to render full-time contracting unprofitable. Before buying machines for full- or part-time contract work, one can analyze the prospect by:

1. Determining the usual average, total, and marginal cost (including wages for the operator) of the use of the machine on typical farms in the community.

2. Adding 20 to 40 percent to the cost of the home use of the machine for risk and management and to cover additional marginal costs likely to be encountered under customs operations.

3. Comparing the calculated contract rate with rates of other contract operators whose services are available.

4. Estimating the number of days that the machine or machine combinations can actually be used per year.

5. Finding out how keen is the competition for such services within a reasonable working distance, and how much of the kind of work is available.

6. Forecasting if prevailing rates for such custom work will hold.

7. Analyzing if the money invested in the machines and the time spent in operating them would earn larger income if used elsewhere?

There are examples in every community of farmers who have failed because, according to their neighbors, they bought too much machinery. Perhaps the numbers who have failed through machinery extravagance exceeds the numbers who have failed because of extreme machinery conservation.

Illustration of Developing a Labor Program for a Farm

Let us now illustrate the development of a tentative labor program for a specific farm. We shall again use the 335-acre class case farm for which a crops program is tentatively developed. It is recognized that a labor program cannot be developed in isolation from the crop and livestock and machinery programs, etc., except for classroom purposes.

Later, after each phase of organization has been examined separately, all phases will be worked out simultaneously as in the real world. This farm business, as tentatively set up, is a large one with three major products produced for sale—namely, tobacco, cattle, and hogs. The feed crops consist of corn, barley, hay, and pasture. Provision has thus been made in the crops and livestock programs for the use of more labor than a farm operator can himself supply. The labor problems then on this farm will center around securing and using additional laborers and using all labor efficiently.

The following questions arise: How many men and machines will be needed? What kind of men? What methods will be used? When will seasonal or harvest laborers be needed? How will they be housed, or boarded and housed? What subsistence provisions will they require? Should enterprises using proportionally more labor be added, or should enterprises using proportionally less be added?

First, we should ask for what crop, livestock, and other work will laborers be needed. Second, we should ask what machines will be used. Then we shall determine the numbers of productive man work units which will be required and at what months during the year. Recapitulating from Table 13.2, summarizing the tentative crops program, and, from Table 15.1, summarizing the tentative livestock program, we have the following:

Table 19.3. Tentative Crops Program for 335-Acre Class Case Farm

Crop	Acres	Production	Disposition
Corn	46	3,680 bu.	Fed
Wheat	23	460 bu.	Sold
Barley	17	510 bu.	Fed
Barley	25	750 bu.	Fed
Mixed hay	20	50 tons	Fed
Rotation pasture	65	55 units	Fed
Permanent pasture	100	50 units	Fed
Tobacco, Burley	17	30,600 lb.	Sold

Table 19.4. Tentative Livestock Program for 335-Acre Class Case Farm

Kind	Number	Weights Beginning	Weights Marketing	Feeding Periods
Stocker cattle	90	(700) 63,000	106,800 (2 culls or losses)	6 mo. winter 3 mo. summer
Hogs	12 sows 160 pigs		(225) 36,000	Fall to spring Spring to fall

Labor production requirements for crops and livestock by areas are available at the various experiment stations throughout the country. The total requirements are frequently broken down by months and half months. On the basis of such studies, data are available to develop a table of labor requirements for the 335-acre case farm. The data used assume the use of "usual" farm machinery.

Looking at the grand total of hours of labor requirements for the year (Table 19.5) (under average rates of labor accomplishment) we find a need for 9,690 hours for the productive work. Estimating that a worker should accomplish 250 productive units or 2,500 productive hours, we find a need for about four full-time men. However, monthly

Table 19.5. Hours Labor Requirements for the 335-Acre Class Case Farm

Enterprise	Scope	March	April	May	June	July	Aug.	Sept.	Oct.	Nov.	Dec.	Jan.	Feb.	Total
Corn, acres	46		46	184	92				184	184				690
Wheat, acres	23				23	23		23	69					138
Barley, acres	17				34	17		34	17					102
Barley, acres	25				50	25	75	50	25					225
M. Hay, acres	20			40	160									200
R. Pasture, acres	65	65					65							130
P. Pasture, acres	100					100								100
Tobacco, acres	17	136	204	357	646	68	799	816	68	969	1,207	68	17	5,355
Clover, acres	17			34	136									170
Cattle, number	90	180	180	180	90	90	90	90	90	90	180	180	180	1,620
Hogs, number	12	96	72	72	72	72	72	96	96	72	72	72	96	960
Total		477	502	867	1,303	295	1,201	1,109	549	1,315	1,459	320	293	9,690
Without tobacco		341	298	510	657	227	402	293	481	346	252	252	276	4,335

distribution varies from 293 hours in February and 295 hours in July to 1,459 hours in December, the great majority of which is on crops. Allowing 250 hours as the maximum accomplishment for summer months, the August requirements of 1,201 hours would require five men. The January, February, March, and April requirements should be done easily by two men with considerable time for work not directly associated with crops and livestock, such as repair, manure hauling, etc. With a four-man size of business, the operator would need to use a considerable proportion of his time for managing and supervising.

It is to be noted that more than half of the total labor requirements are needed for the 17 acres of tobacco. A usual method on farms of this size in tobacco-producing areas is to have the tobacco raised by tobacco tenants. One or two good men could be secured for producing the crop, who would provide all the labor, furnish all the canvas and insecticides, some of the equipment, and one-half the fertilizer and coke in exchange for one-half the crop. What are the advantages and disadvantages of the cropper-tenant system? The principal advantage to the owner is to shift supervision of laborers to others and have the croppers as available men for other farm work such as hay harvest. The principal disadvantage comes through sacrificing that portion of the returns that the cropper tenant receives for risk and supervision. With tobacco at 50 cents per pound and a yield of 1,800 pounds per acre, and further with the tenant getting one-half the crop, the tenant would collect about $12.50 per day for total time spent on the crop. Tobacco tenants usually get wage rates about equal to harvest-time wages for the total time spent.

Using the cropper system of producing the tobacco crop, the farm operator would have left 252 hours of labor needs in January and February, respectively, and a maximum of 657 in June during hay, wheat, and barley harvest. June harvests would require three men. Thus, one full-time hired man in addition to the operator himself should handle the work if extra day laborers were hired in June.

If the tobacco crop is handled by the operator himself he should employ two full-time month hands plus day hands in May, June, August, September, November, and December. A total of some 320 days of day hands is indicated.

The choice between the cropper-tenant system and the hired-labor system would depend upon:

1. Wage rates in proportion to price of tobacco.
2. Personal choice of operator.
3. Availability of day laborers and tenants.
4. How hard the operator wishes to drive himself.

For purposes of illustration, we elect the cropper-tenant system, as it is the most typical on farms using this system of farming.

The students will develop labor programs for their own case problem farms.

Illustration of Developing a Machinery Program for a Farm

How does one proceed to determine the particular pieces of machinery and equipment that he:

1. Should own to run a specific farm business?
2. Should have use of?

It is rather unusual for the farmer to buy a full complement of machinery at one time. The usual practice is to add pieces as a business develops and as new machines come into common usage, provided that the individual thinks it is good business to do so. One is likely to use what he has, borrow, or rent until he finds an appropriate time to make the addition. He is thus able to weigh the advantages of having the new machine against the sacrifices he must make in purchasing other things.

First, one is likely to decide between things for the family and contemplated purchases for the farm. Having decided in favor of the business, he may next weigh other business uses he could make of the money and attempt to analyze returns from the alternatives. For example, if he has $1,500 to use for the business and finds that he could use a pick-up baler to advantage, he should weigh the advantages of the use of the baler against the advantages in spending the $1,500 for fertilizer, seed, livestock, a barn dryer, or other things. If he is limited in capital funds, he might well make a list of all the things he could use to some degree of advantage and choose from among the items on the basis of maximizing returns from the $1,500. Though this requires considerable knowledge of costs and returns, it is possible to improve decisions on the basis of simple comparisons.

The student's present problem is *selecting a complement of machines and pieces of equipment for his individual case farm,* under the assumption of having adequate money resources available for most needs.

Let us then accept the assumptions of rather adequate capital and the need for choosing a complement of machines all at one time for a particular farm. How does one proceed? A simple method is to start with the crops to be grown, and list the machines used on these crops, and then determine:

1. If the scale of the enterprise justifies the machine.
2. The conditions of cost, returns, etc.

After determining the machines for crops, the procedure may be duplicated for livestock. Many of the decisions can be made on the basis of general knowledge. Other choices will need detailed analysis. For example, one knows that he must have a tractor and a set of tillage tools for a 160-acre corn-belt farm, but one would not decide quickly in favor of having automatic milk-handling equipment.

Selecting Machinery for the 335-Acre Class Case Farm

Let us now proceed to illustrate developing machinery programs through the use of the 335-acre class case farm. Referring to Chapter 13, we find that it was decided, tentatively, that the following acreages of crops would be grown in 1952:

Corn,	46 acres	Hay,	37 acres
Tobacco,	17 acres	Pasture,	165 acres
Barley,	42 acres	Wheat,	23 acres

The labor program for this farm was decided on the basis of having power machinery and the tobacco crop grown by cropper tenants. There is relatively little machinery and equipment used on tobacco, and the specialized pieces are usually furnished by tenants.

Machine	Preference Rating	Kind or Size
For the corn crop there is needed:		
1. Power	Indispensable	Tractor—2-plow
2. Plow	Indispensable	2-bottom
3. Disk	Indispensable	8′ tandem
4. Harrow	Indispensable	4 section
5. Cultipacker	Desirable	8′ single
6. Planter	Necessary	2-row tractor
7. Cultivator	Necessary	2-row
8. Picker	Needs analysis	
9. Truck	Needs analysis	
10. Elevator	Desirable	

Machine	Preference Rating	Kind or Size

For the barley there is needed:

1. Power	Provided for corn	
2. Disk	Provided for corn	
3. Grain drill	Necessary	8' disk with fertilizer attachment
4. Combine	Needs analysis	

For the hay there is needed:

1. Power	Provided for corn	
2. Mower	Indispensable	Tractor—7 foot
3. Rake	Indispensable	Side delivery
4. Baler	Needs analysis	
5. Elevator	Provided	
6. Loft dryer	Needs analysis	
7. Field chopper	Needs analysis	
8. Trucks and tractor	Needs analysis	
9. Moisture tester	Depends upon method	
10. Blower	Needs analysis	

For the pasture there is needed:

1. Tooth or chain harrow	Provided for corn	60-tooth frame
2. Fertilizer drill	Provided for barley	
3. Seed sower	Unquestioned	Cyclone hand or wheel

For general farm use there may be needed:

1. Another tractor
2. Truck
3. Farm wagons
4. Power sprayer

For the purposes of illustration, let us analyze the desirability of purchasing a hay baler. What are the other methods of handling hay?

1. Field chopping.
2. Handling loose.

If a silo were to be used on the farm, the field chopper would fill an additional need and the baler would be less needed. There is no silo. Referring to the section on Principal Problems, in this chapter, we consider items 7, 9, 11, and 13. Referring again to the method for determining cost of use, we develop:

Original cost	$1,500.00
Estimated life, 10 years	
Interest on $750 at 5% for 10 years	375.00
Overhead—other	160.00
Total overhead cost of use 10 years	$2,035.00

Cost per year		203.50
Amount of hay to bale	84 tons	
Amount of straw to bale	42 tons	
Total	126 tons	

Hours to do the baling, 80		
Operating cost (plus man and tractor)		96.00
Total operating and overhead		$299.50
Cost per ton (126 tons)		2.38
Marginal cost per ton		0.76

The cost per ton figures somewhat under customary rental rates, and there is a very decided advantage in having one's own baler in order to work on the hour, according to condition of the hay (a subjective measure). Capital being available, the low marginal cost per ton and some promise of custom work would throw the decision in favor of purchase. However, other possibilities such as joint ownership, custom work, or purchase of used machines should be explored.

An analysis of the economy of purchasing and buying a corn picker for this farm can be made similarly as follows:

Purchase price (1-row)	$1,000
Anticipated life, 10 years	
Interest on $500 at 5% for 10 years	250
Other overhead costs	80
Total overhead	$1,330
Overhead per year	133
Days needed, 8	
Operating costs (man and tractor)	96
Total overhead and operating	$229
Total average costs per acre (46 acres)	about 5
Marginal cost per acre	over 2

The cost would be higher than if a contract picker were used, and, since the period for harvesting corn is long, in this area, and risk from reasonable timeliness low, it would be better to plan to hire a custom operator for this job.

A full tentative list of machinery and equipment for the 335-acre class case farm is given in the illustrated budget in Chapter 21.

QUESTIONS AND PROBLEMS
Machinery

1. By rule of thumb what is the annual fixed cost of the use of a machine costing $1,000 when new?

2. In calculating fixed cost of the use of a machine, why is interest charged on but half the original investment?

3. What method is used in calculating depreciation for income tax purposes?

4. What are the limitations of developing a size of business on the basis of complements of machines, as one team, one plow, one disk, one cultivator, one wagon, one binder, etc.?

5. Weigh the advantages of the one-plow tractor against a two-plow job for a small farm; consider the use of a two-plow used tractor vs. a new one-plow one.

6. If a tractor costs $1,600 new and is used 40 days per year how much are the fixed costs per day (estimated life 15 years)?

7. Compare your estimate of the net returns in crop values from a corn, wheat, clover, pasture rotation with the crop value of pasture above (soil treatments equal).

QUESTIONS AND PROBLEMS
Labor

1. If one's earnings are valued at $5.00 per day and the total cost of the use of a machine is $500, how many days does he have to work to pay for the machine?

2. List the reasons that farmers are willing to accept lower wages than factory workers.

3. Why do labor problems differ with different sizes of businesses?

4. If a dollar spent for labor as a variable input is used at a profit, are all dollars (those in fixed and variable inputs) used at a profit?

5. Why do operators of large farming businesses in general farming areas use more beef cattle for converting feed than dairy cattle?

PROBLEM EXERCISE 14
Labor Requirements on Specific Farms

How would you handle this labor program?

"Professor Scotch" has a 60-acre part-time farm business—capital investment, $18,600. He lives on the farm but has a job of teaching vocational agriculture at the county high school, 11 miles from the farm. The farm is improved for production of Grade A milk and produces roughage feed for 20 cows plus replacements. Milk has been sold wholesale. There is no tenant house on the farm and "Prof" has no family labor except his own.

Should he employ a full-time farm hand?

Would you build another house on this farm for a hired worker?

How would an intensive cash crop make a difference in the labor program?

What crops, livestock, and labor programs do you suggest?

How would you provide labor for this farm?

PROBLEM EXERCISE 15
Labor Requirements for Enterprises

1. As a class exercise: (a) Develop a list of the days or hours of man-labor requirements for farm enterprises in your state, or better, type-of-farming area, or (b) secure a list from your professor, or (c) secure a list from your state experiment station publications.

2. Break the total requirements needed down into monthly or bi-monthly periods.

3. Keep a copy of the list of requirements.

PROBLEM EXERCISE 16
Labor Budget—Individual Case Farm

Develop the labor requirements program for the individual case farm being used as illustrated in Table 19.5.

1. Use the labor production requirements of your state or type of farming area.

2. State the requirements by months, or by bi-monthly periods, and by totals.

3. Choose a system of satisfying the requirements, including both the year-round and seasonal workers.

4. Some of the requirements may best be satisfied through contracting production of the enterprise, such as hay to be produced by others, or through contracting such intensive operations as combining, spraying, or baling.

5. Accompany the table with a narrative description of the specific labor problems and methods of meeting them.

PROBLEM EXERCISE 17
Power, Machines, and Equipment for Individual Case Farm

On the basis of (a) the instructor's directions; (b) the crops to be grown; (c) the livestock to be kept; (d) the production practices contemplated; (e) the costs of ownership and use of machines; (f) the analysis and illustration:

1. Determine (a) kinds, (b) sizes and numbers of power units, machines, and pieces of equipment to use on the individual case farm.

2. Place values on each and list them in a table.

3. Estimate annual repairs and depreciation costs for each.

4. Write a description of the farming program from the viewpoint of machinery uses.

Keep a copy of your list and values for the general budget.

CHAPTER 20

Prices for Use in Budgeting

This rather brief introductory discussion will present a classification of price variations (movements), by kind and source, which are important in managing farms. The *kinds* of price variation to be considered are three in number: (1) variations in terms of exchange between farmers and non-farmers, (2) variations in prices of individual farm products, and (3) variations in prices of farm products relative to each other. The *sources* of price variation to be considered here are also three in number: (1) short-run variations which are not associated with changes in the general level of employment and industrial activity, (2) variations associated with the general level of employment and industrial activity, and (3) trend or long-run variations not associated with changes in the general level of employment and industrial activity. Cross classification of the three kinds of price variation with the three sources of price variation yields nine categories.

The remaining tasks of this discussion are: (1) to acquaint the reader with the nature and importance of each of the nine categories in this classification, (2) to illustrate the usefulness of the classification as a guide to farm managers, and (3) to illustrate how prices were assembled for use in budgeting the class case study farm.

Nature and Importance of Each of the Nine Categories

The nine categories can be arranged for reference purposes as in Table 20.1 appearing on the following page.

The nature and importance of each of the nine categories will be discussed in terms of (1) information concerning the extent of the different price changes and the nature of farming and (2) theory concerning the effects of imperfect price knowledge on organization, reorganization, and operation of a farm. In general, no attempt will be made to prove stated empirical facts or relationships; instead, footnotes will be used to refer the student to supporting literature.

Table 20.1. Price Variations Affecting Agriculture, Classified by Kind and Source

	SOURCE		
KIND	Short-run variation not associated with the general level of employment and industrial activity	Variations associated with the general level of employment and industrial activity	Trends or long-run variations not associated with the general level of employment and industrial activity
Terms of exchange between farmers and non-farmers	1	4	7
Prices of individual farm products	2	5	8
Farm product prices relative to other farm products	3	6	9

Category 1. Short-run variations in the terms of exchange (between farmers and non-farmers) which are not associated with changes in the general level of employment and industrial activity. One of the best measures of the terms of exchange between farmers and non-farmers is the ratio between the index of prices paid and the index of prices received by farmers. Another but somewhat less valid measure of the terms of exchange is the income parity ratio. Although the large swings in the ratio of prices received to prices paid by farmers are associated with changes in the general level of employment and industrial activity, a considerable amount of short-run variation is also present.[1] These short-run variations tend to reflect supply changes resulting from short-run factors, primarily weather. Short-run variations in the terms of exchange resulting from changes on the demand

---

[1] United States Department of Agriculture, *1949 Agricultural Outlook Charts* (Washington: U. S. Government Printing Office, 1948). See p. 12 which presents a chart of the ratio of prices received to prices paid by farmers. The short-run variations are easily observable.

side are of some importance. In either case such variations in the terms of exchange are hard to foresee.

Short-run variations in the terms of exchange are important in the year-to-year operations of a farm business; i.e., a shift in the level of prices paid relative to prices received is likely to result in much higher or lower profits than anticipated.

Category 2. Short-run changes in prices of individual farm products which are not associated with changes in the level of employment and industrial activity. Absolute in contrast to relative prices of individual products are referred to here, i.e., the dollars and cents prices of corn, steers, wheat, or grapes. Relative prices of individual products and inputs will be considered in Category 3. Short-run changes in absolute prices have allocative effects. Many of these effects are desirable involving more efficient allocation of resources. Other effects are undesirable; for instance, uncertainty about the future price of wheat not only affects the ability of a farmer producing wheat alone to secure credit for purchasing working capital but also affects his willingness to invest his own money in wheat production.[1] Debt obligations are in absolute, not relative, terms and must be paid out of absolute, not relative, incomes.

Short-run variations in absolute prices of farm products which are not associated with the level of employment are of great empirical importance.[2] Uncertainty and risks resulting from these variations appear to have a moderately important deterring effect on the flow of capital into agriculture and the flow of labor out of agriculture. By and large, these flows should not be stopped or deterred, as they result from (1) technological progress and (2) differentials between the birth rates of rural and urban areas.

Category 3. Short-run variations in prices of farm products relative to each other which are not associated with changes in the general level of employment and industrial activity. Examples of such variations include changes in livestock/feed price ratios, the corn/soybean price ratio, and changes in the cotton/peanut price ratio, to name only three of the seemingly infinite number. Most of the variations in rela-

---

[1] T. W. Schultz, "Capital Rationing, Uncertainty and Tenancy Reform," *Journal of Political Economy*, XLVIII, 1940, pp. 309–324.

[2] United States Department of Agriculture, *1949 Agricultural Outlook Charts* (Washington: U. S. Government Printing Office, 1948); see various charts such as those on pp. 31, 32, 36, and 70 to note empirical importance of short-run variations in absolute prices of particular farm products.

tive prices in agriculture are short run, and only a few of the relative prices are closely associated with depression and prosperity conditions.[1] These variations in relative prices have highly important and desirable allocative and distributive effects. For example, changes in the live-stock-feeding ratios adjust livestock production to changes in feed supplies; changes in the price of meat relative to prices of other food products adjust meat consumption to changes in meat supplies. By and large, these variations are predictable and can be adjusted to by farm managers.

Category 4. Variations in the terms of exchange (between farmers and non-farmers) which are associated with changes in the general level of employment and industrial activity. A large proportion of all variation in the terms of exchange is associated with changes in the general level of employment and industrial activity. The empirically important variations falling into this category have important and undesirable effects on the management of farms. Uncertainty concerning the terms of exchange deters the movement of capital into agriculture made desirable by technological progress; it also deters the movement of labor out of rural surplus-labor-producing areas. In the first instance, it increases interest rates charged to farmers and in the second it reduces the earning power of one of agriculture's principal assets—its labor.

In the interwar period, the very unfavorable terms of exchange which accompanied unpredictable periods of depressed business activity and/or low to moderate employment were responsible for a vast number of farm business failures. Economists generally agreed that the uncertainty concerning the terms of exchange was greater than a major industry should be required to bear, and many accepted the parity concept as a desirable stabilization standard. Large groups of consumers gave "silent consent" and, in some cases, outright approval of the parity concept. The effects of uncertain variations in the terms of exchange associated with uncertain (unpredictable) levels of employment and industrial activity create an important long-run problem in making permanent or semipermanent agricultural investments.

Category 5. Variations in prices of individual farm products which are associated with changes in the level of employment and industrial activity. Most of the variation in prices of individual farm products

---

[1] Glenn L. Johnson, "Allocative Efficiency of Agricultural Prices—As Affected by the General Level of Employment," unpublished doctoral dissertation, University of Chicago, June, 1949.

is associated with the level of employment and industrial activity.[1] It should be noted that absolute, not relative, prices within the farm sector are under consideration in this category. This category of price variations which is more important empirically than category 2 is also highly important economically. As noted under category 2, uncertainty concerning absolute prices (1) deters necessary movements of capital into agriculture; and (2) deters the flow of labor out of rural areas producing surpluses of laborers. As the variations of this category greatly exceed those of category 2, this category has the greater effect on interest rates and labor earnings. Further, the variations in absolute prices considered in this category probably do not result in relative prices which effectively allocate production between products in accordance with the changes in demand associated with changes in employment and industrial activity.

Variations in absolute prices associated with the interwar changes in the level of employment and industrial activity caused many farm business failures between 1920 and 1936. Because changes in the level of employment are difficult to predict, variations in absolute prices associated therewith create one of the most important problems involved in borrowing money for investments in agriculture.

Category 6. Variations in prices of farm products relative to each other which are associated with the general level of employment. It is difficult to isolate empirically that portion of the variations in the price of one farm product relative to another which is closely associated with changes in the level of employment. Changes in the price of a product produced by highly commercialized farms relative to the price of a product produced by less commercialized farms are sometimes associated with changes in the level of employment and business activity. For the most part, however, prices of individual farm products do not change relative to each other in a manner which can be associated with any given level of employment. Thus, from the demand side, movements into and out of depression periods have little effect on the enterprises which should be carried out on a particular farm.

[1] United States Department of Agriculture, *1949 Agricultural Outlook Charts* (Washington: U. S. Government Printing Office, 1948). Again, see charts presenting historical price series for separate products such as those on pp. 31, 32, 36, and 70. These charts indicate that the swings in prices which occur with the swings in the level of employment and industrial activity include most of the variations in the series.

Category 7. Trend or long-run variations in the terms of exchange between farmers and non-farmers which are not associated with changes in the level of employment and industrial activity. Only a small part of the variation in the terms of exchange appears due to trend. This trend is secular in nature [1] and probably reflects differentials in rates of technological development between the farm and non-farm sectors. The fact that such a small proportion of the variation in the terms of exchange appears to be traceable to trend diminishes the importance of this consideration within a farmer's life span and, hence, in the problem of organizing or reorganizing a farm.[1]

Category 8. Long-run variations in prices of individual farm products not associated with changes in the level of employment and industrial activity. Prices of individual products generally display an upward trend since the late 1700's; however, the price level of farm products has fluctuated within wide extremes as the economy has moved into and out of depressions.[1] Little uncertainty is created by trend variations; hence, such variations are of little importance in organizing and reorganizing farms.

Category 9. Trend or long-run variations in prices of farm products relative to each other which are not associated with changes in the level of employment and industrial activity. Although price variations of this nature are of importance for a few pairs and/or between a few groups of farm products, most relative farm product prices do not display long-run trends.[2] Those variations which do occur probably occur as a result of secular shifts in production costs or demand and for these reasons must be considered.

The Task of Pricing Fixed Assets for Budgeting Purposes

Most of the difficulties encountered in pricing inputs involve fixed inputs; this is true with respect to accounting, record making, cost work, and budgeting. Fixed inputs usually do not have market prices as separate items. They are fixed and therefore worth what they will produce in their present employment. What they are worth in their present employment depends on a variety of factors, including: (1) prices received for the products that they are used to produce, (2) the

---

[1] United States Department of Agriculture, *1949 Agricultural Outlook Charts* (Washington: U. S. Government Printing Office, 1948). See chart on p. 1 which plots prices of farm and non-farm products, 1798 to date. Prices of farm products increased relative to non-farm products throughout the period.

[2] Johnson, op. cit.

amount and quantity of variable inputs (working capital) used, and (3) production techniques employed. Ordinarily market conditions do impose upper and lower restrictions on variations in the worth of a fixed asset; i.e., if the worth of a fixed asset becomes sufficiently high, it becomes advantageous to add more of it, in which case it is no longer fixed; conversely, if the worth falls sufficiently low, it becomes advantageous to start selling the asset. The upper of these two limits is often over 50 percent higher than the lower (consider a man with a given amount of hay on hand—it is easily possible for the purchase price laid down at the farm to be $30.00 a ton whereas the net return for hay sold off the farm is $20.00). The same is often true in greater or lesser degree of land, buildings, machines, labor, management, etc. From time to time all of these and other items fall into fixed positions where they are worth what they will produce. When they are in these positions, it is extremely difficult to price them.

One method of pricing fixed assets is to use *replacement costs*. Use of replacement costs causes costs to be overestimated and profits to be underestimated. Another method is use of liquidation prices or opportunity costs, which causes profits to be overestimated. Still another procedure is to not price fixed assets at all but, instead, to subtract from gross income all cash expenses and call the remainder return to fixed assets and profits. Great difficulty is experienced in interpreting the results of subtracting from this remainder arbitrary charges for portions of the fixed assets. This difficulty, the source of much confusion in the profession of farm management, is best avoided by persons unprepared conceptually to make and interpret interfarm analyses of the dollar and physical productivity of the fixed assets.[1] The difficulty is avoided by refraining from making arbitrary charges against gross income for fixed assets. In other words, it is suggested that the farm manager settle for an estimate of farm earnings as explained in Chapter 4, as this figure can correctly be interpreted to represent returns to management, fixed investments, and the operator's labor and can be reached without pricing the fixed assets. For those instances in which it is felt desirable, for traditional or other reasons, to price fixed assets, either (1) estimates of the dollar productivity of the fixed assets or (2) arbitrary fixed asset prices falling between replacement and opportunity costs should be used. In the latter portion of Chapter 11, estimates of dollar productivities were used; in the

[1] See the last portions of Chapter 11.

chapter on use of the general budget, arbitrary fixed asset prices (or charges) will be used, as dollar productivity estimates are not available for farms similar to the class case farm.

The Task of Getting Price Data Together for Budgeting Purposes

When a farm is being organized or reorganized, certain commitments are made on a long-time basis. These commitments are best made on the basis of long-run *price relatives;* they should also be made on the basis of long-run *levels* of prices. The "joker" in the last requirement is that long-run levels of prices are difficult to predict; in fact economists and others have great difficulty predicting depressions, prosperity periods, and the consequent changes in the level of prices.

Not all commitments made in organizing a farm are of a long-run nature, however, and can be adjusted to changes in both (1) the level of prices, (2) the terms of exchange, and (3) price relationships.

About all one can do in "guestimating" long-time price trends is to:

1. Have confidence in the future.
2. Study carefully historical trends.
3. Keep as much of the operations on a short-run basis as feasible.
4. Keep in position to adjust to new information concerning the general price level.
5. Defer heavy outlays for low turnover capital commitments until the individual financial position is reasonably secure, regardless of price trends.
6. Make heavy long-run expenditures out of windfall profits.
7. Insure against price declines by estimating prices conservatively when short on owned equity, percentagewise.

Thus in getting ready to budget a plan for organizing or reorganizing a farm, a set of expected prices must be formulated. Ideally such a set of prices should coincide with the actual prices which will be encountered. Practically this is not possible. Apparently, the best procedure is to construct a set of prices having the following characteristics:

1. The *relationships between prices* should reflect the normal relationships for the farm under consideration.
2. The *level* of prices paid should be about the same as that currently paid for major investment items.

3. The *level* of prices for products should be conservative enough to give the farmer (not the planner) the degree of safety he desires.

4. The variation in prices of different products and inputs should be known.

Sources of Price Information

1. Reports of state extension services and experiment stations. Generally, both long-run price information and current outlook information are available from these sources. Also, price information on local products in local areas is often available.

2. *Agricultural Prices* published about the 29th of each month by the Bureau of Agricultural Economics and containing, in various issues:
   (a) Current prices paid and received by farmers for various products and inputs, by states.
   (b) Average prices, for periods of years, useful in establishing price relationships.
   (c) Series of prices over a period of years useful in establishing measures of price variability.
   (d) Information on current price support programs.

3. *Agricultural Statistics,* published annually by the U. S. Department of Agriculture. This book contains about the same price information as that contained in *Agricultural Prices* except that the emphasis is upon annual data.

4. *Crops and Markets,* published annually by the U. S. Department of Agriculture. This publication is a good single source of monthly and annual prices over a period of years. It is short on area detail and not current.

5. Production and Marketing Administration offices are in position to furnish information on current price-support programs, as well as various price reports and compilations.

6. Offices of the Bureau of Agricultural Economics State Statistician are also often in position to furnish reports and data on prices in areas smaller than one state.

7. The "situation reports" published periodically by the Bureau of Agricultural Economics are good sources of nearly current price information and data. Among the important situation reports are those dealing with demand and prices, feed, wheat, livestock, wool, cotton, tobacco, fruit and vegetables, dairy, meat, and poultry.

8. Various private agencies such as the Doane Agricultural Service also get out good current reports on prices.

9. No listing of sources for price information and data would be complete which excluded such agencies as newspapers, magazines, radio stations, television stations, dealers, banks, and other credit institutions.

Prices Used in the Illustration Budget

Prices used in the illustration budget in the succeeding chapter are prices which were expected to be somewhat readily realizable for the year 1952, during the period of preparation of this book (1950–1951).

It is safer to be on the conservative side of expected income (production and prices) in budgeting, as pointed out in Chapter 3 in the section on degrees of perfection of knowledge. Error on the conservative side results in added unexpected income. Furthermore, since price forecasting cannot be perfect a form of insurance is taken through conservatism or discounting.

Budget prices of products should ordinarily be "on-farm prices" and allowances for low quality or grade should be made. Prices of supplies should likewise be on-the-farm prices.

Conditions existing during the period of formulating prices were:

1. The outbreak of the Korean War and public acceptance of a long-time defense program and world-wide aid, indicating high industrial employment.

2. Consumer resistance to food prices.

3. Institution of the OPS.

4. The 1948 Agricultural Adjustment Act providing for parity income, support prices, marketing quotas on tobacco, the 10-year movable base, and commodity loans.

5. Increasing labor costs and escalator clauses in some industries.

6. Existing prices of farm products.

7. Current parity prices.

In assembling this set of prices, use was made of local sources of price information, such as newspapers, auction prices, and conversations with farmers. Also, outlook talks, presented at the University Farm-Home Week program, and the various "Situation" and "Outlook" reports were used.

Where important fixed assets, such as land, were involved, an intermediate price between replacement costs (what it would cost to buy such land on short notice) and opportunity cost (what such land would sell for on a forced sale basis) was used. The same is true of the prices placed on pasturage and corn silage.

An exercise at the end of this chapter will provide the student with an opportunity to construct, in a similar fashion, a set of prices for his individual case farm.

The prices used in the 1952 class case budget were formulated in 1950 on the basis of the conditions as given above. On the basis of these conditions, it was thought at that time that prices would hold for a few years or work somewhat higher. Parity and support prices were taken into consideration for grains; hay was estimated on the

Prices of Important Items for the Illustration Budget

Real Estate
Land (naked) $200.00 per acre.
Land and improvements $310.45 per acre.

Farm-Produced Feeds
Barley $1.15 per bushel.
Corn $1.75 per bushel.
Hay $25.00 per ton.
Pasturage $25.00 per summer pasturage unit.
Corn silage $10.50 per ton.

Purchased Feeds
Tankage $6.70 per hundredweight.
Middlings $4.00 per hundredweight.
Salt $1.50 per hundredweight.
Soybean meal $5.00 per hundredweight.

Purchased Livestock
Good feeder yearlings $24.00 per hundredweight.

Product Prices
Cattle, good to choice slaughter $27.00 per hundredweight.
Hogs
    spring $22.00 per hundredweight.
    fall $20.00 per hundredweight.
Tobacco   50 cents per pound.
Wheat $2.20 per bushel.
Milk $4.50 per hundredweight.

Commercial Fertilizers and Lime
P_2O_5 7.5 cents per pound.
6-8-6 $45.00 per ton.
10-10-10 $60.00 per ton.
K_2O 6 cents per pound.
Ammonium nitrate $90.00 per ton.
Limestone $3.00 per ton.

basis of local summer price levels; and pasturage was assigned a pasturage unit value at the price of a ton of hay. Corn silage was given a value equal to the estimated value of the corn crop if harvested for ear corn. Purchased feed and fertilizer prices were taken from *Agricultural Prices* (state level), feeder cattle prices were current local prices of good-to-choice cattle to farmers.

In the area of product prices cattle were expected to hold at 1950 levels and hogs to decline. (These forecasts in 1950 (for 1952) proved to be 4 cents low for cattle and 5 cents high for spring hogs. Other predictions proved to be reasonably good.)

PROBLEM EXERCISE 18
Prices for Budgeting—a Class or an Individual Exercise

The problem of forecasting prices can best be handled by each class formulating a set of base prices for the particular area and time in which the members are interested. The source materials and the procedure given in this chapter should prove helpful. Local source materials and student and farmer experiences should not be neglected. Farm prices may vary widely within the state. Prices will be needed for:

1. The crops to be grown.
2. Livestock and livestock products.
3. Real estate values including improvements.
4. Soil amendments and fertilizers.
5. Feeds, seeds, and supplies.
6. Services, commissions, custom operations, taxes, and insurance.

As a class or individual exercise, make a list of prices applicable to the area(s) of individual interests or use prices furnished by the professor somewhat as follows:

Crops	Price per Unit

Livestock	Price per Unit

Livestock Products	Price per Unit

Soil Amendments—Fertilizers	Price per Unit

Feeds Purchased   Price per Unit

_____   _____
_____   _____
_____   _____

Seeds and Supplies   Price per Unit

_____   _____
_____   _____

Services, Commissions, Taxes, Insurance   Price per Unit

_____   _____
_____   _____
_____   _____

Pasturage per Unit

_____
_____
_____

CHAPTER 21

Use of the General Budget

What Budgets Are

A farm budget is a written plan for future actions plus the anticipated results. It is a device for production analysis. Planning is a part of the decision-making process. The plan may be formal, i.e., written in an organized manner and called a budget; or it may be informal to the degree of existing only in the mind of the one who made it. All farmers plan—more or less. More, if the business is large, less, if small; more, if well-organized, less, if haphazard. Thus, budgeting as a process increases in extent and in formality as the business for which it is made increases in size and complexity. A budget can be detailed or general—it can be complete, covering an entire farm (both home and business), or partial, covering only the business aspect of the farm or a small portion thereof.

The plan may be made for a day, a year, or a period of years. Budgets are usually made for a year. The year selected may be the next year or a specific year sometime in advance. It is a wise procedure for one renting a farm, buying a farm, or reorganizing a farm business to make a budget for a typical year's operation under the proposed system of management. If extensive developments are contemplated, 3 to 6 years may be necessary to get the proposed plan into complete use. In such cases, it is wise to make a budget for the business for a year when reorganization will be completed and subsequent budgets for intervening years.

Students frequently voice the observation that few farmers write out their plans. Few farmers have been trained to write plans, but an increasing number are being trained. The process of budgeting farm businesses is usually more important than the paper product, because provisions of the budget exist in the memory of the one who made them and become a production device.

Basically, a budgeting process for a given period converges on two figures. One of these figures is *total revenue* for the period or situation under consideration. The other figure is *total expenses* for the same period. When the difference between these two figures is found, it is called net profit or net return or net loss, depending upon whether net revenues are greater than or less than expenses. All other parts of budgets are details leading up to this result. A budget can be presented in tabular form as follows:

Revenues

Quantity of Y_1 sold or added to inventory $\times$ price of Y_1 = $XXX.XX$

. . . .

. . . .

. . . .

Quantity of Y_n sold or added to inventory $\times$ price of Y_n = $XXX.XX$

Total revenues $XXX.XX$

Expenses

Quantity of X_1 used $\times$ price of X_1 = $XXX.XX$

. . . .

. . . .

. . . .

Quantity of X_n used $\times$ price of X_n = $XXX.XX$

Total expenses $XXX.XX$

Difference (profit or loss) $XXX.XX$

And the above table can be expressed in equation form as follows:

$$[Q_{y_1}P_{y_1} + \cdots + Q_{y_n}P_{y_n}] - [Q_{x_1}P_{x_1} + \cdots + Q_{x_n}P_{x_n}] - FC = \Pi$$

where:

Q = quantity.
P = price.
Π = profit or loss, depending on sign.
$y_1 \cdots y_n$ = different products sold or added to inventory.
$x_1 \cdots x_n$ = different items used or removed from inventory.
FC = fixed costs.

Essentially, a budget is the summation of all expected products (or increased inventories) times their respective price less the summation of all items used in production times their prices for a given time period.

One "joker" in the budgeting process is the problem of getting appropriate prices and quantities to put into the budget forms or budget equations. A considerable amount of discussion has been devoted to appropriate prices and quantities elsewhere in this book. At this point there is no need to extend discussion of variable inputs prices.

The chapters on economic principles and input-output data for pork, dairy, and beef production gave a great deal of attention to principles and methods of adjusting particular enterprises so that (1) the optimum amount of each product would be produced and (2) the inputs would be combined in the most profitable proportions for the production of that optimum amount. These same chapters then presented procedures with respect to particular enterprises for directly ascertaining the *optimum product* and *input quantities* to be used in the budgeting process.

The economic principles upon which the input-output studies reported herein are based locate optimum input and production rates. No further changes in inputs or outputs for the length of run under consideration (fixed conditions) will increase profits. The budgeter who does not use these economic principles for locating optimum quantities attempts to construct "the most profitable budget" by making one change after another. If the budgeter uses economic principles, such changes are confined to those possible in the length of run for which the budget is being made. Both processes lead to the same answer: the one, directly; the other, indirectly, perhaps.

Two changes can be made on the production side: first, changes can be made in the method of producing a product; and, second, within a given production method, changes can be made in the amounts of the variable inputs used and hence, in the level of production. It is hard to say which of these two types of changes is more important. Professor Wilcox has argued that changes dealing with method are more important for small subsistence-type farms, whereas changes in inputs and outputs, leaving method unchanged, are more important for the larger commercial farms.[1] There is probably a great deal of truth in Wilcox's argument.

Why Make Budgets

There are a number of reasons for making budgets, some of which are sufficient to the student or young farmer, regardless of the others.

[1] Walter W. Wilcox, "Effects of Farm Price Changes on Efficiency in Farming," *Journal of Farm Economics*, Vol. XXXIII, February, 1951.

1. Beginners at farming and students of farm management lack experience and also have to decide upon the many items which will, when purchased, become long-run fixed factors in the production processes. Practicing farmers have already fixed many similar items into their businesses. Long-run fixed factors should be selected with more care than short-run. Budgeting assists in selecting factors more wisely. It is a way to experiment in adding other resources to a set of fixed resources in order to compare returns from the whole and from the added resources.

2. Another important reason for budgeting is that of refining decisions for operation. The question of the optimum amount of commercial fertilizer to use on corn is illustrative. If 60 bushels of corn can probably be secured without fertilizer and $1.40 is the current price of corn, should the operator follow his previous practice if the outlook for the ensuing year's crop is $1.50 per bushel? Suppose 70 bushels could be expected with a fertilizer expenditure of $6.00. Or 75 bushels at an expenditure of $16.00. Or 80 bushels at an expenditure of $25.00. Budgeting causes one to think more accurately and to plan more carefully and more completely.

3. A written plan makes a good impression on other people. It shows that one has thought through his production and finance problems. Bankers and suppliers favor men who have written plans.

4. Budgets thus help borrow money. They show money needs for the year, indicate what months the money is needed, and thus establish a basis for budgeted loans. They provide also a basis for setting up repayment schedules.

5. Budgets force one to find items of cost that are frequently overlooked otherwise.

6. The budgeting process is the basis for the capitalization system of farm appraisal used by most lending agencies.

7. It is the basic procedure in the balanced-farming programs of the Extension Service.

8. It is used in farm planning by the Soil Conservation Service.

9. It is used in making and supervising loans by the Farm and Home Administration.

10. A budget is a money saver. It is much cheaper to make mistakes on paper than in business.

Of immediate importance to students at this point is the fact that a budget is an excellent device for learning to organize and reorganize farms.

Extent of Budgets

The most elementary form of budget is a statement of expectations in physical terms, such as:

I expect to produce: I expect to sell:
   10 acres corn   a.
   15 acres cotton   b.
   20 acres pasture   c.

I expect to keep: I will need to buy:
   10 dairy cows   a.
    2 sows and pigs   b.
  300 hens   c.

A complete budget goes into details as to:

1. Use of the specific units of the farm land.
2. Acres of each crop to be grown.
3. Complete details on inputs of the variable factors, such as seed, plant food, labor, sprays, marketing costs.
4. Disposition of production into farm use, home use, and sales.
5. Details of the livestock program.
6. Machinery and equipment items, and costs.
7. Summary and production rates.
8. Consumption expenditures, savings, and investments.

How to Rough Out a Budget

Students are already well on their way to having made a budget of their respective individual case farms. Problem Exercises 8 and 9 are the results of thinking about land use and crops programs. Acres, expected production, values, and sales have been determined roughly. This step in the process of budgeting a farm business followed an appraisal of the family's goals, objectives, and resources (Problem Exercise 6). The next step has likewise been taken in developing livestock plans for the individual case farm (Problem Exercise 13). There remains the further task of adjusting the crop and livestock programs to each other, to existing price relationships, and to the goals, objectives, and resources of the family.

If data similar to that developed in the Marshall County study described in Chapter 10 were available for all farming areas the problems of farm planning would be greatly simplified. This study gives marginal returns for five of the major categories of inputs and thus may be used for Marshall County upland farms, as it indicates good distribution of resources. No such data are available for the area in which this farm is located. It is expected that such data will be developed in many farming states within reasonable time limits.

Optimum or most profitable rates in using units of outlays rationally depend upon:

1. Expected price of product.
2. Marginal product in terms of quantity and quality.
3. Prices of inputs.

The rough budget may be formulated on the basis of rates of inputs with good practices as used by leading farmers and as advocated by the Extension Service, the farm press, and other reputable agencies. Most farmers err on the side of conservatism, i.e., not using purchased inputs in sufficient quantities to bring output up to the point where $MFC = MVP$, rather than on the side of using too much, i.e., using more than enough inputs to bring outputs beyond the high profit point. Purchase of machines may be an exception.

Final budgets should show refinements in input-output expectancy based upon (1) available detailed input-output data of the type presented in the pork, dairy, and beef chapters, (2) less detailed computations matching additional costs against additional returns as a basis for choosing between various alternatives, and (3) reappraisals of the fixed asset organization, and the goals and objectives of the farm family.

Illustration for Developing a Budget

The succeeding pages illustrate the process of roughing out a budget for the class case farm used in the chapters on land, crops, livestock, and labor. This rough budget is a recapitulation of the plans for land use, crops, livestock, and labor uses, plus quantities, prices, and further explanations. This budget is an illustration in procedure—a student's guide for making budgets. There is a flow of problem solving from table to table, corresponding generally to the flow of organization and management problems followed in this book. The student is requested to take the items of Tables 21.A, 21.B, and 21.C and follow them through the budget. For example, there is land to be used for corn.

Corn produces feed; the feed is used for hogs and cattle.
Hogs and cattle involve further quantities and prices.
These are reflected in the budget summary.

Budget Form

A budget is a written plan for the organization and management of a farm for a unit of time—usually 1 year. It may be for the ensuing year, for a typical year or for some year in advance. The purpose of the budget is to develop an accurate, coordinated, and detailed plan. It is to the farmer what a blueprint is to both the architect and the construction engineer. There are many kinds of budget forms. This set of forms may be used to show:

1. The way the land is to be used, the production expected of crops to be grown and the plan for disposition of such production (Table 21.*A*).

2. The seed, fertilizer, and other expense items for the proposed crops (Table 21.*B*).

3. The numbers and kinds of livestock that are to be kept on the farm under the crop production plan and their yearly production requirements for farm-produced feeds (Table 21.*C*).

4. The amount and cost of supplemental feeds that will need to be purchased for such livestock, the cost of the livestock to be purchased, and the miscellaneous livestock expenses (Table 21.*D*).

5. The estimated production of livestock and of livestock products and the disposition to be made of such production (Table 21.*E*).

6. A list of the machinery and equipment needed for the crops and the livestock and their values (Table 21.*F*).

7. A list of the farm improvements and their values (Table 21.*G*).

8. A summary of the farm receipts and farm expenses with provisions for determining the estimated net earnings (Table 21.*H*).

9. The proposed capital investment (Table 21.*I*).

10. Some rough indicators of production efficiencies (Table 21.*J*).

Student's Name *Livestock Major* Farm of *335-Acre Class Case* For Year *1952*

County *Fayette* Location of farm *9 mi N.E. Lexington*

Refining the Budget

The budgeter is confronted in farm management with both the long-run, or more or less organizational, problems of the business, and the short-run, or more or less operational, problems of the business. In both cases the marginality principles are applicable; in the long-run, to a large number of variable inputs; in the short-run, to a correspondingly shorter list of inputs. For example, the student may need to think of some 5 to 20 years as the long-run planning span and 1 month to 2 years as the short-run planning period. Thus the student needs ultimately to examine the business and refine his plans both as a whole and in detail on the basis of marginality principles.

Since it is impossible within the learning process to study all problems simultaneously until they have been examined individually, student attention in the budgeting process has been focused upon the fixed

Table 21.A. Estimated Production and Disposition of Crops to Be Produced

Name of Crop [1] and Number of Field	Slope of Field	Number of Acres	Production [2]		Gross [3] Product Value	Man W.U. Needed	Farm Use		Household Use		Sales [3]	
			Per Acre	Total	$		Feed	Seed	Amount	Value	Amount	Value $
Classes I & II Land												
Corn (rye) 9₁	0-3	23	80	1,840	3,220	34.5	1,840					
Corn (wheat) 4₁	0-3	23	80	1,840	3,220	34.5	1,840					
Wheat (G.M.) 3₁	0-3	23	26	598	1,316	13.8	50				548	1,205
Tobacco (B) 4₂	4-6	17	1,800	30,600	15,300	535.5					30,600	15,300
Barley 3₂	4-6	17	30	510	586	10.2	510					
Clover 9₂	4-6	17	2	34	850							
Class III Land												
Barley 10	7-9	25	30	750	862	22.5	750					
M. Hay 1a	7-9	20	2.5	50	1,250	20.0	50					
R. Pasture 1b	7-10	20	1	20	500		20					
R. Pasture 6	7-9	20	1	20	500	13.0	20					
R. Pasture 8	7-9	25	0.6	15	375		15					
Garden & truck	*Cropper's 1*				(300)					(300)		
Perm. pasture tillable 2 / 7	10-15 / 10-15	75 / 10	0.5 / 0.5	37.5 / 5.0	938 / 125	10.0						
Idle crop land												
Perm. pasture ~~not tillable~~ 5	10-15	10	0.75	7.5	188							
Woods pasture												
Farmsteads, roads, wastelands		14										
Totals	xxx	335	xxx	xxx	$29,230	694.0	xxx	xxx	xxx	xxx	xxxx	$16,505

1 List crops by land classes and by rotations, e.g., Class I, corn, wheat, clover hay.
2 List production of crops in usual units, e.g., bushels, pounds, tons, crates, etc. List production of pastures in units of livestock that the acreage will carry on the basis of the pasture season.
3 Record in full dollars.

Table 21.B. Estimated Requirements of Seeds, Fertilizers, and Other Expenses for Crops

Name of Crop	Number of Acres	Seeds and Plants				Manure, Fertilizer, and Lime				Other Expenses		
		Kind	Rate per Acre	Total[1] Amount	Total[1] Value	Kind	Rate per Acre	Total[1] Amount	Total[1] Value	Kind	Total Amount	Total[1] Cost
												$
Row Corn	46	103	10	8 bu.	$ 96	P_2O_5	60	2,760	$ 207	Picking	4°/a	184
						6-8-6	500	23,000	518			
						Limestone	500	12	36			
						Nitrate	200	9,200	414			
Tobacco	17	16	¼ oz.	4	8	Manure	8	136	(272)	Canvas	255	41
						P_2O_5	200	3,400	255	Sprays	5°/a	85
						10-10-10	1,000	17,000	510	Coke	9	225
										Selling	½ crop	268
Small grain												
Barley	17	1	2	34	51	None						
	25	1	2	50	75	6-8-6	200	5,000	112			
						Lime	2,000	25	75			
Wheat	23	Clarkson	1¼	29	87	6-8-6	300	6,900	155			
Hay and pasture clover	17	Alf.	10	170	102							
		Fescue	10	250	250					Innoc.		12
Mixed	25	Timothy	3	75	56	P_2O_5	100	2,500	188			
			2	50	10	K_2O	100	2,500	150			
		Bluegrass				Lime	400	20	60			
Pasture	100	Ladino } as needed				P_2O_5	10	1,000	75			
		Korean				K_2O	50	5,000	300			
		Fescue										
Total value of items to be bought			xx	$ 735		xx	xxx	xxx	$3,055	xxx	xx	$ 815

[1] Encircle value not to be bought.

$ 735 seeds plus $ 3,055 manure, fertilizer, lime, plus $ 815 other expenses = $ 4,605 cash expenses on crops.

Table 21.C. Livestock. Total Production Requirements (Farm-Grown Feeds). Labor Units Needed.

Kind	Number of Head	Corn, bu.	Barley	Barley Straw	Mixed Hay, tons	Legume Hay, tons	Silage, lb.	Stover, acres or lb.	Units of Pasture	Bedding, tons	Man W.U. Needed
Workstock	2	No			4				2	2	
Dairy cows	4	100				8			4	3	(90)
Beef cattle	90	1,420	600	42	50	30			90	17	180
Sheep											
Hogs Sows	12	300	280						} 8	2	96
Fattening	160	1,960	380								
Poultry											
Total needed [1]		3,780	1,260	42	54	38			104	24	276
Amount produced		3,680	1,260	42	50	34			105	23	xxx
Amount bought											xxx
Cost of purchases		$	$	$	$	$	$	$	$	$	xxx

Total cost of purchases _None_

[1] Check total needed vs. production and purchases within 10 percent.

Table 21.D. Total Production Requirement of Purchased Supplemental Feeds, Livestock Purchased. Miscellaneous Expense.

Kind	Number of Head	Soybean Meal Pounds per Head	Soybean Meal Total Pounds	Middlings Pounds per Head	Middlings Total Pounds	Tankage Pounds per Head	Tankage Total Pounds	Salt Pounds per Head	Salt Total Pounds	Livestock Purchased Number of Head	Livestock Purchased Cost	Misc. Expense Kind	Misc. Expense Cost
											$		$
Workstock	2			or other supplement		or similar supplement							
Dairy cows	4	or C.S. meal		D. cows fed by croppers									
Beef cows												Vet.	20
												Buying	90
Steers	90	150	13,500					20	1,800	90	15,120	Selling	67
												Trucking	100
												Misc.	120
Sheep													
Hogs Sows	12			100	1,200	120	1,440					Vacc.	80
Fattening	160			75	12,000	75	12,000		300			Trucking	100
												Corn	40
Poultry												Misc.	100
Total amount	xx	xx	13,500	xx	1,200	xx	13,440	xx	2,100	xx	xx	xxx	
Price per unit	xx	xx	5.00	xx	4	xx	6.70	xx	1.50	xx	xx	xxx	
Total cost [1]	xx	xx	675	xx	48	xx	900	xx	32	xx	$15,120	xxx	$717

[1] Record to nearest dollar.

[2] Include breeding fees, registration fees, veterinary, medicine, dips, trucking, commission, sheep shearing, blacksmithing, and depreciation not accounted for through sales (Table E) or replacements (Table D). Depreciation on workstock is roughly 10 percent of value; sheep, 15 percent; dairy cows, 10 percent to 25 percent, depending on breed and quality; hens, 35 percent.

Total cost of purchased supplemental feeds $ 2,055

Table 21.E. Estimated Production and Disposition of Livestock and Livestock Products

Kind	Number of Head	Number Animal Units	Total Inventory Value	Production		Disposition of Production					
				Per Head	Total	Farm Use		Household Use		Sales	
						Kind	Amount	Amount	Value	Amount	Value
Workstock	2	2	$ 200								$
Dairy cows	4	4	800					89			
								1100			
								8900			
								89			
								97,900 @ 27¢			
Beef cows— Steers	90	90	19,000	400	Gain					89	26,433
Sheep											
Hogs Sows	12	6	} 1,500							12	768
Fattening	160	32		225	36,000				Spring	74	3,673
									Fall	74	3,330
Poultry											
Totals	xxx	134	$ 21,500	xxx	xxx	xxx	xxx	xxx	$	xxx	$34,204

[1] After making allowances for barrenness and death losses. $34,204 Total livestock (including products) sales minus $ 15,120 Livestock purchased = $ 19,084 Livestock net inc.

Table 21.F. Machinery and Equipment

Kind and Number	Value	Kind and Number	Value
Power:		**Specialized enterprise:** [1]	
Tractor	$	Coke stove 35	$ 175
Tenant 1		Sticks 21,000	420
Owner 1	1,100		
		Farrowing houses 12	600
		Waterers, feeders, etc.	500
Land preparation:			
Tractor plow 1	135		
Tractor disk 1	165	**Other machines:**	
Tractor harrow 1	60	Truck 1½ T.	600
Bush & bog 1	200	Manure spreader 1	160
Cultipacker 1	65	Elevators 1	200
Drag	25	Feed grinder 1	125
		Motors 3	150
		Lime spreader	50
Planting:			
Corn planter	75	Fertilizer drill	50
Grain drill	135		
Plant setter 2			
Grass seeder (hand)	5		
Cultivating:		**Miscellaneous:**	
		Shop tools	500
Tractor cultivator 1	160	Fencing tools	50
		General tools	200
Small	6	Harness 2	100
		Wagons 2	300
		Bags 700	140
Harvesting:			
Combine 1	650		
Pick-up-baler 1	1,200		
Tractor mower	150		
Rake	150		
		Total investment $	8,601
		Repairs 4%	344
		Depreciation 10%	860

[1] As milking machines, etc., on dairy farms, potato diggers, etc., on potato farms, spray rigs, etc., on fruit farms.

Table 21.*G.* Inventory of Real Estate and Improvements, Estimated Amount of Depreciation and Costs of Repairs

Item	No.	Value	Rate of Dep.	Amt. of Dep.	Cost of Repairs	Remarks
Land (acres)	335	$67,000	%	$ xxx	$,xxx	
Dwelling house	1	15,000	2	300	100	
Tenant houses	2	8,000	4	320	50	
Stock barns Hay shed 40x60		1,500	3	45	10	
Silo						
Cribs-granaries	6	1,800	6	108	108	
Special e'prise barns Tob	2	7,000	4	280	140	
Machine shed						
Fences (rods)	1,600	3,200	5	160	80	
Temporary		300	15	45		
Tile drains (ft.)						
Water system		2,000	10	200	50	
Drainage ditches						
Totals	xxxx	$105,800	xxx	$1,458	$ 538	xxxx

Table 21.*H*. Summary, Receipts, and Expenses

Income Summary		Expenses	
		Cash:	
Crop sales (Table 21.*A*)	$ 17,385		
Livestock net increase (Table 21.*E*)	31,645	Cash exp. on crops (Table 21.*B*)	$ 5,093
		Supp. feeds bought (Table 21.*D*)	3,311
_____	___	Grains, hay, past. bot. (Table 21.*C*)	104
Crops used in home (Table 21.*A*)	___	Feed grinding	
Livestock used in home (Table 21.*E*)	___	Salt minerals	25
Fuel used in home	___	Misc. Livestock expenses (Table 21.*D*)	1,370
Use of house (10% of value)	1,500	Hired labor (50 days) 400	5,800
Total farm receipts	$ 50,530	Landlord's 3 yr 5,400	
Total farm expenses	32,030	Value cropper's share of crops	7,650
Farm earnings	18,500	Repairs of M. & E. (Table 21.*F*)	640
Interest on investment (@ 4%)	7,398	Repair of improvements (Table 21.*G*)	813
Net earnings	11,102	Trucking (not chg. above)	
		Truck (operating costs)	700
		Auto (farm shares)	500
		Electric current	156
		Tractor, cash operating costs	600
		Commission (not chg. above)	
		Advertising	___
		Insurance (on farm items)	185
		Taxes on real estate	1,050
		Other:	
		Depreciation M. & E. (Table 21.*F*)	1,600
		Depreciation improvements (Table 21.*G*)	2,433
		Total expenses	$ 32,030

Table 21.*I*. Investment Summary

Land & improvements (Table 21.*G*)	$ 105,800
Livestock (Table 21.*E*)	21,500
Machinery & equipment (Table 21.*F*)	8,601
Feed (beginning inventory)	6,000
Cash to run farm	10,000
Total	$ 151,901

Table 21.*J*. Some Rough Indicators of Efficiency

Receipts per total crop acre	$ 160.55
Expenses per dollar receipts	0.60
Capital turnover, percent	24.4 %
Dollar return per $1 feed fed	$ 1.29

characteristics of the available managerial, financial, labor, and land resources. With this procedure we have:

1. Chosen a farm on the basis of available financial, managerial, and labor resources and personal desires of the family.

2. Tentatively planned to use the land for crops on the basis of land-use classes.

3. Tentatively developed livestock programs largely on the basis of using farm-produced feeds.

4. Used normal or average production requirements as first approximations.

Using these procedures, the student has been able to develop an overall picture or reconnaissance survey of a farming business and to obtain a first approximation of the organization. The job of adjusting the first approximations to a final plan or organization remains. At this point, the student or farmer needs to examine his plan:

1. *From the standpoint of proportions of land, labor, machinery, livestock, land development investments, and miscellaneous expenditures used in the plan.* It may be that more or less land should be used, that a livestock system requiring more or less labor should be used, that the assets he owns would permit borrowing more money or would make it impossible to borrow the money necessary to put the rough budget into operation.

2. *With respect to the cropping system.* Would more or less forage be desired or more or less concentrates? Should grain-producing land, for example, be purchased or rented to supplement the land on the farm well adapted to forage production? Should investments be made in mechanical erosion-control practices to permit more grain production?

3. *With respect to the livestock program.* Does the livestock-program plan fully utilize the management available? Is it adapted to the existing buildings? Would it be more efficient to feed fewer hogs and shift to a beef production system utilizing more grain? Should the hogs be fed to heavier or lighter weights? Could dairy cattle be substituted for beef cattle?

4. *Production rates.* Are the input rates, the yields, and the livestock production expected and planned the most profitable? For instance, could profits be increased by feeding the hogs to heavier weights, by using additional nitrate dressings on the pastures, by

feeding more or less protein supplements, by changing the beef production system to one requiring more or less forage in relation to concentrates?

It is never possible practically, in a budgeting process, to examine all the modifications which could be made on a rough first approximation of a farm budget or plan. It is almost always possible, however, to make modifications in a rough budget which will significantly increase the expected profits of a farm. This appears to be true almost regardless of the "rules of thumb" used in roughing out a farm plan.

Speed, at which the most profitable budget or plan is approached, is increased in direct proportion to the employment of marginality principles. In some instances, involving short-run feeding problems for dairy animals and hogs, the most profitable adjustment can be located almost at once through the use of procedures outlined in Chapters 16 and 17. In other instances, the marginality approach can only be approximated; this is generally true for the beef enterprise, though, here again, the process can be speeded up by referring to the marginality discussions in Chapter 18. In still other instances, marginality comparisons can be made only in terms of rough computations, matching additional costs against additional returns, the cost and returns data being secured from experience and judgment instead of from experimental work.

As pointed out above, the budgeting process can rarely arrive at the most profitable budget or plan. However, it can arrive at one of the more profitable plans. In the pages to follow, the rough budget presented in the first part of this chapter will be modified to illustrate to students, farmers, and professional farm-management men how this process is carried out. A complete modified budget similar to the rough budget presented earlier will be developed and presented at the end of this chapter.

Production Weights on Hogs

Selecting one problem first, let us use available input-output data on hog production as given in Table 16.1. We elected for our first approximation to try producing hogs to 225 pounds. Corn was valued at $1.75 per bushel. The spring sales were budgeted to sell at 22 cents per pound and the fall sales at 20 cents. Referring to Table 16.1, for hogs now weighing 225 pounds, worth 20 cents, with corn at $1.75 per bushel, an additional 50 pounds of gain would necessitate selling the hogs at $20.02 per hundredweight in order to break even for adding the additional 50 pounds. Thus it is readily seen that with prevailing prices of corn it would make no material difference in the fall sales if the hogs were marketed at 225 pounds or 275 pounds since additional returns approximate additional costs. If more corn were available for feeding, the hogs would provide a market for it at the farm price of $1.75 per bushel. On the other hand, 25 additional pounds would prove profitable, whereas 50 pounds barely covers feed costs. Table 16.2 shows that an additional 25.0 pounds could be added for an equivalent of 126.5 pounds of corn (986.3 − 859.8). The additional corn is priced at $3.94, and the additional gain valued at $5.50. Thus one could expect an added $1.56 above feed cost per head by further feeding the fall drove to 250 pounds.

The spring sales were budgeted to sell at 22 cents. An additional 50 pounds could be added for a break-even selling price of around $21.66, indicating an advantage of 34 cents per hundredweight for the added inputs above feed costs increased 25 percent to cover other variable costs. Thus, as long as the hogs could be sold for more than about $21.66 it would pay to take them to 275 pounds.

More Cattle, Less Hogs

Let us now examine more carefully the cattle-hog programs. The procedure used for determining the number of cattle to be handled in the livestock chapter was:

1. To determine the number of cattle that could be pastured, since pasturage once produced is a fixed asset, i.e., it must be used where it is, harvested for hay or silage, or left as green manure during the months of production.

2. To allot as much grain to cattle as required for the tentatively chosen method of beef production.

3. To allot the remaining farm-produced feed grains to hogs.

In the problem under consideration at present (more or less hogs or more or less cattle), only the items involved in shifting from cattle to hogs, or vice versa, need consideration. These items include (at the assumed prices): (a) farm-produced roughage; (b) farm-produced concentrates; (c) purchased feeds; (d) labor; (e) equipment.

Let us narrow the analysis to feed. Other systems than the grass production of 90 steers to weigh 1,100 pounds and the production of

160 porkers to weigh 225–275 pounds suggest themselves. Foremost among these is the allocation of a larger quantity of grain to the grass-pastured cattle and less grain to hogs. It should be recalled that 105 units of pasturage were available. Ninety cattle were selected to use about the 90 units of pasturage, the remaining 15 units for the hogs. For illustrative purposes, let us compare the beef-hog system as first budgeted with a modification of it through feeding additional concentrates to the cattle and reducing concentrates for hogs. This system should result in a higher finish on the cattle commanding perhaps an additional $1 to $2.00 per hundredweight.

Consulting Figures 18.1 and 18.2, we find that 2-year-old steers at the 1,200-pound level may be expected to gain about 8 pounds per 100 pounds of TDN consumed. Morrison[1] reports Minnesota trials using 714 pounds of concentrates with 455 pounds of hay and 899 pounds of silage for 100 pounds of gain for steers from 1,100 to 1,200 pounds in weight. The Morrison feeding standards give 17 to 19.6 pounds of TDN per day for fattening 1,100-pound cattle, or about 8 pounds of gain per 100 TDN. Thus, a daily gain of 2.25 pounds may be reasonably expected from cattle such as those budgeted when put on a full feed of about 16 pounds of grain, 1 pound of supplement, and a small quantity of hay, or hay and silage, per day. Furthermore, 100 days of feeding might produce an added 225 pounds of gain at the expenditure of 1,600 pounds of grain, 100 pounds of supplement, and 800 pounds of hay.

The 1,600 pounds of additional grain per head, totaling 141,400 pounds for the 89 cattle, would have produced around 35,350 pounds of hogs worth $7,660. Adding $5.00 per steer for supplement ($445) and $10.00 per steer for hay ($890), the cattle would need to bring an additional $8,095 ($7,660 less $900 hog supplement + $445 + $890) to equal the income sacrificed from hogs, or 29.28 cents per pound (1,325 pounds × 89 head is 117,925 pounds; $26,433 + $8,095 ÷ 117,925 pounds). Thus, if it appeared that the price of hogs would drop relative to the price of cattle, it would pay to feed cattle further than 1,100 pounds. On the other hand, if the price of hogs rose relative to the price of cattle, it would pay to increase hogs at the expense of cattle. If the price of both increased relative to the price of grains, both longer feeding and purchase of grain would probably result in added returns. It should be added that, if dry-lot fattening were planned to follow

[1] F. B. Morrison, *Feeds and Feeding,* Livestock Edition, p. 643.

grazing as a usual practice, steers weighing less than 700 pounds (perhaps 450) would usually be purchased.

More Corn vs. More Pasture

Let us continue refining the budget with a further consideration of the use of the land resources. The Classes I and II lands are intensively used, and the Class IV land must be kept in sod crops the larger portion of the time to avoid destructive erosion. The Class III land may thus illustrate the use of additional labor and equipment resources, toward increasing profits. This is an illustration of adjustment in the intermediate length of run or planning span. In the original budget this 110 acres of Class III land is planned to be used 1 year each for the production of barley and hay, and 3 years for pasturage. The land is somewhat too sloping for short-rotation use, but, if terraced at an estimated cost of $8.00 per acre, it could well be used for a 5-year rotation of corn, small grain, hay, and 2 years of pasture. The two cropping systems may be compared as follows:

A. The Barley-Sod Rotation

		Production		Value	Days of Labor
Barley	25 A.	30 bu.	750 bu.	$ 862	22.5
M. hay	20 A.	2.5 T.	50 T.	1,250	20.0
R. pasture	20 A.	1 U.	20 U.	500	
R. pasture	20 A.	1 U.	20 U.	500	13
R. pasture	25 A.	6 U.	15 U.	375	
				$3,487	55.5

B. The Corn Rotation

		Production		Value	Days of Labor
Corn	25 A.	60 bu.	1,500 bu. (250 tons silage)	$2,625	37.5
Wheat	20 A.	20 bu.	400 bu.	880	12
M. hay	20 A.	2.5 T.	50 T.	1,250	20
R. pasture	20 A.	1 U.	20 U.	500	8.7
R. pasture	25 A.	1 U.	20 U.	625	
				$5,880	78.2

C. Comparison in Feed on Whole Farm

Corn	3,680 bu.	vs. 5,180 bu. or 3,780 bu. and 250 tons silage
Barley	1,260 bu.	510 bu.
Clover hay	34 T.	34 T.
M. hay	50 T.	50 T.
Pasture	105 U.	95 U.

It is noted that such an adjustment in the cropping program would add an additional 1,500 bushels of corn or 250 tons of corn silage and 880 bushels of wheat at the expense of 750 bushels of barley and 10 units of pasturage. The shift would necessitate only an added 23 days of man and machine labor and the use and maintenance of the $880.00 investment in terraces. It would result in crop values of $5,880, as against $3,487 for the barley system. The added corn could be marketed through cattle or hogs as examined in a later section in the chapter.

Shift from Beef to Dairy

Promise of a larger net income from the use of dairy cattle arises because of the need and opportunity to use additional resource inputs in the form of labor, farm improvements, machinery, feed, and management. Experience indicates that roughage for dairy cattle is most economically produced on the farm. This experience is strengthened by economic analysis of differences in costs of roughage produced on the farm and the cost of that brought in. This reasoning leads one to determine the number of units of dairy cattle which can be kept on the proposed roughage to consist of 84 tons of hay, 80 animal units of pasturage, and 200 to 250 tons of silage. We thus need the requirements for one unit or one animal. The requirements, of course, depend upon the level of feeding most economical for the existing price ratios and the capacity of the cows. What are these ratios? Hay is valued at $25.00 per ton and milk at $4.50 per hundredweight. The hay-milk price ratio is therefore 5.4 to 1. A grain mixture utilizing the farm-produced corn and barley and consisting of 200 pounds of ground corn, 200 pounds of ground barley, 200 pounds of wheat middlings, and 100 pounds of cottonseed meal would cost $3.60 per hundredweight. With the grain mixture at $3.60 per hundredweight and milk at $4.50, the grain-milk price ratio is 0.8 to 1.

Referring to Figure 17.4, one finds the desired grain-feeding level to be 1 pound of grain to 3.6 pounds of milk. Table 17.4 gave data by weights of cows and BF content of milk.

By consulting Table 17.4, we find that cows such as we are planning to use (1,150-pound cows which will give about 7,900 pounds 4 percent FCM milk fed at 1:4) (High Station—Poor Cows) when fed 2.08 pounds of hay equivalent per cwt. per day and a total of 2,343 pounds of grain were fed at the level of 1 pound of grain to 3.64 pounds of milk.

Figuring 1 pound of hay equal to 3 pounds of silage, we find a need for 2,056 pounds of hay and 6,963 pounds of silage per cow per 6-month period. We now have a basis for determining the number of cows, of cows and young cattle, for which the crops program can be expected to provide roughage.

Herd records indicate that one-third to one-fourth of the cows in such herds may need to be replaced each year. The proportion of 3½ cows—1 heifer, two years old; 1 heifer, one year old; and 1 calf—gives about one and one-half units of dairy cattle per milk cow. On our 84 tons of hay, 250 tons of corn silage, and 80 units of pasturage we should therefore be able to keep about 50 cows, 15 heifers, two years old; and 15 heifers, one year old.

The cows would be expected to produce 8,200 pounds of 4 percent fat-corrected milk, according to the data in Table 17.4. By coincidence the amount of corn left for feeding hogs (rough budget) has not been materially changed, and 15 units of pasturage have been reserved for the use of the hog enterprise.

The refined livestock program would budget somewhat as follows:

50 dairy cows	
4,000 cwt. of milk	$17,325
Cull cows, calves	5,375
74 spring-drove hogs	4,477
74 fall-drove hogs	3,700
12 sows	768
Total sales	$31,645
Total inventory value	$26,950

The added inputs in the form of machinery and equipment would consist of a tractor, a field chopper, hay drier, milker, milk cooler, water heater, and smaller items, increasing the machinery and equipment investment from about $8,600 to $16,000.

The additional farm buildings needed would consist of a rest-shed dairy barn, 52 ft. by 130 ft., a calf-and-maternity barn, a milking parlor, two concrete silos, a water system, and some additional fencing, raising the real estate investment from $105,800 to $131,000.

Two additional men would be needed and the owner would spend somewhat more time in managing and somewhat less time in laboring.

The estimated added inputs-added outputs may be summarized as follows:

	Rough Budget	Refined Budget	Additional
Investment	$151,901	$184,951	$33,050
Total receipts	37,089	50,530	13,441
Total expenses	22,435	32,030	9,595
Returns to inv. and mgt.	14,654	18,500	3,846
Returns to mgt. (inv. 4%)	8,578	11,102	2,524

The Final Plan Is Determined by Subjective Values

In the final analysis, a farm organization is an expression of a family's subjective values, i.e., its wants, preferences, and goals. In the preceding pages, several modifications in the rough first approximation to the class case budget have been examined—the question of whether to feed hogs to heavier weights, the question of whether it would be advisable to substitute beef, and the question of whether it would be advisable to feed more grain to beef cattle and less to hogs. Similarly, a considerable amount of time and space was devoted to the problem of whether additional Class III land could be used for corn production. Similarly, the question of whether the farm should be planned for a dairy was examined.

In addition, the authors have examined the possibilities of farming the class case farm in three other phases: (1) on the basis of unimproved pasture only, (2) on a cash crop and pasture basis, (3) on a cash crop in rotation with balance on permanent-pasture basis. It was important to examine these three systems, as they involve less intensive uses of land and resources sometimes desired for farm families because (1) they do not choose to work hard, (2) they are not convinced that intensive farming pays in dollars, (3) management for intensive farming is not available, (4) they are "land poor," i.e., they do not have sufficient working capital, (5) they hold land wholly or partially for other reasons than producing products for profit.

Five alternative systems for farming the 335-acre class case farm are summarized in Table 21.1. The first system is the one developed as a first rough approximation in this chapter. The second is based on the use of unimproved pasture only. The third is based on a cash crop, generally tobacco and pasture. The fourth is largely a pasture system with a high-value cash crop (Burley tobacco) produced in a grain rotation. The fifth is an intensive system involving a high-value cash crop, a large dairy enterprise, and intensive use of land. The fifth system anticipates that the hogs will be fed to the heavier, more profitable weights found to be desirable in the preceding sections. It also keeps a higher proportion of the Class III land in corn than is true for the rough budget. And it includes the dairy enterprise found to be profitable in examining possible modifications in the rough budget.

It is not the intention of the authors to indicate the advisability of making final decisions for farm families. They feel that families and individuals should be informed and then permitted to organize their

Table 21.1. Alternative Systems for the 335-Acre Class Case Farm

Item	Use of Resources in Rough First Budget		Unimproved Pasture Only	Cash Crop Pasture		Cash Crop in Rotation, Bal. in Perm. Past.		Cash Crop, Dairy, Intensive Use of Land	
Crop, acres	Cash	17		Cash	17	Cash	17	Cash	17
	Corn	46				S. grain	17	Corn grain	26
	S. grain	40				Hay	34	Corn silage	20
	Hay	37						Hay	37
	Pasture	170	330	Pasture	313	Pasture	245	Pasture	170
Livestock	Cattle	90	40		35		60	D. cows	50
								Young stock	35
	Hogs								
	12 sows							12 sows	
	160 hogs							160 hogs	
P.M. work units	969		100	590		627		1,522	
Machinery and equipment, dollars	8,601		300	1,200		1,500		16,001	
Buildings invest., dollars	23,800		3,000	10,000		12,120		49,000	
Gross receipts, dollars	37,089		5,500	17,240		20,140		50,530	
Expenses, dollars	22,435		1,900	8,830		9,520		32,030	
Net earnings, dollars	8,578		−400	3,250		6,380		11,102	

own business according to their own preferences, goals, and judgments. As stated, one of the five tasks of management is the acceptance of responsibility.

It is assumed, by the authors, that the class case farm family has asked themselves and answered affirmatively the following questions:

1. Is the extra amount of effort in supervisory and managerial services repaid by the additions indicated in the steps on refining the rough budget?

2. Does the more intensive crop-dairy program fit the family's particular managerial aptitudes?

3. Does the extra amount of income offset the heavier borrowings and repayments the family must make?

4. Is the age of the operator and of his children desirable for addition of the dairy enterprise?

5. Are the children likely to be interested in continuing a dairy enterprise?

6. Can the added credit needs be met and safely assumed?

Table 21.A.R. Estimated Production and Disposition of Crops to Be Produced

335 A. Refined

Name of Crop[1] and Number of Field	Slope of Field	Number of Acres	Production[2]		Gross[3] Product Value	Man W.U. Needed	Farm Use		Disposition of Production			
									Household Use		Sales[3]	
			Per Acre	Total			Feed	Seed	Amount	Value	Amount	Value
					$							$
Classes I & II Land												
Corn (rye) 9	0-3	23	80	1,840	3,220	34.5	1,840					
Corn (wheat) 4	0-3	23	80	1,840	3,220	34.5	1,840					
Wheat (G.M.) 3	0-3	23	26	598	1,316	15.8	50				848	1,205
Tobacco (barley) 4₂	4-6	17	1,800	30,600	15,300	535.5					30,600	15,300
Barley 3₂	4-6	17	30	510	586	10.2	510					
Clover 9₂	4-6	17	2	34	850							
Class III Land												
Silage corn 10	7-9	25	10	250	2,625	37.5						
Wheat 1a	7-9	20	20	400	880	12.0					400	880
M. hay 1b	7-10	20	2.5	50	1,250	20.0						
R. pasture 6	7-9	20	1	20	500	8.7						
R. pasture 8	7-9	25	1	25	625							
Garden & truck		1			(300)					(300)		
Perr. pasture tillable 2 7	10-15 10-15	75 10	0.5 0.5	37.5 5.0	938 125							
Idle crop land												
Perm. pasture not tillable 5	10-15	10	0.75	7.5	188							
Woods pasture												
Farmsteads, roads, wastelands		9										
Totals	xxx	335	xxx	xxx	$31,623	706.7	xxx	xxx	xxx	(300)	xxxx	$17,365

[1] List crops by land classes and by rotations, e.g., Class I, corn, wheat, clover hay.
[2] List production of crops in usual units, e.g., bushels, pounds, tons, crates, etc. List production of pastures in units of livestock that the acreage will carry on the basis of the pasture season.
[3] Record in full dollars.

Total feed

    95 units pasturage
    3,780 bu. corn
    510 bu. barley
    84 tons hay

Table 21.B.R.   Estimated Requirements of Seeds, Fertilizers, and Other Expenses for Crops

Name of Crop	Number of Acres	Seeds and Plants				Manure, Fertilizer, and Lime				Other Expenses		
		Kind	Rate per Acre	Total¹ Amount	Total¹ Value	Kind	Rate per Acre	Total Amount	Total¹ Value	Kind	Total Amount	Total¹ Cost
					$							$
Row I+II Corn	46	103	10	8 bu.	96	P₂O₅	60	2,760	207	Picking	4.a	184
						6-8-6	500	23,000	518			
						Lime	500	12 T	36			
Corn	25	Silage	10	5	60	Nitrate	200	9,200	414	Terracing		200
						P₂O₅	100	2,500	188			
						Manure	8	200	(400)			
Tobacco	17	16		4 oz	8	6-8-6	500	12,500	281	Canvas		41
						Manure	8	136	(272)	Coke	9	225
						P₂O₅	200	3,400	255	Selling	½crop	268
						10-10-10	1,000	17,000	510			
Small grain Wheat	23	Clarkson	1¼	29	87	6-8-6	300	6,900	155			
Wheat	20		1¼	25	75	Lime	2,000	25	75			
						6-8-6	300	6,000	135			
						P₂O₅	100	2,000	150			
						K₂O	100	2,000	120			
Hay and pasture	17 Clo 20 Mix { Kenland	10	170	102						Innoc.		12
		Alf.	10	200	200							
		Fescue	3	60	48							
		Timothy	2	40	8							
Pasture Per.	100	Blue grass Ladino Korean Fescue } as needed				Lime	400	20	60			
						P₂O₅	10	1,000	75			
						K₂O	50	5,000	300			
Total value of items to be bought			xx		$684		xxx	xxx	$3,479	xxx	xx	$930

¹ Encircle value not to be bought.
$684 seeds plus $3,479 manure, fertilizer, lime, plus $930 other expenses = $5,093 cash expenses on crops.

Table 21.C.R.   Livestock.   Total Production Requirements (Farm Grown Feeds).   Labor Units Needed

Kind	Number of Head	Corn, bu.	Barley			Mixed Hay, tons	Legume Hay, tons	Silage, tons	Stover, acres or lb.	Units of Pasture	Bedding, tons	Man W.U. Needed
Workstock	2					4				2	2	
Dairy cows	50	600	600			26	34	174		60		500
2-yr Heifers	15					12		36		12	} 51	100
1-yr Heifers	15					6		18		6		
~~Beef cattle~~												
Sheep										10		96
Hogs Sows	12	480										
S. feeders	80	1,360										
F. feeders	80	1,224										
Poultry												
Total needed [1]		3,664	600			48	34	228		90	53	696
Amount produced		3,780	510			50	34	250		95	53	xxx
Amount bought			90									xxx
Cost of purchases	$	$	$104	$	$	$	$	$	$	$	$	xxx

$104 ....Total cost of purchases

[1] Check total needed vs. production and purchases within 10 percent.

12 sows, 20 litters, 160 hogs
80 spring feeders to 275 lb each (17 bu. corn)
80 fall feeders to 250 lb each (15.3 bu. corn)

Table 21.D.R. Total Production Requirement of Purchased Supplemental Feeds, Livestock Purchased. Miscellaneous Expense

Kind	Number of Head	Soy Bean Meal / Cotton Seed Meal — Pounds per Head	Soy Bean Meal — Total Pounds	Middlings — Pounds per Head	Middlings — Total Pounds	Tankage — Pounds per Head	Tankage — Total Pounds	Salt — Pounds per Head	Salt — Total Pounds	Livestock Purchased — Number of Head	Livestock Purchased — Cost	Miscellaneous Expense — Kind	Miscellaneous Expense — Cost
		or									$		$
Workstock													
						or other supplement						Vet.	300
Dairy cows	50	335	16,750	670	33,500	{150	2,750	20	1,000			Breeding	400
Heifers	30					{Calf meal			360			Selling	50
												Other	300
Beef cows													
Sheep										None			
Hogs Sows	12			100	1,200	120	1,440					Inn.	80
S. fattening	80					100	8,000		300			Trucking	100
F. fattening	80					50	4,000					Com.	40
Poultry												Other	100
Total amount	xx	xx	16,750	xx	34,700	xx	16,190	xx	1,660	xx		xxx	
Price per unit	xx	xx	5	xx	4	xx	6.70	xx	1.20	xx		xxx	
Total cost [1]	xx	xx	838	xx	1,388	xx	1,085	xx	25	xx	$	xxx	$ 1,370

[1] Record to nearest dollar.

[2] Include breeding fees, registration fees, veterinary, medicine, dips, trucking, commission, sheep shearing, blacksmithing, and depreciation not accounted for through sales (Table E) or replacements (Table D). Depreciation on workstock is roughly 10 percent of value; sheep, 15 percent; dairy cows, 10 percent to 25 percent, depending on breed and quality; hens, 35 percent.

Total cost of purchased supplemental feeds $ Feeds $3,311   Salt 25

Grain mixture 200 lb corn
200 lb barley
200 lb bran
100 lb S.O.M. or C.S.M.
7 lb salt

Table 21.E.R.   Estimated Production and Disposition of Livestock and Livestock Products

Kind	Number of Head	Number Animal Units	Total Inventory Value	Production [1]		Disposition of Production					
				Per Head	Total	Farm Use		Household Use		Sales	
						Kind	Amount	Amount	Value	Amount	Value
Workstock	2	2	$ 200								$
Dairy cows	50	60	20,000	8,000	4,000 cwt			150 cwt	675	3,850	17,325
2-yr heifers	15	12	3,000	60	calves	15				15	4,500
1-yr heifers	15	6	2,250							35	875
Beef cows											
Sheep											
Hogs Sows	12	6	} 1,500	275	20,350				Spring	12	768
Fattening	160	32		250	18,500				Fall	74	4,477
										74	3,700
Poultry											
Totals	xxx	118	$26,950	xxx	xxx	xxx	xxx	xxx	$	xxx	$31,645

[1] After making allowances for barrenness and death losses.

$31,645 Total livestock (including products) sales minus $ —— Livestock purchased = $31,645 Livestock net inc.

Table 21.*F.R.* Machinery and Equipment

Kind and Number		Value	Kind and Number		Value
Power:			**Specialized enterprise:** [1]		
Tractor	2	$2,200	*Tobacco stoves*	*35*	$ *175*
			sticks	*21,000*	*420*
			Hog houses	*12*	*600*
			feeders, etc.		*500*
			Dairy		
			Milker units (3)		*600*
			Cooler		*600*
			Cans		*200*
			Heater		*100*
Land preparation:			*Other*		*100*
Tractor plan	*1*	*135*			
Tractor disk	*1*	*165*	**Other machines:**		
Tractor harrow	*1*	*60*	Truck	2	2,000
			Manure spreader	*1*	*160*
Bush & bog		*200*	Elevators		*200*
Cultipacker		*65*	Feed grinder	*1*	*125*
Drag		*25*	*Motors*	*3*	*150*
			Lime & fert. spreader		*50*
Planting:			*Fert. drill*		*50*
Corn		*75*			
Gr. drill		*135*			
Plant setter	*2*	*300*	*Hay dryer*		*1,500*
Seeder		*5*			
Cultivating:			**Miscellaneous:**		
Tr. cul.		*160*	Shop tools		*500*
Small		*6*	Fencing tools		*50*
			General tools		*200*
			Harness	*2*	*100*
			Wagons	*2*	*300*
			Tr. wagons	*2*	*500*
			Bags	*700*	*140*
Harvesting:					
Combine	*1*	*650*			
Pick-up-baler					
Mower	*1*	*150*			
Rake	*1*	*150*			
Field chopper		*2,500*	Total investment	$	*16,001*
			Repairs *4%*		*640*
			Depreciation *10%*		*1,600*

[1] As milking machines, etc., on dairy farms, potato diggers, etc., on potato farms, spray rigs, etc., on fruit farms.

Table 21.G.R. Inventory of Real Estate and Improvements, Estimated Amount of Depreciation and Costs of Repairs

Item	No.	Value	Rate of Dep.	Amt. of Dep.	Cost of Repairs	Remarks
Land (acres) 335		$67,000	xxx	$ xxx	$ xxx	
Dwelling house	1	15,000	2	300	100	
Tenant houses	5	20,000	4	800	125	
Milk parlor (6 cow)		3,000	3	90	50	
Stock barns 24x30		1,500	4	60	40	Calf & maternity
52 x 130		6,000	4	240	100	barn
Silo concrete	2	3,000	2	150	20	
Cribs-granaries	6	1,800	6	108	108	
Special e'prise barns Tob	2	7,000	4	280	140	
Machine shed						
Fences (rods) 1,600		3,200	5	160	80	
Temporary		300	15	45		
Tile drains (ft.)						
Water system		2,000	10	200	50	
Water supply		1,200				To dairy barn
Drainage ditches						
Totals	xxxx	$131,000	xxx	$2,433	$ 813	xxxx

Table 21.*H.R.* Summary, Receipts, and Expenses

Income Summary		*Expenses*	
		Cash:	
Crop sales (Table 21.*A.R*)	$ *17,385*	Cash exp. on crops (Table 21.*B.R*)	$ *5,093*
Livestock net increase (Table 21.*E.R*)	*31,645*	Supp. feeds bought (Table 21.*D.R*)	*3,311*
		Grains, hay, past. bot. (Table 21.*C.R*)	*104*
Crops used in home (Table 21.*A.R*)	——	Feed grinding Salt minerals	*25*
Livestock used in home (Table 21.*E.R*)	——	Misc. Livestock expenses (Table 21.*D.R*)	*1,370*
Fuel used in home	——	Hired labor (*50* days) *400*	*5,800*
Use of house (10% of value)	*1,500*	Landlord's *3 yr 5,400*	
Total farm receipts	$*50,530*	Value cropper's share of crops	*7,650*
Total farm expenses	*32,030*	Repairs of M. & E. (Table 21.*F.R*)	*640*
Farm earnings	*18,500*	Repair of improvements (Table 21.*G.R*)	*813*
Interest on investment (@ 4%)	*7,398*	Trucking (not chg. above)	
Net earnings	*11,102*	Truck (operating costs)	*700*
		Auto (farm shares)	*500*
		Electric current	*156*
		Tractor, cash operating costs	*600*
		Commission (not chg. above)	
		Advertising	——
		Insurance (on farm items)	*185*
		Taxes on real estate	*1,050*
		Other:	
		Depreciation M. & E. (Table 21.*F.R*)	*1,600*
		Depreciation improvements (Table 21.*G.R*)	*2,433*
		Total expenses	$ *32,030*

Table 21.*I.R.* Investment Summary

Land & improvements (Table 21.*G.R*)	$*131,000*
Livestock (Table 21.*E.R*)	*26,950*
Machinery & equipment (Table 21.*F.R*)	*16,001*
Feed (beginning inventory)	*6,000*
Cash to run farm	*5,000*
Total	$*184,951*

Table 21.*J.R.* Some Rough Indicators of Efficiency

Receipts per total crop acre	$ *218.74*
Expenses per dollar receipts	*.634*
Capital turnover, percent	*27.3* %
Dollar return per $1 feed fed	$ *1.70*

The affirmative answers to these questions indicate that the fifth alternative system of organization is the best of the five for the class case farm family. It is better than the rough first approximation because it provides more income, it meets the needs of the family, they can handle the larger operation, and it makes more efficient use of the land and feed resources of the farm.

The intensive dairy, cash-crop budget and plan are selected as the final budget, and its details are presented in the following pages. This budget should be carefully compared with the rough budget presented earlier in this chapter. The student should carefully note how the process of refining the budget has resulted in a farm plan better adapted to the needs of this farm family and capable of utilizing its resources more effectively.

QUESTIONS AND PROBLEMS

1. The general budgets do not include inventories. Why?

2. Relate budgeting to (1) farm appraisal, (2) capitalization of rents, (3) farm records, (4) land-use planning.

3. Criticize the use of historical prices in budgeting. Criticize the use of current prices in budgeting. What is relationship of price levels to national debt? How long did the major price decline in agricultural products last after 1865? After 1921?

4. In budgeting it is easier to overestimate receipts than expenses. Why?

5. What checks on accuracy can one use in budgeting?

6. What objections may be found to the use of normal production requirements?

7. Why do farmers making net earnings (business gain) of, say, $6,000 a year usually accumulate more in a life span than men on salaries equaling that amount?

8. Referring to Chapters 9, 11, and 21, explain what is meant by the reservation price on one's own services.

9. How do relative costs in producing grain and roughage influence choices between use of the beef and use of the dairy enterprise? Between systems of beef production?

10. Show that the addition of the dairy enterprise in the class case farm involves fixing a number of long-run variable inputs.

PROBLEM EXERCISE 19
The General and Refined Budgets

Prepare a general budget for the individual case farm.

1. Make blank forms similar to those illustrated or use those provided by the instructor.

2. Two sets of budget forms are needed: one set for the rough draft bringing together the planning done in Problem Exercises 7, 8, 9, 11, 13, 16, 17, and 18; the other for the refined plan of operation. Each set will require two copies of the forms—one for the pencil work, the other to be handed in.

3. Some of these data from earlier exercises will probably require reworking because of knowledge acquired subsequent to making them. For example, the original land-management plan (Problem Exercise 8) might have provided for using all the corn grown in the form of grain. Subsequently, when the livestock plan was being made, a need for corn silage might have been found. If a decision was made to use a portion of the corn crop as silage, a readjustment in acreage, yield, value, and disposition would be necessary. The same type of problem might have arisen in the use of hay, or as between hay and pasturage. Again a reconsideration of labor or machinery programs might have revealed that an economy would arise by readjusting the crops or the livestock program.

4. Any good farm management handbook published for your state or region will likely contain most of the base data needed. Textbooks on crops, soils and livestock, particularly *Morrison's Feeds and Feeding,* are good references. Your own state bulletins and circulars are good source materials, though usually time consuming, for this purpose.

5. Use pages opposite the forms used for descriptions. Use additional blank sheets if necessary. Cross out column heading or items not applicable to your farm and write in those that are applicable.

Part 3

OPERATING A FARM BUSINESS

The last eighteen chapters culminated in Chapter 21, giving the final organization of the class farm and directing the student to present his plan for the organization of his individual case farm.

Farm management, however, consists of much more than organizing farms. Farms must be operated. Operation involves management. A review of Part 1 will indicate that the adjustment of businesses to (1) change and (2) improvements in knowledge *is the essence of management*. Organization, though very important, occurs sporadically, but all businesses are operated every day. The student should reread the introductions to Chapter 1 and to Part 2 at this point.

Chapter 22 expands the principles presented in Chapter 3, and Chapter 23 illustrates those principles. Chapter 24 discusses the problems of securing and maintaining control over productive resources. Chapter 25 illustrates some managerial problems of an operational nature connected with a specific farm and provides the student with an appropriate problem exercise in planning and budgeting over a period of years. Chapter 26 considers some additional conceptual problems involved in the study of management.

CHAPTER 22

Principles for Increasing the Efficiency with Which the Managerial Tasks Are Performed

Chapter 3 dealt, in general overall terms, with some principles useful in increasing the efficiency with which management is carried out. This chapter presents in a more concise (but still rather general) manner some principles which are useful to managers in deciding (1) how to perform the various managerial tasks and (2) how much of these tasks to perform. The student could profitably reread Chapter 3 at this point.

The first and foremost managerial principle is not to spend more (in time, effort, foregone alternative opportunities, and money) performing additional amounts of any of the managerial tasks than such additional performance is worth.

I. Principles Involving Deductive Learning. 1. One of the most traditional methods of thinking used by farm management men is *budgeting*. The usual budget is, essentially, a thought system which an analyst uses in deducing the outcome of operating a farm business on the assumption that the production requirements and price data he uses are correct. The principles of budgeting are not repeated at this point as they were covered in detail in previous chapters of this book.

2. Another important, more recent method of farm-management thinking (also very closely related to budgeting) is marginal analysis or, by its more commonly known name, ordinary (static) *economic principles*. This body of deductive thought processes concentrates upon problems of defining and locating the most profitable combinations of inputs and enterprises as well as the most profitable levels of output. This set of principles was covered in detail (from the standpoint of farm management) in Chapters 8 through 12.

3. Several other systems of thinking have developed in the field of farm management which are particularly valuable in organizing the thinking of farm managers. One of these systems (largely deductive in nature) is known as the land-use approach. Under this approach attention is given to the physical capacities of the land; then a cropping system and livestock enterprises are selected within these physical capacities to utilize the crops produced. At first thought this system appears to be unrelated to marginal analysis; however, upon closer scrutiny, the two systems are more closely related than was apparent from superficial examination.

In certain areas of the country other resources tend to be more important than land as limitations on the type of farming which can be carried out. For example, near certain industrial areas labor is often a very important limiting agent of production and certain farm-management men have evolved ways of thinking which can be dubbed the labor-use approach to farm management. Here, again, when studied more closely this approach is rather closely related to the principles of marginal analysis.

Both the land-use approach and the labor-use approach are ways of analyzing and appraising the influence of fixed assets on a farm business. Another such approach is via the available capital or assets. All three of these approaches, if applicable, are basic to both the budgeting and very similar marginality approaches, inasmuch as specification of the fixed-asset structure is basic to both. Farm organizations or reorganizations based roughly on any of the three approaches described above depend for refinement on the marginality approach of matching additional costs against additional returns.

II. Principles of Inductive Learning. Most of the principles of inductive learning are of a statistical nature. The statistical principles which appear most applicable to the managerial processes are as follows:

1. The accuracy of estimates, choices between alternatives, and decisions increases at a decreasing rate as the number of observations made and used increases.

2. The per unit cost of observations in time, money, and effort often increases as the number of observations made and used increases.

3. The optimum number of observations is being made and used when the cost of an additional observation is just offset by the value of the additional information derived from it (as previously noted, such costs and values are often personal and subjective in nature).

4. The use of deductive thought processes (such as those referred to in the section above) decreases the cost of making and analyzing observations by concentrating the attention of the observer on the most important information to be gathered; this helps insure that the necessary information will be gathered and eliminates expenditures of time and effort on the observation of relatively useless information.

5. When information becomes available slowly with the passage of time it is often worth while "to keep track" of the sequence in which the information occurs, because (a) sequence information often helps explain the overall situation, and (b) series of events often contain lags and trends which, if observed, are very useful for purposes of predicting short-run outcomes.

6. When valuable information is becoming available with the passage of time, it often pays to spend money, time, and effort acquiring ability to postpone decisions until more information is at hand. Such ability is referred to as flexibility.

7. Flexibility (as defined above) should be used only to the point at which the cost of additional flexibility is just offset by the value of the acquired ability to postpone the decisions.

8. The optimum amount of analysis is being carried out when the cost of additional analysis is just offset by the value of the additional analysis (as previously noted, such costs and values are often personal and subjective in nature).

9. The seriousness of a given mistake or error depends (among other things) upon its size, whereas the accuracy of an estimate, choice, or decision depends upon the chances per hundred of making the mistake or error, as well as upon the size of the mistake or error.

10. A decrease in the size of a probable mistake without an increase in the chances per hundred of making the mistake is an increase in accuracy, and vice versa. Similarly, a decrease in the chances per hundred of making a mistake without an increase in the size of the mistake is an increase in accuracy, and vice versa.

11. In choosing between two alternatives, two kinds of errors can be made: (a) the first alternative can be accepted as correct when, in fact, it is wrong, and (b) the second alternative can be accepted as correct when, in fact, it is wrong. As the seriousness of the two types of errors often differs, it is important to consider them separately in choosing between alternatives.

12. It is important to note that all proposed separate actions involve two possible choices: (1) *to act,* or (2) *not to act.* The two conse-

quent possible errors (noted above) often have different consequences and must be considered separately. For instance, the result of isolating and testing a new cow for Bangs when such action is not necessary is loss of the expense involved, whereas the result of not carrying out this procedure when it is necessary may be infection of an entire herd.

III. Principles Applying to Both Inductive and Deductive Reasoning or Learning Processes. 1. It pays to substitute habit, custom, and tradition for learning procedures whenever the cost of the resultant errors does not exceed the cost of learning. Conversely, it pays to engage in learning whenever the value of additional learning exceeds its cost, both costs and values being measured in personal subjective terms.

2. Learning (either inductive or deductive) is a cumulative process; hence, in appraising the value of learning, allowance must be made for the value of the "experience gained" as well as for the immediate value of the results.

3. Insistence on high degrees of accuracy increases the costs and time required to make decisions, choices, and estimates. It follows, especially when the amount of information available depends upon the passage of time, that insistence on unusually high degrees of accuracy causes delay, unemployment of assets, and probably reduced but more certain incomes.

4. On the other hand, high tolerance for inaccuracy decreases the time and costs required to make decisions, choices, and estimates. It follows, when the amount of information available depends upon the passage of time, that tolerance of inaccuracy eliminates delay, keeps assets more fully (but not necessarily more efficiently) employed and results in less certain and often (on the average) lower incomes.

IV. Principles of Strategy. The list (incomplete) of strategy principles to be presented will cover insurance principles, flexibility principles, miscellaneous strategic principles for handling impersonal situations, and miscellaneous strategic principles for handling personalities.

1. It cannot be worth while insuring against losses unless the personal value of losses increases at an increasing rate. The odds of successful insurance schemes are sufficiently against the user to pay the cost of, and perhaps profits for, operating the insurance scheme. Users of insurance exchange a larger (but less sure) average expected income for a lesser (but more certain) average expected income. It is worth while insuring only when the lower, more certain average

expected income is worth more, on a personal subjective basis, than the higher, less certain average expected income. This is true whether the insurance scheme is a formal, contractual one such as life insurance with a reputable company or an informal non-contractual scheme such as that of "putting your eggs in more than one basket."

2. Informal insurance schemes can be set up in three main ways: (*a*) A manager can set up an informal insurance scheme by refusing to take action except when prospective returns are high enough to pay the cost of bearing the risks taken. The cost of operating such insurance schemes is foregone income. Thus, as additional income opportunities are foregone in insuring a business against risky ventures, such foregone incomes must be evaluated as costs against the value of the additional insurance (security) attained.

(*b*) A manager may also set up an informal insurance scheme by combining risks as protection against complete failure. The costs of such insurance schemes occur as a result of participating in more activities than would be profitable in the absence of risk. Such additional costs must be matched against the value of the additional protection secured. Diversification, the addition of enterprises to a business beyond that number known to be advantageous because of supplementarity and complementarity for purposes of spreading risk, is an example of this type of informal insurance. The cost of diversification is reduced productive efficiency. Such costs should be equated, on a marginal subjective basis, with the value of the insurance or security.

(*c*) Another general type of informal insurance often set up by managers involves the maintenance of reserves against unfavorable developments. The costs of such insurance schemes result from the reduction in the earning power of assets held in reserve. Such additional cost must be matched against the value of the additional safety acquired in determining the size of reserves to be held.

3. The flexibility principle was previously listed as (6) under the section on inductive thought processes. It is, however, more properly classified as a strategic principle because it deals with present allocation of assets so as to be able to adjust to an evolving or changing situation. Whenever information is becoming available through time, it may pay to acquire the ability (even at a cost) to postpone decisions until more information is available. The costs of acquiring such ability to postpone generally run in terms of inefficiently employed assets while the passage of time is making additional information available. Flexibility is being used in an optimum manner when the anticipated value of additional information to be acquired is equal to the cost of

acquiring such additional information, including the cost of flexibility.

4. A principle often followed in choosing between alternative dangerous situations is that of selecting the course of action which minimizes the maximum losses which can be incurred.

5. A principle often followed in choosing between alternative desirable situations is to select the alternative course of action which maximizes the minimum gain which could be made. One might also decide to maximize the maximum gain which can be incurred.

6. When farm managers accept, in exchange for a certain situation and at unfair odds, the joint possibility of incurring (a) a small probability of making a very large gain and (b) a large probability of making a small loss, it is necessary that the value of possible gains increase at an increasing rate. This is the long-chance principle. If progress is to be made in developing a farm and accumulating necessary productive assets, farm managers must often apply this principle.

7. Farm managers must continually deal with the businessmen they sell to (including other farmers), the businessmen they buy from (including other farmers), members of their own families, their hired laborers, government officials, and others whose operations have an impact upon the farm business. All of these personalities are capable of reacting to strategy; hence, special strategy principles are applicable in dealing with them: (a) Uncovering of the intentions of, or logic patterns of action, of an individual being dealt with makes it easier to handle him. (b) Covering up of one's own actions often confuses the strategy of the individual being handled. (c) A random, non-logical course of action often confuses the strategy of the personality being handled. (d) Non-revelation of intentions prevents the personality being handled from taking counter action. (e) The use of force resources (economic, social, political, etc.) and deception (within legal and moral limits) to restrict the actions which the other personality may take is necessary when one is competing in personal relationships with a personality employing similar strategies. (f) Reconstruction of a person's beliefs on a basis advantageous to the business makes it easier to handle that person.

Some Psychological Patterns Which Serve as Bases for Managerial Actions

Fairly strong evidence indicates that normal reaction patterns exist among persons with respect to the importance attached to gains and losses in income. These patterns are useful in deciding upon managerial actions, in understanding the managerial actions of other people, and, hence, in handling other people in business matters. 1. Persons "normally" attach increasing importance to additional losses up to a limit and then decreasing importance to additional losses beyond such levels; hence, persons ordinarily insure against losses up to some limit beyond which they do not insure.

2. Persons "normally" attach increasing importance to additional gains; hence, persons ordinarily do not take long chances, at unfavorable odds, beyond some limit.

3. Although the patterns of uniformity noted above apparently exist, the importance attached to gains and losses varies among individuals in accordance with their psychological natures, their family obligations, the beliefs and values of their laborers and members of their community, their education, the amount of analytical experience that they have had, their equity position, their debts, their ages, their moral and esthetic training, and a wide variety of other influences.

4. Among the other influences affecting the importance which individuals attach to gains and losses is any recent, large change in the income of the individual concerned. Newly rich and newly poor persons are apt to be "abnormal" with respect to the importance attached to losses and gains. The abnormalities do not follow readily apparent patterns.

5. As people become adjusted to greater incomes they simultaneously acquire the ability to (1) sustain greater losses, and (2) spend a higher proportion of their income on security or accuracy. They also gain experience in performing the managerial functions; hence, the tendencies to take long chances and to insure do not seem to bear consistent relationships to the income received by people or to recent changes in their incomes. Similarly, the value attached to accuracy and learning does not seem to bear a consistent relationship to the incomes received by people or to recent changes in their incomes.

6. Abnormalities, among people, with respect to the importance attached to losses and gains, include both the extreme gambler and the extreme security seeker. The extreme security seeker is willing to pay abnormally large amounts for security (perhaps even at the expense of his own and his family's welfare). In contrast, the extreme gambler is willing to pay abnormally large amounts for a long-chance of "hitting it rich" (perhaps even at the expense of his own and his family's welfare).

QUESTIONS AND PROBLEMS

Reread Chapters 2 and 3 at this point and answer the following questions:

1. List three examples for each of the five different degrees of perfection and imperfection in knowledge outlined in Chapters 2 and 3. Draw these examples from your personal experience with farm people.

2. List five detailed subjects under each of the five general subjects about which managerial knowledge is often imperfect. Again, draw these examples from your personal experience with farm people.

3. List as many principles as you can think of under each of the three categories of managerial principles outlined at the end of this text.

4. Read the following, and then write a short essay on the five degrees of perfection and imperfection in knowledge:

F. H. Knight, *Risk, Uncertainty and Profit,* Chapter VII.

A. G. Hart, "Risk, Uncertainty, and the Unprofitability of Compounding Probabilities," *Readings in the Theory of Income Distribution,* Philadelphia: The Blakiston Company.

Glenn L. Johnson, "Needed Developments in Economic Theory as Applied to Farm Management," *Journal of Farm Economics,* pp. 1140–1156, 1951.

CHAPTER 23

Uses of Managerial Principles in Farm Operation Illustrated

Chapters 1 and 3 indicated that a center is needed in each business for the purpose of acquiring and analyzing information and adjusting thereto. *That center is management*, and its functions are those of observing, analyzing, deciding, taking action, and bearing responsibility.

Reflection on these concepts indicated that managers are mainly concerned with problems falling into five subject-matter areas, i.e., changes and lack of knowledge concerning (1) prices, (2) production methods and responses, (3) inventions, (4) personalities, and (5) economic, political, and social institutions.

Further thought indicated in Chapter 3 that managers find themselves in one of five different knowledge situations with respect to a given problem encountered in the day-to-day and year-to-year operations of their businesses. Examination of these five situations provided a useful basis for learning managerial principles. The five situations were: (1) the *inactive situation* in which available information is inadequate for a decision concerning a contemplated action and in which the cost of acquiring more information exceeds its value, (2) the *learning situation* in which available information is inadequate for a decision and in which the value of acquiring knowledge exceeds its cost, (3) the *forced action situation* in which available information is inadequate but in which action is forced by outside circumstances, (4) the *subjective risk situation* in which available knowledge, though imperfect, is adequate for action and in which the cost of additional knowledge equals its value, and (5) the *subjective certainty situation* in which knowledge is complete enough for managers to *act as if* they had perfect knowledge. As the first four of these situations all involve inadequate knowledge, they can be grouped together under the label *subjective uncertainty*.

373

Several principles in economic and statistical literature, it was found, serve to increase the efficiency with which the five managerial functions, outlined in the first paragraph above, are performed. These principles have to do with learning (observation, analysis, and, in part, decision making) and strategies with certain psychological patterns serving to explain partially the risks which managers will accept and the degrees of security that they try to attain. These principles were summarized in Chapter 22.

Examination, in the following pages, of a number of managerial situations faced by farmers serves to illustrate the wide applicability of the principles and generalizations in Chapter 22.

The Introduction of Hybrid Seed Corn

When hybrid seed corn was first introduced into the corn belt all farmers did not start using it immediately. Hybrid seed corn was first tried by isolated farmers more or less closely associated with people doing research work on corn breeding. A few individuals who were in a position to secure advanced and relatively large amounts of information concerning the new hybrids were among the first to try them. Other farmers held back waiting for more information about results obtained by the innovators. Most corn producers remained in the learning situation for a number of years. In general, the typical corn producer felt that he did not know enough about hybrid corn to be ready, willing, and able to invest in the more expensive seed; on the other hand, he was highly interested in learning about this new development and spent a considerable amount of time reading literature and advertisements and visiting the fields of his more audacious neighbors. In this learning period one of the costs of learning was the lower yields obtained by persons who failed to attempt the new production technique. Eventually, the greater part of the commercial corn producers in the corn belt learned enough about hybrid-corn production to be ready, willing, and able to act. They were not necessarily sure that hybrid seed corn was more profitable (given the high price of seed) than open-pollinated corn but, nevertheless, they were convinced enough to "give it a try."

The spread of information concerning hybrid corn and the cautiousness with which farmers shifted from open-pollinated to hybrid-corn production illustrate very clearly the way in which farmers proceed through the learning situation to a risk situation. At present

(1953), a great proportion of the commercial corn producers is in the "perfect knowledge" or certainty situation with respect to corn production, i.e., they now act as if they were certain that production of hybrid corn is more profitable than production of open-pollinated varieties.

Price Variations Affect the Decisions Which Farmers Make

Price variations have a particularly important effect upon the willingness of farmers to borrow money. All present-day farmers experienced financial difficulties due to the price changes of the 1920's and 30's or are acquainted with people who did experience such difficulties. Since early in the World War II period, economists, financial advisers, and others have been warning about the danger of price declines. In 1946 a postwar depression similar to the one which occurred in 1921 was widely predicted. Hence, all present-day farmers are more or less aware of the dangers of price declines. They see clearly that a 50 percent equity in real estate, equipment, or livestock can be entirely wiped out by a 50 percent decline in prices. For this reason, farmers are reluctant to borrow money even though it is obvious that, under stable conditions, such money (1) would often produce an income three or four times the interest charges involved, and (2) would make it possible to execute badly needed developmental programs.

When a farmer has a use for money which will produce, on the average, three or four times the costs of borrowing that money and fails to borrow it, he is in either an uncertain or a learning situation. If he is in the uncertain situation, he is convinced that he cannot learn enough about price changes to make him ready, willing, and able to borrow money. If he is in the learning situation, he knows that he does not now have possession of enough information to be ready, willing, and able to borrow but has confidence that he might be able to learn enough to want to borrow the money at a later date. In the learning situation, a farmer continues to be interested in price developments and devotes time and effort trying to learn enough to increase his confidence to a point which will permit him to go ahead and make the investment. The cost of learning in such a situation is, of course, the foregone income which he would have earned had he borrowed money and invested it in the profitable alternative. The value of learning arises in part from the greater security which the farmer feels as a result of not having invested in the face of his lack of knowledge. Another value which he may derive from the learning process is the greater assurance that he will actually earn the amount of money which he anticipates the investment will yield.

Lack of Knowledge Deters Investments in Soil Conservation Practices and Programs

Despite years of earlier work on the part of the agricultural experiment stations, the recent work of the Soil Conservation Service, and all the work of interested private and semipublic agencies, many farmers are still far from being perfectly informed concerning the costs and benefits of various soil-conservation practices and programs. In many instances, the farmer does not know what is involved in carrying out various soil-conservation practices and, hence, cannot compute their costs. In other instances, farmers have only vague ideas as to the probable increases in costs and yields which would result from the various recommended practices. Further, even if a farmer knows, with some precision, the yields which may be expected under various practices, he is still imperfectly informed concerning the prices which he will receive for the products he produces.

Thus, when a farmer becomes interested in soil-conservation practices one of the first things that he needs to do is to inaugurate a program of learning about the costs and benefits of the various practices which might be carried out on his farm. Actually, until a farmer becomes interested in conservation work he is in the uncertainty situation previously defined, i.e., he does not know enough about soil conservation practices to be ready, willing, and able to carry them out and does not value prospective increases in his knowledge enough to cover the costs of making such increases. Once, however, a farmer becomes convinced that it is worth while to learn about conservation practices, he begins to spend time getting together and analyzing information. As long as he is in the learning stage with respect to any particular practice, he does not necessarily adopt it. He may, before becoming completely convinced that a practice should be started on his farm, experiment with it on a small scale. The authors know of few farmers who have decided to terrace an entire farm at one time. In fact, most of them have started with a few terraces. On the basis of such experience, some farmers have continued to terrace and have extended terrace systems over their entire farms. Others, on the other hand, have decided on the basis of their experience with a small amount of terracing that they should not terrace the entire farm.

Two Kinds of Mistakes Can Be Made in Choosing between Alternatives

It has been observed that the cash-grain farmers of east central Illinois are more responsive when planting soybeans to changes in the soybean-corn price ratio than are the livestock and grain farmers of northern Illinois and Iowa. When an individual farmer is considering the substitution of soybeans for corn in his cropping plans he runs the danger of making two kinds of errors. He can make the error of choosing grain and being wrong or he can make the error of choosing soybeans and being wrong. These are two distinct types of errors which may have different consequences on different types of farms.

On the cash-grain farms of east central Illinois, the error of choosing soybeans when corn should have been chosen results in loss of the differential in profit. The same kind of a loss is involved when the east central Illinois cash-grain farmer erroneously chooses corn in preference to soybeans. The livestock-grain farmer of northern Illinois and Iowa, however, suffers considerably *different consequences in making the two different types of errors*. If the livestock-grain farmer erroneously chooses corn in preference to soybeans, he loses only the profit differential; if he erroneously chooses soybeans in preference to corn, he suffers the additional consequence of eliminating a part of the feed base for the livestock enterprise of his farm. Thus, the farmers in the livestock-producing areas tend to require larger and more certain price differentials in favor of soybeans before shifting to soybeans than do the farmers of east central Illinois. Prior to World War II, Iowa and north central Illinois were relatively unimportant producers of soybeans for seed. With the introduction of relatively high guaranteed support prices for soybeans during the World War II period, the livestock farmers switched to soybean production.

Imperfect Knowledge about Future Yields Makes Maintenance of Feed Reserves Important in Many Farm Areas

In many parts of the United States, especially west of the Mississippi River, forage and grain yields are highly variable. The amount of grain available for pork and beef fattening enterprises in many areas may vary more than 100 percent from a low in one year to a high in the next. The same is true about the amounts of pasturage and hay produced. Under such variable conditions, farmers find it difficult to maintain orderly feeding and breeding operations. Over a period of years, the importance of feed reserves as a source of stability for livestock enterprises has become apparent and such reserves are fairly widely used.

These reserves are part of an informal insurance scheme. Such reserves protect the farm business against the need to liquidate livestock enterprises in poor crop years. These reserves, however, are not maintained without cost. First, they represent rather sizeable investments upon which an interest charge must be made. Second, feed reserves are subject to deterioration. And, third, the structures used to house such reserves are expensive to maintain and build. Thus, it is necessary for managers employing feed reserves as a source of insurance against poor weather to balance the value of such insurance against the costs of maintaining the reserves. Here again the obvious problem is one of trying not to pay more for additional insurance than such additional insurance is worth.

Liquid Assets Are (1) Important Components of Insurance Schemes and (2) Sources of Flexibility

A liquid asset is an asset which can be quickly converted into cash. Cash, of course, has perfect liquidity. A checking account is slightly less liquid; a savings account still less liquid; and bonds, though still liquid, are generally less liquid than savings accounts. Grain in the bin is a fairly liquid asset as it can be rather quickly converted into cash. Land and building investments are examples of assets which lack liquidity.

Farmers often maintain reserves of liquid assets for use in case of unfavorable developments. Such liquid assets are parts of informal insurance schemes designed to protect the farm business against such developments. Such reserves have costs which should be balanced (generally subjectively) in marginal terms against their value.

Liquid assets, however, have another important function to play in farm businesses. Oftentimes, liquid assets are held, in contrast to being invested, because a farmer is in a learning situation, i.e., because he does not know enough to be ready, willing, and able to invest his funds but nevertheless anticipates that he will shortly acquire enough knowledge to make such investments. Hence, he maintains his assets in a liquid position, even at a cost of foregone income derivable from alternative employments for such assets, until he can learn more about the proposition currently interesting him. Here the manager is purchasing the right to postpone an investment decision, i.e., he is using liquid assets as a source of flexibility. Such flexibility has value because it permits him to learn more about the alternative investments and, hence, to increase his income and/or personal satisfaction. Here again, the obvious problem of a manager is one of trying not to spend more on additional flexibility than such additional flexibility is worth. The value of flexibility, like many of the values associated with management, is a personal, subjective thing, depending upon such considerations as a manager's ability to learn, the importance which he attaches to accuracy, the importance which he attaches to alternative investments for his liquid assets, and a wide variety of other more or less personal considerations.

Strategic Considerations Play an Important Role in the Purchase and Sale of Farm Land

In contrast to trading in the standardized commodities, trading in land often involves local, special, and more or less monopolistic elements. If a farm has special location value, the supply of similarly located land is strictly limited. The supply of land adjacent to a given farm is, of course, limited, and prospective buyers and sellers of such land negotiate on a personal, strategic basis. Such land is often worth more to both the present landowner and the adjacent farmer trying to buy it than it is to anyone else; hence, the bargaining process becomes one of establishing a price somewhat above the going price for land. In such situations, buyers often wait for years for the strategic time at which to purchase. Such strategic times are likely to occur in connection with financial difficulties for the seller, settlement of estates, retirement, etc. On the other hand, a seller of land is likely to try to overimpress an adjacent farmer with the value of his particular tract of land. In the negotiations involved in buying and selling adjacent tracts of land all the principles of strategy are likely to be utilized. Both buyer and seller are likely to try to cover up their real intentions; they may even negotiate through intermediaries. Similarly, both buyer and seller are likely to spend considerable time uncovering the intentions and logical patterns of action of each other. Attempts bordering on deceit and even fraud are continuously made, in such instances, to "run down" the value of the farm in the eyes of the seller and to "build up" the value of the farm in the eyes of the buyer.

The results of such negotiations are highly important to successful management of farms. Unwise or fortunate purchases are likely to affect the operation of a business for many years. Acquisition of land at bargain rates strengthens the financial position of a farm operator tremendously, thus making it possible for him to secure access to credit for operational and developmental purposes. Conversely, the farmer who is "stung" in the purchase of land goes to a poorer credit position and has difficulty financing both ordinary and developmental operations.

Some Imperfect Knowledge Problems in Beef Production

Beef-cattle raising and specialized feeding are widely practiced. While the production method adopted depends on a farmer's resources and other enterprises, the type of cattle raising carried on depends also on knowledge concerning levels and variations in livestock prices, feed supplies, and production practices. Thus, where beef herds fit into the farm organization the farmer has a number of alternative lines of action.

A basic cow herd may be maintained and feeder calves sold. Such an organization is rather inflexible if pasture is short or the hay crop fails, for the alternatives are buying high-priced feed or selling part of the cow herd. If calf prices become unfavorable, barn space may not be available to carry the animals over. When one's facilities are used to capacity, his organization is relatively inflexible.

A second alternative is that of raising and holding over calves for sale as yearlings or even as two-year-olds. This method is suitable for the farmer who feels he cannot foresee the future well enough to take a more positive action but values prospective gains in his knowledge in regard to prices and yields more than the cost of making such gains.

In the first alternative, the farmer obtains rapid liveweight gains with little ability to adjust to change. The second system allows the farmer to adjust his plans as conditions seem to warrant. Under the more flexible plan, steers may be marketed when there is no economic advantage in keeping them longer, the planned grazing period can be shortened, winter feeding can be cut out if feed supplies are short, and yet the basic cow herd can be maintained. The second system is also such that expansion is relatively easy and capital outlays are not heavy in either getting started or in expanding. Thus, the choice between the two systems depends, in part, on whether the ability to adjust offsets reduced efficiency in securing liveweight gains.

Dual-purpose cattle also play an important role in beef production in many areas. They appear to persist largely because they offer the farmer a chance to shift between milk and cream or calf production as price relationships and needs for labor income change. This ability to change (flexibility) has both a value and a cost, the cost arising from the fact that dual-purpose cattle are relatively less efficient than single-purpose cattle both in beef and in milk production.

A cattle feeder has a number of alternatives facing him both before a feeding operation is started and while it is being carried on. Cattle feeding is a business fraught with price dangers. Those operators who feel these price dangers are too great and do not value prospective improvement in knowledge higher than its cost seek other alternatives. Some feeders vary their production plans on the basis of current knowledge, going from light to heavy cattle, from a straight roughage system to heavy grain feeding, from many animals to a few or none, depending on expected changes in prices and costs. The latter type of action has earned some operators the derogatory name "in and outers" when actually such actions reflect good management in many cases, depending on their ability to observe and analyze.

Those who undertake feeding operations may be said to be in a continual learning situation with respect to the enterprise. With respect to any given group of feeder cattle, an operator often finds himself forced to take somewhat irreversible actions, regardless of his state of knowledge and willingness. Before purchasing feeders, the operator can decide to buy a few or many, depending on the prospective feed supply and other factors. The age of animal purchased depends somewhat on one's feed supplies and experience but also on one's estimate of the future strength of the fat-cattle market. If the short-run market seems to be the safest bet, the feeders favor big cattle to finish in 2 to 4 months or long-fed, young animals that do not require a large initial investment. Calves and yearlings offer more flexibility and involve the feeder in fewer forced-action situations than older animals, allowing the operator to change strategies as long as heavy grain feeding has not progressed far. Calves are particularly flexible, provided that the farmer has available pasture and roughage to make it possible to postpone their fattening period by roughing through one winter and grazing through the following summer, perhaps even roughing through still another winter before he is finally forced to feed grain to finish them out. Such a feeder, of course, always has the alternative of remarketing the steers as feeders.

Changing Governmental Arrangements Create Managerial Problems

Governmental arrangements are always more or less temporary. Thus, farm incomes which depend on governmental arrangements are never perfectly foreseen. Milk-marketing agreements, production control, and price-support programs are sources of such more or less artificial incomes.

One of the most outstanding of such governmental arrangements affecting farm incomes exists in the Burley-tobacco-producing states, mainly Kentucky and Tennessee. In these states, the acreage control and price-support programs have maintained an artificially high price for Burley, which has, in turn, caused acreage allotments to have values ranging over $1,000 per acre in areas having the highest comparative advantage in Burley production.

In these areas farmers have to adjust to the possibility that the acreage control and price-support programs might be eliminated and the value of investments in acreage allotments destroyed. First, the farmers have the problem of securing some idea of what an acreage allotment for a particular farm is worth for a given year. Second, they have the problem of appraising how many years such increased incomes will exist. Then, on the basis of such information, they have to determine the present value for a particular farm of an acreage allotment.

Early in the operation of the programs, it became evident that the programs were affecting land values. Farmers found this out through different reasoning processes. Some reasoned that land prices should be increased if the programs affected Burley prices. Others observed that land prices were increasing. The first type reasoned deductively; i.e., they mentally determined an implication of a fact known or assumed to be true. The other set reasoned inductively, i.e., they reasoned that what was happening to the price of the relatively small number of land parcels sold was happening to all similar land.

Because the future of the programs has never been perfectly foreseen, farmers have never been completely confident that the increased income from an acre of allotment would continue to exist. One study of the control programs indicates that in 1948 the program probably maintained the price of Burley more than 10 cents above the level which would have existed had no programs been in effect.[1] At a yield of 2,000 pounds per acre this would be worth over $200 an acre of allotment per year. Figured at 5 percent interest, a series of $200 annual incomes extending indefinitely into the future would be capitalized at $4,000. Yet allotments seldom bring more than $2,000.

[1] Glenn L. Johnson, "Burley Tobacco Control Programs—Their Overall Effect on Production and Prices, 1933–1950," *Kentucky Agr. Exp. Station Bulletin* 580, February, 1952.

More commonly they bring about $1,000 per acre in the areas of high comparative advantage. This difference indicates that farmers are setting up safety factors and heavily discounting the future incomes which might be received under the programs. Apparently farmers think, on the basis of what they can learn about the operation of the programs, that it is safe to count on the continued existence of the programs for another 5 to 10 years. These safety factors protect land purchasers against full losses. However, these safety factors have a cost; i.e., if a farmer refuses to pay more than $1,000 for 20 annual $200 incomes, he loses $3,000 (no allowance for interest; $1,580 if an interest allowance is made).

Thus, the safety factor has both a cost and a value. These costs and values are personal and subjective in nature. Obviously, it does not pay to use so much safety that the last "unit of safety" costs more than it is worth.

Uncertain Hog and Corn Prices

Sometime in the summer of each year, hog producers begin to think about the number of gilts to be kept for the next year's spring pig crop. On particular farms this decision is ordinarily affected by prospective prices for hogs, corn, protein supplements, prospective corn supplies, and the health of the current drove of hogs. As the feeder hogs on a particular farm approach market weights it becomes increasingly important that a decision be reached as to how many gilts will be taken off the fattening ration and placed on a ration more favorable to the development of thrifty breeding animals.

In this period hog producers ordinarily find themselves in a learning situation; i.e., their knowledge of hog and corn prices and their own supply of corn is not sufficient for them to decide on the size of their breeding herd while, at the same time, they value at more than its cost the additional information which they can learn. Thus, hog producers spend time evaluating current trends in hog and corn prices. They also begin to make tentative estimates as to size of their own corn crop and the amount of it which will be left over to feed the crop of spring pigs.

If the day when the gilts must be separated from the market hogs approaches before the producer acquires enough information to be ready, willing, and able to act, he may desire to follow a strategy which will keep him from getting into a forced-action position. One way of avoiding the final decision as to size of breeding herd is to keep a fairly large number of gilts on a tentative basis—a few extra gilts can be held on a non-fattening ration for a month or two at a relatively low cost. The costs would include, among other things, (1) the possible incurrence of a seasonal decline in the per pound value of the gilts if they are eventually marketed, and (2) reduced efficiency in their gains when placed on a breeding-herd ration. Here the problem is to avoid paying more for additional flexibility (the ability to postpone decisions) than such additional flexibility is worth.

If ability to postpone the decision as to size of breeding herd is acquired, the learning situation is prolonged. Consequently, more time has to be devoted to learning about prospective supplies of corn, protein supplements, prospective hog and corn prices, and the health of the hogs on the farm. However, the date is eventually approached beyond which breeding for the spring pig crop can no longer be postponed. If, on that date, the manager has not accumulated enough information to be ready, willing, and able to decide on the size of his breeding herd, he may further postpone the decision by breeding extra gilts and then keeping them until just before they get so "piggy" as to be heavily docked on markets for slaughter animals. It is logical for a manager to follow such procedures provided that he values prospective improvements in his knowledge more than (1) the cost of providing the flexibility necessary to use such knowledge, plus (2) the cost of acquiring such knowledge through time.

If a manager has not acquired enough information to be ready, willing, and able to decide on the size of his breeding herd by the time his gilts begin to get piggy he may find himself in a *forced-action situation;* i.e., despite the fact that he does not know enough to be ready, willing, and able to act, he may be *forced* to act. There is, of course, the alternatives of disposing of bred gilts, but the decision as to whether to produce bred gilts or slaughter animals is forced.

Variations in Forage Yields and Requirements Create Important Problems

Pasture, hay, and grass silage yields are highly variable even in areas of high annual rainfall—they depend on changes in weather, the season of the year, grazing and harvesting practices, and a wide variety of other factors. Similarly, the need for hay and pasture on particular farms varies with weather, the seasons, the kind of livestock produced, and the production plans followed. Thus, farm managers often face the problem of not knowing enough about forage yields and requirements to completely coordinate their forage and livestock production plans.

Some farmers in such situations feel that they do not know enough about forage and livestock production to engage in commercial production of forage-consuming livestock. Among such farmers are two types. Farmers of the *first* type feel that what they could learn would not be worth the effort; hence, they do not engage in commercial production of forage-consuming animals and do not try to learn about such production problems. Farmers of the *second* type, on the other hand, feel that what they could learn about such production processes would be worth the cost and effort of learning. As a result, the second type of farmer engages in various learning processes with the object in mind of eventually engaging in such operations.

By and large, the learning techniques fall into two categories. In some instances, farmers concerned with forage and livestock production problems reason inductively to general conclusions from observed experiences, experimental data, and isolated facts. In other cases, farmers reason deductively from budgeting and economic principles to arrive at detailed conclusions.

In pasture production, it is never possible to acquire perfect knowledge concerning yields. Hence, managers often devise strategies to reduce the impact of variation in pasture yields on their business. One publication indicates that farmers can reduce variation in pasture yields by four main methods: [1] (1) choice of plant mixtures, (2) such practices as rotation grazing, seasonal applications of fertilizer, mowing and underutilization of pasture to leave residuals for consumption in short periods, (3) storage of surplus pasture forage for use in deficit periods, and (4) control of the soil water supply. Each of these methods has a cost; each produces valuable stability in feed supplies; some also contribute additional production. Obviously, it does not pay a farmer to spend more for additional stability than such stability is worth.

Antibiotics Make Learning Important

Technological changes create the need to learn. What kind of evidence or knowledge should be on hand before adopting a new product or idea? The old adage is "Be not the first by which the new is tried nor yet the last to lay the old aside."

[1] E. J. Nesius, "Allocation of Farm Resources for Economic Production of Pastures," *Kentucky Agr. Exp. Station Bulletin* 568, July, 1951.

Antibiotics are a case in point. These compounds, like streptomycin, aureomycin, penicillin, and B_{12}, have been reported as giving (1) phenomenal feed savings through increased daily gains and reduced death losses when they are added to hog and broiler rations, and (2) increased egg production and feed efficiency when they are used in laying mashes.

Feed and pharmaceutical companies advertise widely. Many farmers know neighbors who have had seemingly good success with these compounds. Yet some people, farmers and researchers, have found evidence to the contrary. In analyzing such conflicting evidence, farmers discover that the difficulty may be due to a number of things. Antibiotics are, among other things, germ killers. Therefore, when used in hog feed, antibiotics rid the hogs of certain bad (and good) microorganisms. This, in turn, often makes them thrive, thereby increasing gains and bringing about feed savings not otherwise possible. It follows that hog herds not infected with such bad microorganisms do not give as favorable responses as herds of hogs so infected. The same compounds fed to ruminants (cattle, sheep) could actually destroy the organisms that synthesize proteins in their digestive systems. Researchers have found that some antibiotics and combinations of antibiotics give responses, that others do not, and the why's are not fully known as yet.

Now just what should the individual farmer do in this and similar situations where technological changes are introduced? In this case, the cost of trying antibiotics is small and the gains may be great. The cost of incorrectly concluding that antibiotics should be used when they should not is low; the cost of concluding that they should not be used when they should may be high. Thus, as long as the information to be gained has a fairly high prospective value, a considerable number of farmers are experimenting with antibiotics as a method of learning about them.

Long-Chance Takers Trade Secure Incomes for Large Risky Incomes and Benefits

Farmers, agricultural economists, and businessmen experience great difficulty in foreseeing future land value. Individuals, however, attach great importance to landownership. And, because they attach such importance to incomes from land and the benefits of owning land, they often take chances at apparently unfavorable odds in trying to establish ownership.

In taking such risks, elements of speculation are involved. Under such circumstances an individual exchanges a relatively low, stable, real income for chances at two other levels of real income; i.e., he receives (1) a small probability of "making the grade" and becoming an owner with all attendant rights and privileges while (2) running a large chance of failing and receiving a lower level of real income. *depends where he thinks he belongs*

Sensible people do not take long chances unless the combined chances of getting the resultant high or low incomes are worth enough more to them than their present certain income to offset the unfavorable odds necessary to cover administrative costs. In a gambling establishment such costs are referred to as the "cut for the house," whereas in business gambles (e.g., in long-chance land purchases) such costs often include brokerage fees, title fees, and, in short, all land transfer costs. Very few long-chance situations exist which do not involve administrative costs of some nature, and the odds are often sufficiently against the taker to cover such costs. Thus it is necessary for the income which might be gained by taking a long chance to have increasing value to the chance-taker.

It is normal for people to ascribe high values to increases in income capable of shifting them between various social strata, i.e., from farm laborer to renter, or from renter to landowner, or from small owner to large landholder. The desires to make gains which permit such shifts are in no sense abnormal or pathological and the taking of long chances of making such gains is not gambling in a sense to be particularly deplored. Similarly, the taking of long chances at the introduction of new production methods or in the development of such methods is not to be deplored. In fact, the taking of such chances is necessary in a free-enterprise economy. If such chances had not been taken in the past, the agricultural economy of the United States would not be one of the most efficient in the world. Thus, whether one likes it or not, it is evident that the principles of long-chance taking (or, more plainly speaking, of gambling) are useful in increasing the efficiency with which the managerial functions are performed.

Long-chance taking can, of course, take on a diseased or pathological nature in business as well as in gambling houses. The desire for gain without work or the contribution of assets can eventually become so strong that productive activity on the part of a manager ceases. This pathological case, of course, is similar to that found in the extreme security seeker who spends so much time seeking security that his resources (1) are kept continually out of productive employment, and (2) have to be sold to pay his formal and informal insurance premiums. Apparently, the danger of pathological gambling is more important for individuals, whereas the danger of extreme security seeking becomes more important in organized groups, especially in political bodies. Such bodies are often inclined to legislate away, or decree away, the productive capacity of a nation in an elusive quest for security of one form or another.

Farmers Prefer to Maintain Credit Reserves in Contrast to Cash Reserves

A farm family may do three things with the income which it has left after paying production expenses and current debt commitments. First, it may spend a portion of such income for consumption purposes. Second, it may invest a portion. And, thirdly, a family may use part of the income as a reserve against unfavorable developments and as a source of flexibility.

Subjective wants, preferences, and desires are the dominant considerations in allocating income among these three uses. Money is spent for consumption purposes so that members of the family may enjoy the items or services consumed. Money is spent for investment purposes because members of the family want the extra income which will probably result from such investments. Money is held in reserve because the members of the family want the security of reserves and/or the ability to postpone decisions which such reserves grant. A farm family derives the maximum amount of satisfaction from these three uses of income when the satisfactions derived from the last dollar devoted to each of the three uses are equal. Because the family actually owns the money held in reserve, the satisfaction derived from cash reserves must be great enough to cover the satisfaction securable from the income that such reserves would have earned had they been directly invested.

Similarly, the farm family has three uses for the amount of credit which it could obtain. Credit can be used for (1) investment purposes, (2) consumption purposes, and (3) a reserve against unfavorable developments and for flexibility. The credit sources of a farm family are yielding the farmer a maximum of satisfaction when the satisfactions derived from each credit dollar devoted to each of the three uses are equal. As long as money which could be borrowed is not borrowed, the only cost of holding it in reserve is the profit which could have been made had the money been borrowed—this is a net opportunity cost. Thus, the satisfaction derived from credit reserves only needs to be large enough to be equal to the satisfaction which would have been derived from the *profit earned* had the credit been used. This is in sharp contrast to the amount of satisfaction which must be derived from *cash* held in reserve. Satisfaction from the last dollar of cash held in reserve must be great enough to cover the total earnings of the cash asset in contrast to only the profits earnable with a dollar's worth of credit.

This difference is fundamental in understanding the actions of farmers in dealing with monetary matters. Farmers ordinarily have much greater reserves of unused credit than of unused cash. The typical farm family rarely has at its disposal more than a small cash balance for reserves and flexibility purposes; on the other hand, the typical farm family ordinarily has at its disposal a rather large reserve of unused credit, even at moderately low rates of interest. At higher rates of interest, such as those paid in connection with consumer credit, most typical farm families have very large reserves of unused credit.

Diversification Is a Technique for Reducing Risks

Cropping systems are sometimes diversified beyond the point most advantageous from the standpoint of complementarity; i.e., additional crops are sometimes grown to reduce variability in total income from a cropping system. Some farmers prefer a steady income to a highly variable income, even when the latter would probably give them a greater income over time.

Certain rotation systems adopted by farmers illustrate this procedure. In small-grain areas of the great plains, summer fallowing is an important weed-control and moisture-conservation practice. One year in four is usually adequate for weed control, and more than one in three or four for moisture conservation means that a large proportion of the land is not in direct production. But a number of great plains farmers are adopting cropping systems involving large acreages of fallow land in order to stabilize grain yields, and thereby stabilize incomes. By following such crop sequences they forego high total production in order to secure protection against dry weather.

In farming areas where a particular product (or group of products) has a high comparative advantage and yet this same product (or products) experiences great price or yield uncertainties compared to other products, it is a common strategy to combine such enterprise with one that is relatively more certain. The latter enterprise provides the farmer with a stable income component at a sacrifice in total income over time, while the former provides the bulk of the income. Dairy cows on many corn-belt farms are a case in point. Forage-consuming livestock on farms having a high comparative advantage in cash grain production in the great plains provide another example of this. More cattle are sometimes kept than are necessary to utilize non-arable or rotated pastures. This practice reduces the land available for grain production. The comparative advantage of wheat and other small grains is often such that every arable acre taken from this use (beyond that required for economic soil management) and put into livestock uses represents foregone income. The gain offsetting this cost is the more stable income for any one year. Yields and prices have been so high and stable since 1940 that many great plains livestock enterprises have disappeared, the farmers feeling presumably that this source of income stability is no longer needed or is too costly relative to the income foregone.

CHAPTER 24

Getting and Using Resources

This chapter, the third having to do with the year-to-year, month-to-month, and day-to-day management of a farm business takes up a subject which has been more or less slighted in the past chapters. Back in Chapter 6, we started illustrating a procedure for organizing a farm business. This procedure started with an appraisal of the assets and resources at the disposal of a farm family. All the subsequent chapters dealing with organization of a farm assumed that a given amount of resources were at the disposal of the farm family or that they had access to all the resources required.

In managing a farm over a period of time, two of the most important problems which a manager faces are those of accumulating and maintaining control over productive resources. Sometimes farm management men are prone to think of productive assets as being primarily monetary and physical in nature; however, a moment's reflection indicates that personal assets are also productive. It is as important for a farmer to accumulate technical know-how and managerial capacity as it is for him to accumulate land, buildings, and monetary assets.

The general problem of resources falls more or less under two headings: first, the problem of getting control of sufficient assets to operate or develop a business; and, second, the problem of using and maintaining the assets which one has. If assets in use are overmaintained, savings occur; if undermaintained, dissavings occur.

Getting Control of Resources

Farm families acquire control of resources through four main methods. Resources, both personal and physical, *may be inherited;* i.e., individuals inherit property, social position, mental capacity, and many other traits, any of which may turn out to be business assets at some future date. Another source of assets, probably more common than realized, are the *windfall gains* which people pick up. Oftentimes, an unexpected source of income provides the initial capital so important in "getting started" in the farming business. The third source which will be mentioned is *earnings;* i.e., asset control can be accumulated through the process of saving part of one's earnings. In practice, this source of control is probably less important than we commonly think. A person is not likely to be able to save enough to get started in the farming business unless he either receives an inheritance, a windfall gain of some sort, or, in addition to his own earning power, has the earning power of certain assets, such as property or educational investments in his personal capacity. Probably the most important way of getting control of assets in farming is through *borrowing* which is the fourth and last to be listed here. The first three, however, generally provide the credit base for use in borrowing.

Inheritance. The first assets which a farmer or prospective farmer gets together are inherited. Personal capacities are inherited, and, in addition, each person inherits varying amounts of training from his family and the society in which he lives. The personal physical and mental capacities of a young farmer just getting started are almost entirely inherited, and, in addition, previous generations generally pass on to the members of a given generation various physical assets, such as land, in the old days—a team of horses, in current days—some purebred livestock, a tractor, and a great variety of other physical assets. In addition, a young farmer may inherit such assets as a good family name and reputation, a community organization conducive to rapid development, roads, and market facilities.

Inherited assets, in turn, become the base for the expansion of future farming operations. The expansion process is likely to involve the accumulation of earnings, the receipt of windfalls, and the expansion of earning power by borrowing on the basis of the assets which a person inherits.

Earnings. The earnings of the assets under the control of a farmer provide a second way of accumulating control of assets. The process of accumulating control through earnings involves both income and expenses, as assets are not accumulated unless expenses are below income.

The level of earnings which a man can attain, of course, depends upon the assets which he has at his disposal. Some farmers have only their labor and, in some instances, a very low grade of labor, as a source of earnings. Others are skilled laborers. Still others are skilled, have strong bodies, and in addition, are well informed and capable of earning fairly large incomes even without physical assets. Still, others are capable as laborers, mentally well trained, and, in addition, have inherited sufficient assets to place their incomes at a relatively high level.

On the consumption or expenditure side, some farm families are in a position to run along at a low level of expenditures; others have heavy consumption demands on their incomes. One farm-management professor has said that a young farm family, without children, with the wife teaching in the local school, is like a team of horses pulling an empty wagon and that the real problem of saving money does not arise until the wife and three children get in the wagon and start riding.

The above paragraphs serve to emphasize the fact that control of resources can only be accumulated from current earnings when expenses are held down. Thus, it is especially important that farmers and farm families recognize the periods in their lives when it is possible to set up differentials between income and expenses. It is easy to save $1,000 before marriage. With conservative spending habits and the absence of children, it is probably still easier to save $1,000 immediately after marriage. Once, however, family expenses reach their more normal levels, savings are possible only if high earning power has been accumulated.

Windfalls. Though we do not like to admit it, the "initial shot" of capital for establishing farm businesses or for inaugurating developmental programs on farms is often of a windfall nature. A favorable, unforeseen turn in prices; an unusually high yield; a G.I. pension; an insurance payment; the accident of being properly located; and a wide variety of other instances often result in the receipt of unforeseen incomes. In many instances, the farmer recipients of such incomes are quick to see that, if invested, these windfall incomes will provide the basis for the establishment of the farm or the expansion of a subsistence farm business into a commercial operation.

Not all apparently unearned increments, however, are windfalls— some result from deliberate chance taking, i.e., the purchase of a farm "on a shoestring," the taking of a "long shot" in planting a specialty crop or feeding cattle, etc. One cannot help but be impressed by the proportion of farmers who secured their start by deliberate chance taking. Oftentimes, the chances that they take are not as unfavorable as they themselves think. For instance, one of the authors has talked and taken records from many farmers who thought they were taking long chances in fertilizing and seeding pasture on worn-out farms—actually, what they were doing was almost a sure thing, at least as sure as other ordinary farming operations.

Borrowings. To him that has something, borrowing offers one of the most rapid ways of acquiring control of assets and a portion of what the assets earn. In almost all instances, some assets must be on hand as "security" for the loan. Even the 100 percent loans occasionally supplied are likely to be 50 percent loans if the physical earning power and the technical know-how of the borrower are considered; i.e., a healthy, physically fit family, well trained in technical agricultural problems and of average or better moral standards, is often a sounder basis for a $5,000 loan than $4,000 worth of corn in a crib or 15 steers in a feed lot.

Borrowing is often looked upon as a source of danger, but, by and large, most farm-management men readily agree that borrowing for productive purposes is desirable. They often see that borrowing is necessary in order to get the larger categories of inputs properly combined on a farm. A young man representing a considerable quantity of labor, possessing over 120 acres of land, but no working capital, has to borrow money in order to get his land and labor resources properly combined with machinery, livestock, and other forms of capital. In connection with the dangers of borrowing, it should be pointed out that the borrowing of money has probably put about as many people in a position to reap the benefits of windfall gains due to price increases as it has in a position to suffer the consequences of price declines. Further, it is probably true that, among the farm businesses now in existence, by far the largest percentage have received the benefits of such windfalls; i.e., many of those which suffered the consequences of price declines are not now in operation.

Renting of land and buildings is basically only another way of borrowing. The young physically capable, well-trained farmer, with command over some working capital, often finds it advantageous to acquire control over the necessary land resources through rental contracts. This is especially true in the midwestern areas of the United States. In many of the southern areas, tenure arrangements are primarily ways whereby a landowner, in a position to furnish much of the working capital, manages to acquire control over labor resources. This is in sharp contrast to the tenure arrangements in the midwest and probably most of the west where the tenure arrangements permit a farmer businessman, in possession of both labor and working capital, to acquire control of the land resources.

Both borrowing and renting are alternatives to saving in the process of accumulating control. Judicious borrowing and renting often greatly increase the earning power of the assets which a man owns. Borrowing and renting often widen the differential between earnings and expenditures and, in turn, often make additional savings possible. It is, of course, these savings which make it possible not only to pay interest on the money borrowed or rent on the land rented but also, in addition, to pay back principal or accumulate bank accounts for the purpose of buying land.

The Control of Resources

In Chapters 3 and 22, certain principles of use in understanding insurance and flexibility were discussed. It will be recalled that insurance schemes are broadly defined to include procedures whereby a manager exchanges an uncertain higher average expected income for a much more certain, but lower, income, the difference between the two generally going to pay the cost of maintaining the insurance scheme. The flexibility principal, on the other hand, is involved when a manager so handles his affairs as to be able to reallocate his resources, at a later point of time, on the basis of the additional information which he may be able to secure. In the case of flexibility, a manager ordinarily anticipates that the subsequent reallocation of resources will be advantageous enough for him to more than make up the costs involved in maintaining a flexible position.

In controlling resources, managers commonly keep both insurance (security) and flexibility principles in mind in addition to income-producing possibilities. Both of these principles restrict the amount of resources which a manager finds it advantageous to use. Therefore, these two principles form the basis for a general overall discussion of resource control and use in operating a business. By and large, the economic principles presented in Chapters 8 to 12 and in the budgeting procedures outlined in Chapters 13 to 23 did not give much attention to the problems of (1) insuring against undesirable developments and (2) keeping businesses in a position so that it is possible to adjust to the changes which occur to take advantage of favorable opportunities and to avoid undesirable events.

In the field of agricultural economics, three terms have grown up which are useful in describing these situations and in understanding the procedures followed by managers.[1] These terms are (1) *internal cash or asset rationing*, (2) *internal credit rationing*, and (3) *external credit rationing*.

[1] T. W. Schultz, "Capital Rationing, Uncertainty and Farm Tenancy Reform," *Journal of Political Economy*, XLVIII, 1940, pp. 309–320.

Internal Cash or Asset Rationing. The distinction maintained between cash and credit is essentially the distinction between owned and borrowed assets. What we will have to say, with respect to cash rationing, applies almost without modification to all owned assets. The economic principles presented in Chapters 8 to 12 assume that the use of an asset will be expanded as long as it returns more at the margin than it costs. When one is using his own assets, this means essentially that he continues to expand the use of an asset as long as the income which is earned at the margin is worth more to him than the asset would be worth in alternative uses. By and large, the economic principles include only consumption and production uses and ignore the use of assets as a source of security (insurance) and flexibility.

If the reasoning used in the economic principles and the budgeting procedure actually conformed to reality, the amount of assets which a person uses for income-producing purposes would be the amount AC in Figure 24.1; the amount of assets used for consumption purposes would be BC. In that figure, the line labeled MU_{MVP} represents the satisfaction which the farmer and/or his family receive from the additional incomes earned when an additional unit of the resource is devoted to income-producing purposes. The line labeled $MU_{Consumption}$ represents the satisfaction or the utility which the farmer and/or family derive from using additional units of the resource for consumption purposes. The amount of resources used for income-producing purposes (including savings for income purposes) is measured from left to right, starting at A, whereas the amount of resources used for consumption purposes is measured from right to left, starting at B. AB is the amount of cash assets available for both consumption and income-producing possibilities.

Figure 24.1 is, we know, very unrealistic. Very few farmers use all their assets for either consumption or direct income-producing purposes. There is a tendency to reserve assets for two additional purposes: (1) as a source of security (insurance) and (2) as a source of flexibility, so as to be able to take advantage of favorable opportunities or to avoid undesirable events.

Figure 24.2 is the same as Figure 24.1 except for two modifications. The MU_{MVP} line of Figure 24.1 has been discounted enough to give the safety margin which the farmer or the farm family requires; a second modification is the introduction of an additional curve labeled $MU_{Flexibility}$. The flexibility curve measures the utility or usefulness which the farmer and/or his family feel they can derive from maintaining a portion of their assets in a flexible position to take advantage of favorable opportunities and avoid undesirable events. Study of Figure 24.2 indicates that if the farmer or farm family uses the amount AD of their assets for income-producing purposes and the amount BE

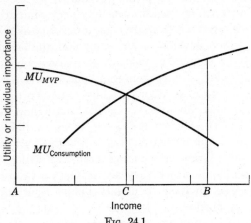

Fig. 24.1.

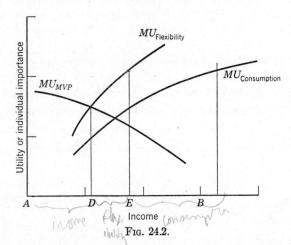

Fig. 24.2.

for consumption purposes, they will have the amount DE left as a source of insurance against undesirable developments on the income-producing side of the farm business and as a source of flexibility. Figure 24.2 is related to the discussion in connection with inheritance, earning, and windfalls. The total amount of incomes and assets to be divided among the four uses is, of course, made up of income and assets from all sources. As can be seen from the chart, the higher the farm family's demands for consumption, the less there will be available for investment for income-producing purposes. Similarly, the more cautious the family is, the more they discount returns, in order to acquire safety margins; the smaller the proportion of their investments which will be invested for income purposes, the smaller will be the proportion of the assets which will be used for consumption. Similarly, the greater the farmer's demand for flexibility in order to take advantage of the situations which develop or to avoid undesirable situations, the smaller will be the amount of incomes and assets which will be used for income-producing and consumption purposes. When one looks at Figure 24.2 and thinks rather carefully about its meaning, he sees that farm management involves a great deal more than the maximizing of farm incomes. If sufficient assets are to be available for income-producing purposes, the farmer and his family must give careful attention to their consumption or spending habits. Further, they must be sure that the discounts which they are setting up in order to acquire security are not so great as to unduly hinder their investments for income-producing purposes.

Internal Credit Rationing. The term, internal credit and asset rationing, refers to the self-imposed restrictions which a business places upon itself in borrowing money. As in the case of the restriction which the business places on itself in using the assets which it owns, these restrictions are placed on the business in order to obtain security and flexibility.

In Figure 24.3, the amount of credit which a farm business would be able to obtain is represented by the line labeled SS, the supply of credit

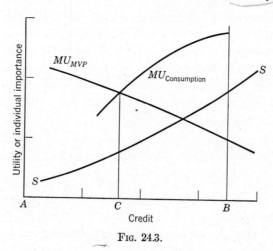

Fig. 24.3.

available to the business. As can be readily observed, this line indicates that the amount of credit available to a farm business depends upon the amount of interest that it is willing to pay. For instance, a farm business may be able to obtain \$10,000 at 4 percent by giving a first mortgage on its land. It might be able to obtain an additional \$5,000 at 5 percent interest by placing a second mortgage on its land. By borrowing against its working capital, a farm business might be able to borrow another \$4,000 or \$5,000 at 6 per cent. Beyond this, additional credit could be brought into the business, mainly, by moving into various retail trade channels. A car or major item of equipment might be financed on a monthly payment schedule with the rate of interest about 12 percent. Still less advantageous forms of credit, mainly for consumption purposes, are likely to be obtainable at rates of interest in the neighborhood of 30 percent per year. The economic principles and budgeting procedures presented have, by and large, disregarded the changes and imperfect knowledge of farm managers and have tended to assume that a farmer would use an additional dollar's worth of credit as long as what he was able to get back from it, either in the way of income or consumption pleasures, more than covered the cost of that dollar's worth of credit. This situation is presented diagrammatically in Figure 24.3. The line MU_{MVP} represents the satisfactions obtainable from the income obtainable from additional amounts of borrowed resources. The line $MU_{Consumption}$ represents the utility or satisfaction obtainable from borrowing additional amounts for consumption purposes. The credit used for income-producing purposes is measured from left to right, starting with A. Conversely, the amount of credit used for consumption purposes is measured from right to left, starting with B. Assuming perfect knowledge, Figure 24.3 indicates that a man would borrow the amount of money AB and use the amount AC for income-producing purposes and the amount CD for consumption purposes. The distance AC as contrasted to CB has no empirical meaning in Figure 24.3 which was drawn to illustrate a principle.

Just as Figure 24.1 was unrealistic with respect to the use of owned resources, this figure is unrealistic with respect to the use of borrowed resources. Farmers do not borrow all the money that they can borrow for two reasons: (1) they wish to maintain reserves of borrowable funds as a source of insurance against various risks which they run and (2) they wish to maintain reserves of borrowable funds for the purpose of taking advantage of favorable opportunities or to avoid undesirable consequences which may be revealed to them by their study of the situation in which this business is operating.

Thus, Figure 24.3 has been modified in Figure 24.4 in two ways. First, the MU_{MVP} curve has been discounted sufficiently to make the farmer willing to take the risks involved in investing borrowed money. Secondly, an additional curve labeled $MU_{Flexibility}$ has been introduced; this curve indicates the utility which the farmer derives from having borrowable reserves available to take advantage of his developing

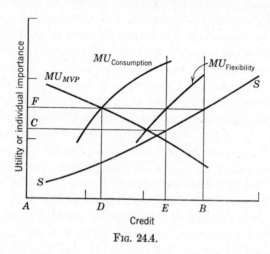

FIG. 24.4.

store of information concerning the future events which his business and family are likely to face.

Figure 24.4 indicates that it would be possible for the family to borrow the amount AB. Of this amount, the quantity AD would be used for income-producing purposes and the quantity DE could be used for consumption purposes. The quantity BE would be maintained as a borrowable reserve, which would serve as a source of both security and flexibility. Only the amount AE would be borrowed at a rate of interest having a disutility EC but returning a utility DF.

As was the case when internal cash or asset rationing was considered, all the lines of relationship in Figure 24.4 represent personal subjective values. As the intersections of these lines of relationship determine the amounts of money which a farmer borrows for income-producing purposes, the amount which he borrows for consumption items, and the amount which he holds in reserve for purposes of acquiring security and flexibility, it is apparent that here again farm management involves far more than production techniques, methods, and prices. In order to do a good job of using credit, then, a farmer needs to know how much income is personally worth to him, how much the security derived from discounting prospective returns is personally worth to him, how much the various consumption items, such as refrigerators, automobiles, clothing, etc., which he might buy with credit, are worth to him, and how much the ability to adjust to change is worth to him. It follows then that farm managers need to know themselves and their families and to adjust the values which they place upon these various items, such as income, security, and consumption. The process of adjusting the values which one places upon these items is really the process of self-discipline. Many of the old expressions, having to do with virtues, pertain to this aspect of management. For example, "a penny saved is a penny earned," "look before you leap" (security).

What we are really saying is that in borrowing money, or for that matter, in renting assets, far more than dollar incomes and costs are involved. The income to be derived from the use of credit must be worth more to the farmer than the interest paid on the amount borrowed. It must be enough more to offset the risks run in borrowing money. The income earned with borrowed money must be worth, in a personal sense, at least as much as the maintenance of unutilized credit is worth, as a reserve to take advantage of favorable opportunities and to adjust to unfavorable situations.

In the case of internal cash rationing, the utility of flexibility had to be sufficiently large to cover the foregone earning power of an "idle" dollar as well as the profit which would have been made on that dollar. In the case of internal credit rationing, the utility of flexibility derived from an unused dollar's worth of credit only has to be sufficiently large to cover the utility of the profit which would have been earned. This difference explains why farm managers acquire most of their flexibility from unused reserves of credit rather than unused reserves of cash.

External Credit Rationing. The term, external credit rationing, refers to the self-imposed restrictions which a credit or lending agency places on the amount of credit which it will extend to its customers. These restrictions, in turn, restrict the amount of money which the customers can, as a totality, borrow. External credit and asset rationing, thus, is important in a community sense—it has to do with the amount of money which the banks and other lending agencies of a community are willing to pour into the community at a given rate of interest.

Figure 24.5 has to do with the credit agency's business; it does not deal directly with the business of any one of the credit agency's customers. In this figure, the amounts of loanable funds which the agency is able to obtain at various rates of interest is represented by the line *SS*. The amounts of money which the agency could lend at varying rates of interest is represented by the line *DD*. If the agency knew that every loan made would be repaid, it would find it profitable to loan the money represented by *OA*. This, however, we know to be unrealistic.

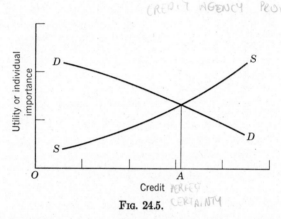

CREDIT AGENCY PROFILE

Credit *PERFECT CERTAINTY*

Fig. 24.5.

Creditors often fail to collect both the interest and the principal on loans which are extended. Thus, most credit agencies discount the amount of interest that they charge. If the contract rate of interest is, say, 6 percent, they say that actually they are really netting, say, 4½ percent, the difference of 1½ percent being necessary to offset the bad loans which are occasionally made.

This realistic situation is represented by the dotted line labeled *DD* in Figure 24.6, this line being the utility of the discounted rate of interest. In addition to the discounting of interest rates as a safety factor, the lending agency finds it advantageous to maintain reserves of loanable funds for purposes of taking advantage of favorable opportunities and of adjusting to unfavorable situations. Even a credit agency, therefore, derives a value from unextended funds. The line $MU_{\text{Flexibility}}$ represents the value of such funds to the credit agency. We now find that the total amount of money which the agency could acquire at a given rate of interest *OR* is *OD*. Of this amount, the amount *OA* is actually loaned to its customers. The amount which is not loaned to its customers is *AD*.

In addition to using assets, farmers desire to maintain control over their assets. The insurance process of discounting was discussed in the preceding section. The next section will discuss insurance more formally as a means of protecting a farm business or family from a major loss of assets.

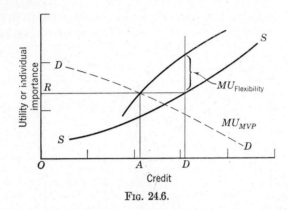

Fig. 24.6.

Desires and Insurance [1]

Most people owning assets and, hence, having earning power try to insure or protect their continued ownership of these assets or possession of this earning power. Barns are insured against fire, crops against hail, life (earning power for a family) against death, etc.

Two kinds of insurance exist. In addition to the *formal* contractural examples listed above, people, including farmers, insure or protect themselves by *informal* arrangements. Money is often held aside for a "rainy day"—extra feed may be held as a reserve against crop failure. People often engage in "discounting"—the process of refusing to act in risk situations until prospective returns exceed those necessary in non-risk situations by a margin large enough "to protect one" against the "bad years."

Both types of insurance are basically the same. Both have costs, i.e., premium payments, in the case of formal insurance and loss of income in the case of informal insurance. Further, the dollar costs often exceed, on the average, the dollar gains, i.e., *premium payments* to an insurance company must exceed payments to those insured by an amount large enough to pay the administrative costs and profits

[1] M. Friedman and L. J. Savage, "The Utility Analysis of Choices Involving Risks," *Journal of Political Economy*, LVI, 1948, pp. 279–304.

of the company, and *the costs of holding reserves and discounting* reduce the total earning power of the assets owned by the individual concerned. This excess of dollar costs over dollar returns makes it evident that people do not insure to make money; they insure to get security or safety.

Let us examine the kind of security a person obtains when he insures. In the first place, such a person exchanges a risk situation for a certainty situation. Before insuring, the person is ordinarily running a chance (P) of incurring a loss as well as a chance $(1 - P)$ of

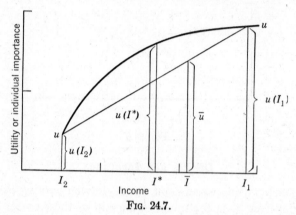

FIG. 24.7.

not incurring a loss, or conversely, of retaining his present income earning power (I_1). After insuring, the person is certain that he will possess some earning power I^*, which is ordinarily less than I_1. *That new lower* income earning power must be "worth more" to the individual taking out the insurance than the *average of the two possible developments in the uninsured situation.* This implies that losses become increasingly important as they increase in size. If we measure the importance (utility) of a given income-earning position on the vertical axis and the income-earning situation on the horizontal axis, we arrive at Figure 24.7,

where I_1 = uninsured income position if no loss occurs.
    I_2 = uninsured income position if a loss occurs.
    $\bar{I}$ = average of I_1 and I_2 weighted according to probability of loss.
    I^* = income position if insured.

In order to insure, the utility or importance of I^* must be greater than the average utility or importance of I_1 and I_2. The line uu indicates the utility derivable from each income. The distance $u(I_1)$ represents the utility of the uninsured income-producing situation, without a loss. The distance $u(I_2)$ represents the utility of the uninsured income-producing situation, with a loss. If the chance of the loss occurring is P and of it not occurring is $(1 - P)$, then the average utility of the uninsured situation, $\bar{u}$, is given by the equation: $P[u(I_2)] + (1 - P)[u(I_1)] = \bar{u}$. This utility is not measured from the utility line, as it is the average of two other utilities $u(I_1)$ and $u(I_2)$ weighted by the probabilities of their occurrences. The average dollar income $\bar{I}$ is $PI_2 + (1 - P)I_2$. If the importance or utility of an insured situation producing a non-risk income I^* is greater than the importance or utility of $\bar{I}$, which is $\bar{u}$, a person takes out the insurance. In Figure 24.7 $u(I^*)$ is greater than $\bar{u}$; hence, insurance would be taken out.

It is important to note that $u(I^*)$ cannot be greater than $\bar{u}$ if utility fails to fall at an increasing rate to the left of I_1. This is the same as saying that the losses must increase in importance at an increasing rate as they increase in size if insurance is to be possible. In more technical economic terms, it is the same as saying that increasing marginal disutility of losses is a prerequisite for insuring.

Apparently, most people who are adjusted to possession of a given amount of income-producing power fear the loss of that power. Small losses of income appear to be much less important *proportionally*. The question of insurance becomes particularly important when the loss involved is sufficiently large to bring about a change in social status—people are willing to make sacrifices in average income in order to insure against such events. For example, homes are insured against fire, crops against storms, incomes against law suits arising from automobile accidents, etc.

One of the most common forms of informal insurance used is the refusal to make investments involving rather minor chances of large losses and rather large chances of moderate profits. Farm people commonly refuse to borrow for investments which would be profitable "on the average" because one year of poor prices might cause them to "go broke." These people insure by staying in their present position in preference to moving to an uninsured position which would be more profitable "on the average." This preference is a major obstacle to expansion of investments in forage and livestock production in many of the southern states. Because the obstacle is a matter of preference, dollar data are not particularly effective tools for extension men to use in dealing with such problems.

The above discussion has proceeded from a consideration of the "good" of insuring against losses to a consideration of how the quest for security can prevent people from taking advantage of opportunities. Security seeking also has its "bad" aspects; carried to its extreme, it can prevent the taking of action on the basis of calculated risks and acceptance of responsibility therefor. These two or three functions it will be recalled are among the five essential functions of management. We are now ready to consider the opposite of insuring—chance taking, an absolutely essential subject in the study of management.

Human Desires—Chance Taking and Getting Control over Assets

Unavoidably managers take chances: they operate in a changing economy; they are never perfectly informed; and, above all, their function is that of adjusting to change and improvements in knowledge.

Two kinds of chance taking exist—formal chance taking, known as gambling, and the informal chance taking of everyday business operations. The stigmas attached to formal gambling do not obviate the facts (1) that the economic principles are basically the same in both cases and (2) that the need for management arises primarily from the need for chance taking.

Both types of chance taking are basically the same—a person exchanges a non-chance situation for a chance situation involving probabilities of both a gain and a loss. The gains generally involve control over additional assets; hence, chance taking is one means of getting control over assets. Further, as in the case of insurance, the average income of the loss and the gain situation is often less than what the income would be if the chance were not taken.

Let us examine the nature of chance taking (see Figure 24.8). Before taking a chance a person has control of assets and a situation yielding a given income I^*. After taking a chance he is running a chance, P, of securing a greater income, I_2, and a probability, $(1 - P)$, of receiving a lesser income, I_1. The average chance-taking income $\bar{I}$ is, of course, equal to $PI_2 + (1 - P)I_1$. The utility or importance of this income is the average (weighted by P and $1 - P$) of the utilities of I_1 and I_2; hence, $\bar{u} = P[u(I_2)] + (1 - P)[u(I_1)]$. If this average utility, $\bar{u}$, is greater than the utility, $u(I^*)$, of the income before the chance is taken, then the chance is taken. If the utility of the gain is sufficiently large, the $\bar{u}$ can be greater than $u(I^*)$. This implies that the utility or value of gains in income-producing ability or income must increase at an increasing rate—in technical economic terms this is the same as saying that income and income-producing capacity have increasing marginal utility for people who take chances at unfavorable odds.

A diagram similar to the one on insurance can be constructed.

where I_1 = chance-taking income with loss.
   I_2 = chance-taking income with gain.
   $\bar{I}$ = average of I_1 and I_2 weighted according to chances of gain or loss.
   I^* = income without chance taking.

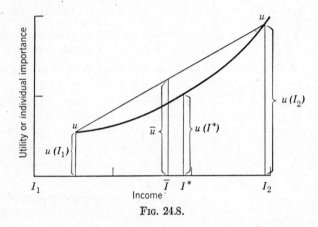

FIG. 24.8.

In the situation diagrammed, chance taking can be logically engaged in, as the importance of the gain is sufficiently large to make the chance situation preferable to the non-chance situation. In farming, people often attach great importance to landownership due to the social and economic amenities going along with it. Thus, farm families often enter chance-taking situations at unfavorable odds in order to acquire the chance of becoming landowners. Here again, dollar data—average dollar income under chance taking versus dollar income without chance taking—are not relevant. The relevant things are the desires and preferences of people which make the possible gain so important. And, when the gains are desired, as they often are, in order to get out of a subsistence level of living not permitting support of churches, education, recreation, adequate medical care, etc., who would argue with the preferences? If a man or family wants to risk moderate losses in order to get important gains, who would say that he (they) should not?

Insurance, Chance Taking, and Subjective Values

The discussion of insurance gradually converted into a discussion of chance taking, and the discussion of chance taking converted into a discussion of questions of right and wrong. Both discussions involved preferences—personal subjective considerations—which could not be adequately handled in dollar terms.

Questions of what the preferences of people should be (in contrast to questions of what the preferences are) are questions for the humanities—religion, philosophy, ethics, etc. This basic consideration needs to be realized by all public farm-management workers, as the tendency to advise the pursuit of security or, conversely, chance taking in connection with the adviser's "pet projects" is widespread. The shaping of preferences, desires and personal schemes of values is part of the function of leadership and is often referred to as "motivating people to get things done." Nothing is wrong with this if the "leader" is qualified, i.e., if he understands what he is doing and why and has "adequate standards" to serve as a basis for his advice. To the authors, the apparent widespread aversion for courses in the humanities in our land-grant colleges raises a question whether rank and file public farm-management men are, first, interested and, second, trained sufficiently to advise farmers what their wants and preferences should be.

Both insurance (security seeking) and chance taking (gambling) can become pathological or dangerous. Members of a farm family (or a man) can become so obsessed with security seeking that they (or he) (1) devote(s) their (his) income to formal and informal insurance premiums at the expense of vital components of their standard of living and, in some cases, their (his) integrity and (2) devote(s) their (his) time and energies to provision of security to the exclusion of productive activity. People falling in this category are known to all and condemned as "afraid to do anything," "Milquetoasts," etc. The person who uses insurance (both formal and informal) properly, in a non-pathological way, is considered, on the other hand, to be foresighted, sound, judicious, provident, etc.

Similar contrasts exist among risk takers. A family or man can become so obsessed with the value of possible gains as to take odds so unfavorable and to spend so much time and effort in the search for "long chances" and "sure things" that its or his income and productivity fall unduly low. The phrase "unduly low" refers to incomes so low that vital components of living and integrity standards are necessarily sacrificed. On the other hand, however, are the judicious chance takers, the backbone of the free-enterprise system, who are referred to as men of action, possessing good judgment, etc.

Insurance, Chance Taking, and the Importance of Income and Income-Producing Power. The analyses of insurance and chance taking combined with two facts indicate a considerable amount of information concerning the desire to obtain income and accumulate income-earning power. The two facts are:

1. Rational, sound judicious people simultaneously insure and take chances.
2. Formal gambling schemes, such as lotteries, have more than one prize instead of one big prize.

If people both insure and take chances (1) the loss of utility accompanying decreases in incomes below their present income must increase at an increasing rate and (2) their gain in utility for incomes higher than their present income must increase at an increasing rate for certain increases at least. The use of multiple prizes in formal gambles indicates that utility does not continue to increase indefinitely at an increasing rate. It is quite likely that utility increases at an increasing rate for that increase in income which would permit a man or family to make some much-longed-for, significant step forward in standards of living.

This reasoning would indicate that the following utility function may be rather typical among people.

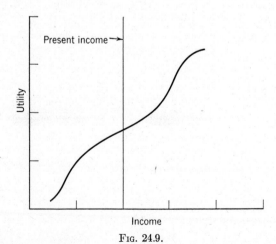

FIG. 24.9.

Such a relationship between utility and income permits a person to insure and take chances simultaneously. It would also cause him to place an upper limit on the size of gain for which he would take chances. Incidentally, the nearly straight section of the utility line near his present income would permit him to gamble for small stakes at fair odds as would be done among friends but not for small stakes at odds in favor at a gambling house; this again appears very realistic. It is also consistent with the farmer's willingness to take long chances for big gains and to insure against major losses but to refuse to take small chances or engage in petty insurance schemes except for the "joy of risk taking" and the "joy of surprise."

CHAPTER 25

Farm and Home Planning

The discussion in the last three chapters makes it apparent that a realistic illustration of the managerial process needs to (1) cover a series of time periods, (2) be concerned with the consumption pattern and value structures of the farm family, and (3) allow for change and imperfect knowledge. This chapter, therefore, presents such an illustration. Individual professors can work out similar illustrative problems applying to farms in their particular geographic localities. (See Problem Exercise 20 at end of chapter.)

The Situation January 1, 1951

This problem deals with the farm *business* and *home* of a particular farm family—the family of Mr. I. Malearner.

Mr. Malearner is assumed to be in possession of a 160-acre farm, 150 acres of which are rather loosely classed as cropland by agencies operating in the area. The area, as a whole, is somewhat pressed for cropland. Figure 25.1 is a plat of the farm. This figure and its legend give the student a rough concept of Mr. Malearner's land assets.

Under moderately good weather, yields per acre last year were as follows: field 1, 55 bushels of oats; field 2, 60 bushels of corn; field 5, 45 bushels of corn; field 3, about 70 bushels of corn (partially hogged down); field 4 produced 10 tons of alfalfa-brome hay and supported 8 brood sows, 40 pigs, and 3 cows. These yields represent about what Mr. Malearner feels his land should produce under present agronomic and animal-husbandry practices.

A year ago, a neighboring farmer offered $250 per acre for the farm. The present real estate debt is $25,000, the farm having been acquired three years ago. Malearner owns a two-bottom, row-crop tractor purchased in 1948, a 1946 Ford automobile, an 8-foot tandem disk, a two-bottom plow, a harrow, a corn planter, a corn picker, a two-row tractor cultivator, spreader, endgate seeder, side-delivery hay rake, hay loader, corn elevator, two wagons with two beds, one rack, and the necessary

411

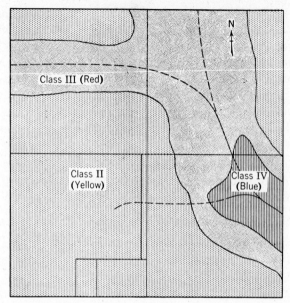

Fɪɢ. 25.1. The I. Malearner farm showing field and land-use capability
boundaries.

supplementary tools and minor equipment items. He has been trading
corn picking for oats combining with his neighbor. All of his equipment, though not new, is still less than four years old and has an estimated present value of $4,500. He owes $1,500 to various individuals
and companies on purchases of this equipment. His livestock consists
of 8 gilts bred to farrow in April and 3 cows now valued at $1,000. He
has 4,000 bushels of corn on hand worth $1.25 a bushel. Thus, he
now owns $55,500 worth of assets on which he owes $26,500.

Buildings on the farm consist of a six-room frame house, an old horse
barn, chicken house, machine shed, corn crib and granary capable of
holding 5,000 bushels of corn and 2,500 bushels of small grain. The
present well is taxed to capacity with existing livestock.

The Malearner's home is equipped with adequate but rather old
furniture, refrigerator, gas stove, electric washer, and central heating
but no plumbing other than a pitcher pump. While comfortable, the
home still lacks many conveniences and arrangements which would
contribute to the efficiency of Mrs. Malearner and the well-being of
the entire family.

Mr. Malearner is 50 years of age and in strong, robust health; Mrs. Malearner, 48, is in rather poor health. They have three children, the oldest of whom is a veteran of 26, living at home while working in a factory 10 miles away and helping at home at odd times. An unmarried daughter, 22, is teaching and living away from home. The youngest, a boy, is just finishing high school.

Mr. Malearner, who acquired ownership of the farm in 1948, now feels that he is in position to embark on a farm-development program. What does he need to learn? What should he do? How should he do it? These are the types of questions which Mr. Malearner needs to have answered. And, as the first step in answering them, an *inventory of the information* in possession of the Malearner family is needed.

The State of Knowledge in Possession of the Malearners

Mr. Malearner is aware that the cropping system on his farm could be revised to (1) increase the amount of livestock his farm would support, (2) increase the number of man-hours which the farm would profitably employ, and (3) consequently increase the income which the farm would produce. He is aware that such procedures would require further learning on his part about pasture and livestock-production techniques. He knows that additional investments would be required and that possible price changes make such investments dangerous even to the extent of possibly depriving him and his family of landownership and all the amenities attached thereto. Mr. Malearner, of course, is aware of the wants and desires of the members of his family. Mrs. Malearner's present need for medical care and better home equipment has to be ascertained and evaluated against the need for investments to produce future income. The goals and aims of the sons and daughter need to be ascertained (or perhaps even created) and the value of investments in the farm matched against attainment of such goals.

In short, Mr. Malearner needs to acquire, integrate, and use information concerning production techniques, prospective changes in techniques, prices, family goals, and the general environment in which he lives.

No attempt will be made in this chapter to work "things" out for Mr. Malearner and his family; instead, one way in which the affairs of the farm could be organized and planned and in which these affairs could develop will be described.

Development and Integration of Individual and Family Values into Goals

Probably the first task of the Malearners is to develop and integrate their value structures, beliefs, and schemes of importances into a set of goals. In the United States where society places high values on free expression of individual wants and preferences, it does not always seem appropriate for authors, program administrators, or others to impose schemes of values on others; it does appear "proper," however, to point out the necessity of developing and integrating one's (and his family's) concepts of the relative importance of various objectives into goals. In this connection time-tested religious principles and ethical concepts are invaluable. In the Malearner case the importance of extra income, soil conservation, individual accomplishment, ethical goals, home employment for sons, church, home improvement, educational investments, family health, financial risks, security, accuracy, a new car, different types of livestock production, and a wide variety of other objectives need to be integrated and ranked in importance as part of the overall goals of Mr. Malearner and his family. The degree in which various objectives can be obtained, of course, depends upon the efficiency with which the production end of the business can be organized.

Thus, the next question for consideration is what and how much needs to be learned in order to increase the efficiency of farm production.

Production Plans

Consultation on Mr. Malearner's part with other farmers, agricultural extension agents, and soil conservation men would probably indicate changes in his cropping system which would increase his crop production and protect his soil. These changes would probably involve some refencing of the farm in accordance with the land-capability classes indicated in Figure 25.1. Such a change would also probably entail setting up a separate grain-producing rotation for the Class II land and a hay-pasture-limited-grain rotation for the Class III and IV lands. The lack of legumes in the last year's cropping system for fields 1, 2, 4, and 5 indicates that the introduction of legumes and, perhaps, commercial nitrogen fertilizers would be profitable; probably a need for liming and the application of phosphorus and/or potassium would be indicated by soil tests. Some water-control structures might appear desirable in the northeast corner of the present field 5. Reference to published material of the type presented in Chapters 7 and 13 of this book would probably increase the efficiency with which Mr. Malearner acquires and analyzes the necessary agronomic information. Even though little marginal or incremental data are available on fertilizer application, the thought structures presented in Chapters 8 and 9 would prove valuable to Mr. Malearner in using and in organizing fragmentary, non-incremental data. The three chapters of this book on input and enterprise combinations (Chapters 9 to 11) would probably be useful in steering Mr. Malearner toward enterprise combinations which would more fully utilize inputs over the year, furnish by-products, such as humus, nitrogen, manure, and straw, and protect the soil.

The next type of production information needed by Mr. Malearner would be information on livestock enterprises. As the farm was operated last year, it produced 8 litters of pigs, a few chickens, and the milk and calves from 3 cows. The appropriate livestock system is related to the proportions in which different forages and grains are produced. Chapters 14 and 15 provide useful guides for collecting, assembling, and analyzing information useful in integrating the crop and livestock enterprises of the farm. Similarly, Chapter 19 on labor and equipment utilization provides useful guides. Chapter 11 on enterprise combinations also is helpful in deciding on the number and combination of enterprises. Chapter 23 contains principles for handling the risks involved in operating the various crop and livestock enterprises. Chapter 24 also contains very general managerial principles useful at all stages of the problem, as they deal fundamentally with the problems of learning, acting, and deciding.

Integration of Production Knowledge

Once the crop and livestock potentialities of the farm are determined in general terms, i.e., once the production data are available, Mr. Malearner is likely to want to employ various analytical thought processes or procedures in order to see the overall meaning of his production information.

Budgeting procedures (summarized in Chapter 21) are helpful in this integration procedure. The principles of marginal analysis are of particular significance in studying the influence of price changes on profitable combinations of inputs, level of output, and combinations of enterprises. When specific input-output data are available, as is the case for pork and milk production, such data are useful as direct indicators of profitable levels of output. When specific input-output data are unavailable, the marginality concepts presented in Chapters 8, 9, 10, and 11 serve as frames of reference for use in organizing and analyzing such data as are available. The cost of production concepts presented in Chapter 12 have similar uses—i.e., (1) actual cost data in meaningful economic form are directly usable and (2) the economic concepts of costs are useful in organizing the use of more fragmentary data.

The above discussion makes it clear that a major portion of this book is aimed at increasing the efficiency with which the production data can be observed and analyzed as a basis for decision and action. Another portion of the book is aimed at increasing the efficiency with which goals are set and reconsidered, action taken, and responsibility borne.

After Mr. Malearner acquires and analyzes production information to the extent that he feels that results of further effort along such lines would not be worth the cost, he would probably try to match his income potentialities against the overall goals previously considered.

Reconciliation of Goals with Income-Producing and Financing Capacity

Eventually, in the planning processes, a point is reached at which goals and costs must be reconciled. If a farm is capable of producing a high income and desires are modest, reconciliation is easy. If, however, a farm is not capable of producing a high income and desires are high, reconciliation is difficult. Ordinarily, the need for developmental and expansion programs arises from low income which, in turn, results in a high desire for investment in conflict with heavy consumption demands for the low income. Contrariwise, the need for developmental and expansion programs is not felt so acutely on high-income farms and it is easy to invest at a slight expense in terms of reduced consumption of relatively unessential items.

Assume, for purposes of illustration, that the Malearners have set the following goals for their farm:

1. Support of two families; the oldest son wants to marry and go into business with his parents.
2. A college education for the younger son.
3. Complete medical and surgical treatment for Mrs. Malearner.
4. Installation of a plumbing system and $600 worth of new equipment for the main home.

5. Eventual modernization of an additional old home or construction of a new home for the oldest son in connection with the purchase of additional land.

6. Landscaping of the present homestead.

7. Support of community organizations (church and community recreation center) with both time and money.

8. Eventually a higher general standard of living as a result of investments to increase the productivity of the farm.

9. Maintenance of economic security through the use of formal and informal insurance schemes.

10. Other miscellaneous smaller goals, including farming methods and conservation methods which will serve as a basis for family pride and dignity.

The Job of Reconciling Goals (Ends) with Income-Producing and Financing Capacity (Means) Is the Core of Economics (Management). Even superficial examination of the Malearner farm plat indicates that the farm, in its present condition, is not capable of producing the level of income required to meet the goals outlined above in the period of time required.

The labor supply is large (two grown men and a summertime college student) relative to the land and livestock available. Could land, labor, and livestock be brought into better balance with the assets at the disposal of the Malearners? Could an additional 160 acres be rented or purchased, and, at the same time, additional investments in livestock be made without unduly curtailing short-run goals? Mr. Malearner owes $1,500 on working capital and $25,000 on real estate having a combined value of $55,500. He now has 4,000 bushels of corn on hand.

If an attempt were made to buy land, either a beef or a dairy herd, and additional machinery and construct the necessary buildings, as much as 60,000 additional dollars would probably be required. This would raise the total assets to about $115,000 to $120,000 on less than a one-quarter equity; if such financing could be carried out, it would be done at heavy sacrifice of other goals, including, especially, sacrifice of security against the danger of price declines wiping out the entire equity of the family. Thus, it appears that the Malearners would probably seek other methods of expanding land and livestock, though such a decision could only be made after possible financing arrangements had been thoroughly investigated. Renting of land appears to have some advantages—the capital outlay is low and the equity position remains unaffected leaving the credit position of the Malearners available for financing operating capital.

Similarly, several alternatives are open in financing and developing the livestock enterprises. Hogs, cow-calf beef production, beef fattening, and dairying are suitable enterprises for adoption or expansion and the indicated cropping system would support both roughage and grain consuming livestock. Immediate establishment of a 30-cow dairy herd to produce Class I milk would entail a $15,000 to $20,000 investment in herd and buildings. Similarly, immediate establishment of a 40-cow, cow-calf plan would involve an investment of over $10,000. Inauguration of a beef fattening program would also involve an investment of over $10,000, though for a shorter period of time. All three of these enterprises would be new for the Malearners and, hence, subject to hazards of inexperience.

The hog enterprise, on the other hand, could be expanded relatively rapidly on a $4,000 investment in gilts and individual hog houses and would benefit from the past experience of the Malearners. Reasoning indicates certain advantages for the Malearners in an immediate, large expansion in hog production with some investments in either a small dairy or beef foundation herd to (1) use the current production of forage, and (2) serve as foundation stock for herds to be accumulated as forage-production capacity is expanded, housing constructed and experience gained. Such a procedure would leave some cash and credit available for machinery purchases, medical care, home improvements, etc.

Thus, in view of the goals and assets (income-earning capacities) of the Malearners, it appears that

1. The following production program might be feasible: acquisition of land through renting; immediate investment in more machinery; expansion of pork production; redesign of the cropping system; inauguration of a foundation herd to become the basis of a forage-consuming livestock herd; perhaps a trial run at beef fattening on a small lot of steers.

2. The following consumption and expenditure pattern might be feasible: immediate medical attention for Mrs. Malearner; marriage and establishment of a new household for the older boy; college (with limited help) for the younger boy; home improvements for Mrs. Malearner with special attention to efficiency (perhaps the water system required for both the home and expanding livestock enterprises could be worked out simultaneously).

The above program has in it several safety features and features which permit acquisition of knowledge. Equity has been held higher than it would be in alternative, more risky, and, quite likely, somewhat more profitable alternatives. These security-seeking techniques would need to be matched against the Malearners' need for security and if found wanting supplemented by additional forms of protection against risk. Some such forms of protection might be (1) diversification of the grain-producing enterprises, (2) diversification of hay and pasture crops, (3) maintenance of grain and hay reserves, (4) life, fire, crop, theft, etc., insurance, and a wide variety of other procedures. (See Chapter 24 for principles involved in learning, handling risk, and deciding on the chances to take.) The student should recognize that an expansion such as contemplated here involves, at times, long chances more or less of a gambling nature. When a present relatively certain income is being exchanged for the joint possibility of failure or considerable additional income, the "long-chance principle" is applicable.

At this stage in the planning procedure, static budgeting and static economic principles would be needed again. Overall budgets are needed to find out how much income various feasible alternatives might produce (see Chapter 21). Detailed budgeting and economic principles are needed in choosing between alternative systems of beef production (Chapter 18 and the principles of Chapters 8, 9, 10, and and 11). In addition, written or unwritten household, general expenditure, and debt-repayment budgets would need to be made up as a basis for reconciling the investment consumption expenditures and debt repayments.

In the operation or action period, favorable and unfavorable events occur. Value structures and consumption patterns change. Productive resources change as a result of both plans and accidents, about half of the changes due to accident being decreases. Thus, all the steps and procedures described above need to be carried out continuously.

Once the final plan is set up and budgeted, either in written form for the satisfaction of the Malearners and their creditors or in unwritten form for similar purposes, the period of action (i.e., of putting the plan in effect) would get underway. The opening of the action does not bring about cessation of learning and decision making; instead, these functions continue and have added to them acceptance of economic responsibility. The result of such operations might indicate that the expansion plans would have to proceed more slowly or that they could be speeded up. Slowing down might involve borrowing less, renting of smaller acreage, and further off-farm work for the older son, whereas speeding up could involve more borrowing, land purchase, a larger foundation herd, and accelerated soil improvement.

PROBLEM EXERCISE 20

The following procedure is suggested as the final exercise in a course in farm management. The teaching experience of the authors indicates that steps 2 and 3, below, introduce sufficient variation in student work to make it unnecessary to have separate problems for each student. Such individuality is further encouraged by the "contest" aspect of the work resulting from non-revelation of data to be presented by the professor in steps 4 and 5 for each of the 3 years which the problem covers.

Step 1. The professor should describe a local (probably hypothetical) farm-family situation, using the Malearner description as a general pattern. The description should include actual physical and business inventories for the farm. The home and family descriptions may well be hypothetical.

Step 2. (a) Each student should work out a set of integrated goals or objectives for this family situation. (b) Each student should work out a land-use pattern, cropping systems, and livestock enterprises in general terms. (c) Anticipated prices for the first year of operations should be worked out individually by the students on the basis of outlook information, local data, and general economic and political information.

Step 3. (a) Preliminary production budgets leading to income estimates should be constructed and matched against expenditure budgets based, in turn, on the integrated goals worked out as step 2. (b) Financing possibilities for both consumption goals and production investments should be worked out on the basis of the current asset position of the family, prospective incomes, and its credit resources. (c) Goals and possible incomes should be weighed against each other as a basis for reconciling consumption-investment conflicts within the financing and income limits of the farm family. (d) Final plans for the first year's operations should be made and production and expenditure budgets should be developed, the students being asked to demonstrate how their plans provide: (1) for continually learning and adjusting to change; (2) protection against price, life, production and other hazards; (3) specifically, for the money they plan to use in carrying out the plans.

Step. 4. (a) The professor should introduce reasonable changes (heretofore unknown to the students) occurring hypothetically in the first one-half year in which the plan is in operation. These changes should be both favorable and unfavorable, as well as realistic; at least one change should occur in each of the following: prices, production methods, yields, personalities, and institutional arrangements. In particular, one price change requiring an adjustment of livestock rations and level of feeding and, also, opportunities to purchase additional livestock, machinery, land, and/or buildings should be offered. Situations requiring use of personal strategy should also be created. (b) The students should then be asked to modify their production plans and goals on the basis of the changes presented in step 4(a).

Step 5. (*a*) The professor should present, as of the end of the year, final "actual" yields, prices, and both favorable and unfavorable events (the actual yields should vary reasonably from expectations and should not be known in advance by the students). (*b*) The students should then figure "actual" income for the year, and allocate that income among debt retirement, production expenditures, consumption expenditures, and reserves.

Lastly, steps 2 through 5 should be repeated for an additional 2 years in order to train the students in further operation (the process of making adjustments to changing events and opportunities).

CHAPTER 26

Some Miscellaneous Conceptual Problems Involving Management

The discussion in the preceding chapters leaves a considerable number of loose ends undiscussed; hence, the purpose of this chapter is to bring these problems together and "conclude" the discussion of management in about as orderly a form as permitted at the present stage in the development of managerial principles.

Returns to Management

The computation of returns to management for a particular farm and period of time has been one of the most difficult problems in farm accounting. In fact, it has been so difficult that it has often been dismissed in an arbitrary and rather meaningless manner by assigning to management the difference between gross income and direct plus indirect expenditures on physical inputs and services. Conceptually, the problem has been just as difficult as it has been at the accounting level. Some of the problems which have plagued farm-management workers when thinking about returns to management include: (1) the problem of explaining just how management produces anything of value and, hence, of how management earns an income, (2) what should be done with profits of a windfall nature, i.e., gains which arise "accidentally" as a result of forces operating outside the farm business, and (3) the similar problem of what to do with losses of a windfall nature, i.e., losses which arise "accidentally" as a result of forces operating outside the business. The problem of handling charges for fixed assets was discussed in Chapter 12 on cost of production; that chapter did not include a discussion of the problem of handling charges for management.

The Earnings of Management. This book has placed emphasis on five managerial tasks or functions and the discussion of management has concentrated on performance of these functions. In discussing the value of performing such functions, the authors have pointed out repeatedly that these values are often personal and subjective in nature. Hence, not all the services performed and products produced by management are expressed in dollars and cents, and few of the services produced by management are sold in the market place. It follows that dollars and cents accounting systems and "going charges" for professional farm-management services are inadequate ways of measuring the *returns* to management. This is not to say that dollar returns to management do not exist; it is to say that dollar returns are only part of the returns to management.

A manager may perform the functions of observing, analyzing, and deciding in order to make more dollar income. If a given manager is better (i.e., more efficient) at learning, observing, and deciding about profit-making matters, it follows that there should be a differential between his income and the income of a manager who is less efficient in these respects and that this differential is a return attributable to management. Such a return will show up in a system of farm accounts and may quite possibly be sorted out of gross income and designated as a return to management. However, no system of farm accounts known to the authors is capable of doing this sorting completely.

On the other hand, a good (efficient) manager may use his superior ability to observe, analyze, and decide in acquiring accuracy and, hence, security for his business. Security dependent upon accuracy in decision making is a real thing; it has value to a person just as consumption of a candy bar has value or architectural design has value to a homeowner, but its value does not show up accurately in dollar and cents accounting systems.

Earlier in the book, a distinction between management and skilled labor was made as follows. It was argued that a person is managing when he goes through the process of acquiring a skill. And it was argued that the receipt of the skill constitutes payment for the managerial effort involved in acquiring it. Once the skill is acquired, however, it was argued that sale of that skill constitutes sale of skilled labor rather than sale of managerial capacity. Thus, the farm man learning to be a good herdsman is managing his own affairs, and the payment for such management of his personal affairs is the skill which he acquired as a herdsman. Later sale of this skill, however, is not regarded as sale of a managerial service. It is regarded as the sale of an ability produced by managerial activity.

Commonly, management is devoted to acquiring "one use" information or skill, and value of the skill or information is the payment to management. In such instances, the process of management is continuous, involving acquisition and use of information or skill having no repetitive value.

This type of discussion about the nature of the returns to management could be continued almost indefinitely with respect to values and costs of performing the various managerial functions. Such discussion, however, would not lead beyond the conclusion that dollar and cents accounting systems can only partially cover the value of performing the different managerial functions and the costs of performing them. The authors know of no way in which to handle this accounting problem. They do know, however, that these non-monetary values and costs are real things which cannot be forgotten by anyone hoping to fully understand the managerial functions and the various types of returns to management.

At this point, reference should again be made to the shortcomings of estimating earnings of management by deducting from gross income actual and arbitrary charges for the other factors of production. The arbitrary deductions for certain fixed factors tend to be too high when based upon replacement values. Conversely, the arbitrary charges tend to be too low when based upon opportunity costs. In either event, the inaccuracies introduced by the arbitrary charges result in inaccuracies in the residual commonly dubbed "earnings of management." When non-arbitrary estimates of the earning power of the fixed factors of production are available, non-arbitrary residuals ascribable to management can be secured. Even this method, however, has the shortcoming of not being directly related to the process whereby management produces anything of value.

Windfall Profits and Losses. According to everyday terminology, a windfall profit or loss is a change in income resulting from factors outside the business, over which the manager had no control and which he was unable to predict or foresee. The five degrees of imperfection in knowledge (listed in Chapter 3) were differentiated from each other on the basis of how *individual managers* feel about the adequacy of the knowledge that *they* possess about certain events and processes. These degrees of knowledge indicate that the outside forces which create or bring about changes in income are almost always more or less imperfectly foreseen and predictable by actual managers and are *allowed for.* In examining managerial actions it was found that managers often feel ready, willing, and able to take the consequence of a considerable amount of error in their own predictions and foresight. Thus, if conceptual definitions of windfall profits and losses are to be developed, variations in income due to "calculated risks" concerning outside influences have to be eliminated from the windfall category. Similarly, when a manager takes a long chance for an important gain and succeeds, such gains should be excluded from windfall profits by definition.

In making choices between alternatives, managers run risks of making errors. Ordinarily, in risk situations, prospective returns have been sufficiently discounted subjectively to offset the consequences of errors which may be made. As an alternative to discounting, various insurance schemes may also be employed.

1. There appears to be some logic in classifying as windfall profits returns so large as to more than cover future *expected* losses from the same operation.

2. There also seems to be some logic in classifying as windfall losses, losses so large as to more than offset future *expected* gains from the same operation.

3. There does not seem to be much logic in classifying as a windfall gain a gain resulting from deliberately taking a long chance. Similarly, there does not seem to be much logic in classifying as a windfall loss a loss resulting when a person deliberately runs a risk in preference to insuring.

It should be pointed out that, in any event, *both windfall profits and windfall losses involve losses.* This is seen when it is realized that windfall profits as well as losses result from errors; if a manager could know before he makes a windfall profit how profitable his actions were to be, he would greatly extend such actions and greatly increase his profits. Therefore, it is apparent that, even when windfall profits are made, large opportunity costs and losses are involved.

The Thought Patterns of People Partially Determine Their Concepts of Management

The concepts of management held by the authors grow out of their system of thinking. In general, following the classification of C. W. Churchman, the authors would probably be classified as experimentalists.[1] The authors generally presuppose [2] that:

[1] C. W. Churchman, *Theory of Experimental Inference*, New York, The Macmillan Co., 1948, p. 53.

[2] The apparent inconsistency between (1) and (3) does not bother the authors who have inherited answers to some questions of fact and some questions of law (theory) from previous generations.

1. The answering of any question of law (theory) presupposes the answering of at least some questions of fact.

2. There exist answers to at least some questions of law (theory).

3. The answering of any question of fact presupposes the answering of at least some questions of law (theory).

4. There exist answers to at least some questions of fact.

Inasmuch as the authors tend to reason within the above four presuppositions, they tend to conceive that managers also reason within the same set of presuppositions. Thus, the authors conceive of managers as simultaneously deductive and inductive thinkers capable of using the deductive processes of budgeting and theoretical analysis as well as the inductive processes of statistical reasoning.

Had the authors been inclined to reject the first of the four presuppositions above, they would have been classified by Churchman as naive empiricists. And, having rejected the first of the above presuppositions, they would not have used theory as a guide in their study of management. And, because the authors would not have used theory in studying management, they would not have conceived that managers would use theory in their (the managers') reasoning processes.

Had the authors tended to reject (1) and (4) or (1) alone, Churchman would have classified them as rationalists. Had the authors been rationalists or theorists to the exclusion of empirical work, this book would have been a book in pure theory, the basic assumptions of which might not have corresponded to reality. And, had the authors been rationalists, they might not have conceived of managers employing inductive empirical thought processes. Instead, they would have conceived of managers as being abstract theoretical reasoners.

It should be obvious to the reader that either of the two concepts of management portrayed in the last two paragraphs above would be unrealistic. Lest the reader think that no one would hold such concepts of management, the authors hasten to point out that certain groups of farm-management workers can be classified as empiricists and that they hold corresponding concepts of the managerial processes. Similarly, among the pure economic theorists, many rationalists hold corresponding concepts of management. If this book has made progress in integrating the so-called old traditional approach to farm management and the so-called new theoretical approach, the integration has come about as the result of the experimentalist approach which causes them to conceive of managers as reasoners simultaneously employing all the tools of deductive and inductive logic.

Study of Dynamic Managerial Principles Reduces the Importance of the Distinction between the Business and Home Aspects of Farming

For many years teachers of ordinary economic principles have differentiated between the production and consumption units of the economy. They have referred to production units as *firms* and to consumption units as *households*. Similarly, workers in our land-grant colleges have differentiated between the production and the consumption aspects of farming. Departments of farm management have carefully worked out principles for organizing and administering the production or business end of the farm, and departments of home economics, as separate administrative units, have worked out similar principles for the home side of farming. This distinction arose in economic theory and principles because theorists tended to assume perfect knowledge, perfect foresight, and the absence of change in production techniques and consumption patterns. The similar distinction which arose in the land-grant system appears to be based (1) on attempts to abstract from the bothersome changes and imperfections in knowledge which have plagued the analyses of both farm management and home economic workers and (2), more particularly, on the tendency to regard farm management as a synthesis of the physical (agricultural) sciences rather than as a field of science in and of its own right.

The last four chapters of this book have concentrated upon the managerial principles useful in handling imperfect knowledge, imperfect foresight, and various types of changes. As these principles have been discussed it has become apparent that a great number of personal values, wants, and desires are encountered on the production side of farming. In fact, it becomes apparent that a major part of management consists of appraising the subjective costs and values of performing the various managerial functions. Further reflection indicates that, on the other hand, a great deal of production occurs on the household side of farming. Farm wives are producers in a very fundamental sense. They produce such services as the canning and preservation of food, the care of hired help in many parts of the United States, as well, of course, as producing the amenities found in the homes of most housewives, rural or urban. Thus, it becomes apparent that the distinctions maintained between the business and the home sides of farming are artificial and unrealistic. Consumption occurs on both sides. Subjective values are important on both sides, and production occurs on both sides.

The unrealism of the distinction between the firm and household in farming, or, stated differently, between the home and business aspects of farming, has been realized by several groups during the last few years. Economic theorists became aware of the consumption aspects of management as a result of work done by such theorists as Knight, Hicks, Keynes, Kaldor, Hart, Tintner, and Reder. As a result, the theoretical distinction between the firm and household, once apparently drawn so clearly in economic theory and principles, is becoming vague and confused. Similarly, farm-management men have been increasingly aware of the relations, within an individual farm business, between consumption and the availability of savings for investments and development of a farm business. Farm managers have also become highly aware of the importance which farmers do or do not attach to such things as material gains, accuracy, progress, and family living in the motivation of farm people. Home economists are becoming increasingly aware of the need to balance consumption against income-producing power.

The University of Missouri took the lead in extension work aimed at synthesizing study of the production and consumption ends of farming and developed a "Balanced Farming Program." Other states soon followed Missouri's lead. At the University of Kentucky a corresponding program is referred to as the "Farm and Home Development Program." Extension workers, in administering this type of program, have made a special point of getting members of the farm family to plan jointly their production, borrowing, saving, investment, and consumption patterns over a period of years, so that the investment and consumption needs of a farm family (for all purposes) could be balanced against the earning power of the farm involved.

It is significant that the balanced-farming approach originated in a state having many farms needing extensive development and redevelopment. It is especially among the low-income families that the need for close integration of production and consumption plans exists. Among the smaller farms credit for expansion and developmental programs is often unavailable, and, hence, such programs must be financed out of the current low levels of income. Thus, states, such as Missouri and Kentucky, having large numbers of low-income families, were rather quick to become aware of the unrealism of the distinction between the home and business aspects of farming.

Divergencies between Overall Values and Individual Managerial Values

Social, economic, and political bodies, as such, often express concern about problems. In the mid-thirties most of the countries of the Western World were concerned with the overall problem of unemployment. For many years the people of the United States have been concerned about the need to conserve our agricultural resources. The segment of economics which studies such overall problems is often referred to as *macro-economics*, whereas the segment of economics which studies the individual problems of producing and consuming units is referred to as *micro-economics*.

In the thirties, a group of economists, commonly referred to as Keynesians, pointed out that relationships exist between the overall level of employment in an industrial economy and the desire of individual managers (including wage earners as managers of themselves) for cash reserves, price (including wages) stability, and liquidity in their business. They also pointed out that overall opportunities for employment at a given money wage are related to the propensity of people to consume their incomes. Thus, an overall or macro-problem of unemployment arose because large numbers of individual managers and consumers had special wants and preferences which led to overall unemployment of manpower and other resources.

Coming more closely to agriculture, reflection indicates that the soil-conservation problem has a somewhat similar origin. The people of the United States, speaking through various organizations and their normal political channels, have indicated dissatisfaction with the rate at which agricultural resources are being used and dissipated. The rate of use and dissipation actually going on is partially determined by the wants and preferences of the individual persons owning and using the resources of our agricultural economy. The soil-conservation problem results, like the unemployment problem, therefore, from the failure of the totality of individual consumption and production decisions to conform with "national beliefs" as to the proper degree of conservation.

The problem of reconciling the conflicting ends and values of individuals with the ends and values of various political, economic, and social groups is really a problem in welfare economics. It is mentioned in this farm-management book merely because attempts at reconciliation of such conflicts involving agriculture must be based in part upon the managerial practices of individual farmers.

Index